COLLECTIONS

BENEATH ANOTHER SKY

Program Authors
Richard L. Allington
Jesús Cortez
Patricia M. Cunningham
Sam Leaton Sebesta
Robert J. Tierney

Program Consultants
Molly S. McLaurin
Robert Slavin
Zena Sutherland

Critic Readers
Karen Fletcher
Dorothy French
Margaret Young

Pupil Readers
Kimberly Burks
Rebecca Jalil
Jason Kee
Sandy Linke
Michael Marino
Datheia Washington

Scott, Foresman and Company

Editorial Office:
Glenview, Illinois

Regional Offices:
Sunnyvale, California
Tucker, Georgia
Glenview, Illinois
Oakland, New Jersey
Carrollton, Texas

Acknowledgments

Text

Page 9: Chapters 8 and 9 from *Jake* by Alfred Slote (J. B. Lippincott). Copyright © 1971 by Alfred Slote. Reprinted by permission of Harper & Row, Publishers, Inc. and Curtis Brown, Ltd.

Page 43: "Jim" from *Bronzeville Boys and Girls* by Gwendolyn Brooks. Copyright © 1956 by Gwendolyn Brooks. Reprinted by permission of Harper & Row, Publishers, Inc.

Page 49: From *Rebecca of Sunnybrook Farm* by Kate Douglas Wiggin, 1903.

Page 75: "Protest" from *At the Top of My Voice and Other Poems* by Felice Holman. Text copyright © 1970 by Felice Holman. Published by W. W. Norton and reissued by Charles Scribner's Sons.

Page 75: "Truly My Own" by Vanessa Howard from *The Voice of the Children* collected by June Jordan and Terri Bush. Copyright © 1968, 1969, 1970 by The Voice of the Children, Inc. Reprinted by permission of Henry Holt and Company, Inc. and Julian Bach Literary Agency, Inc.

Page 84: Excerpt from introduction and "Narcissus and Echo" from *Heroes, Gods and Monsters of the Greek Myths* by Bernard Evslin. Copyright © 1966 by Scholastic Magazines, Inc. Reprinted by permission of Scholastic Inc.

Page 94: "Light and Water" from *Selected Writings of Juan Ramón Jiménez*. Copyright © 1957 by Juan Ramón Jiménez. Copyright renewed © 1985 by Farrar, Straus and Giroux, Inc. Reprinted by permission of Farrar, Straus and Giroux, Inc.

Page 94: "Luz y Agua" from *The Selected Writings of Juan Ramón Jiménez*. Reprinted by permission of the author.

Page 95: "The Legend of the Hummingbird" and excerpt from the introduction from *Once in Puerto Rico* by Pura Belpré. Copyright © 1973 by Pura Belpré. Reprinted by permission of Viking Penguin Inc.

Page 99: "Half Moon" and "Media Luna" by Federico García Lorca from *Obras Completas*. Copyright © Aguilar S. A. de Ediciones. Reprinted by permission of Manuel F. Montesinos for the Estate of Federico García Lorca.

Page 100: "Maui Traps Sun" by Vivian L. Thompson from *Hawaiian Myths of Earth, Sea, and Sky* by Vivian L. Thompson. Copyright © 1966 by Vivian L. Thompson. Reprinted by permission of the author.

Page 106: From *The Sun Is a Golden Earring* by Natalia M. Belting. Copyright © 1962 by Natalia M. Belting. Reprinted by permission of Henry Holt and Company, Inc.

Page 113: Reprinted by permission of Dodd, Mead & Company, Inc. from *Mumbet: The Story of Elizabeth Freeman* by Harold W. Felton. Copyright © 1970 by University of Nebraska Foundation.

Page 141: "Hold Fast Your Dreams" by Louise Driscoll. Copyright © 1918 by the New York Times Company. Reprinted by permission.

Page 147: From *Anastasia on Her Own* by Lois Lowry. Copyright © 1985 by Lois Lowry. Reprinted by permission of Houghton Mifflin Company.

Page 179: "I Am Running in a Circle" from *The New Kid on the Block* by Jack Prelutsky. Text copyright © 1984 by Jack Prelutsky. Reprinted by permission of Greenwillow Books (A Division of William Morrow) and William Heinemann Ltd.

Page 185: Excerpt from pp. 147–191 of *Dragon of the Lost Sea* by Laurence Yep. Copyright © 1982 by Laurence Yep. Reprinted by permission of Harper & Row, Publishers, Inc. and the author.

Page 227: "The Paint Box" by E. V. Rieu from *The Flattered Flying Fish and Other Poems*. Reprinted by permission of Associated Book Publishers, Ltd.

Page 233: Excerpt from *Homesick: My Own Story* by Jean Fritz. Copyright © 1982 by Jean Fritz. Reprinted by permission of G. P. Putnam's Sons and Gina Maccoby Literary Agency.

Acknowledgments continued on page 543

ISBN 0-673-73356-4

Copyright © 1989,
Scott, Foresman & Company, Glenview, Illinois
All Rights Reserved.
Printed in the United States of America.

1234567890—RRW—979695949392919089 88

Laurence Yep:
The Pleasure and Power of Reading

Reading was always fun. When I was twelve, I visited my grandmother in Chinatown, and she asked me to buy a box of incense sticks. I could read English well enough, but I could not read Chinese, so she handed me the label from an old box of incense sticks, which was written in Chinese.

When I arrived at the store, I couldn't find anything with a label like the one in my hand. Worse, the store owner could not speak English. Eventually, after I realized that the manufacturer had redesigned the label, I matched the Chinese characters on the old label with the ones on the new label. I had never felt so helpless in my life. It was then that I knew that reading was more than pleasure. Reading was also power.

Larry Yep

Laurence Yep is a Newbery Honor Book author. His novel *Dragon of the Lost Sea* begins on page 188.

Contents

Alfred
Slote

JAKE

Introducing

JAKE

You probably have goals. Maybe you want to earn money to buy a poster or a new jacket. You decide to look for odd jobs in your neighborhood, such as washing cars, walking dogs, or babysitting. Your plan sounds good, but you can't find anyone who wants a car washed and someone else in the neighborhood already has taken the dog-walking and babysitting jobs. Reaching your goal may not be simple.

One Character's Goal

Jake is the main character in Alfred Slote's realistic novel. (For information about realistic fiction, see your Handbook of Literary Terms.) Jake has a clear goal: to find a coach for his baseball team by the time the game starts late in the afternoon. If the team doesn't have a coach, they have to forfeit the game. Will Jake be able to find a coach?

What Makes You Want to Keep Reading?

Jake seems to have a simple goal. He'll either find a coach or he won't. Slote introduces several complications—twists in the plot in which unexpected things happen. You've probably faced complications. Let's say you go on a picnic, get all the food laid out—and then there's a sudden rainstorm! What do you do to overcome the complication? How will Jake and his teammates overcome the complications they face?

As you're reading this excerpt on your own, discover how Jake and his teammates think they have solved their problem when another one arises.

JAKE

Jake's baseball team needs a coach—quickly! Jake and his teammates on the Print-Alls team have already tried hard to find a good coach but haven't had any luck. Jake lives with his Uncle Lenny, a hot-shot college athlete who's now a musician. Lenny might be a good coach, but he must go to Detroit every evening for rehearsals.

I f that man isn't in the batter's box by the time I count to three," the ump shouted, "this game is forfeited."

My hands were sweating and the bat was so heavy I couldn't pick it up.

"One," he called out.

I grabbed the bat with both hands and tugged.

"Two," he said.

"Help, Lenny," I screamed.

"Three!"

Darriinnnnnnnnnnnnnnnnnnng!

Lenny groaned. "What's the matter?"

I opened my eyes. I sighed with relief and turned off the alarm. "That's the new clock."

"Oh," he said, and went back to sleep.

I just lay there, thankful at being wakened from the nightmare of a bat too heavy to pick up and the umpire threatening to forfeit our game unless I picked the bat up.

That was the worst dream I ever had in my life.

I got up out of bed and pulled up the window shade. A cloudy gray day. It looked like it might rain. If only it would rain. We'd have an extra day in which to look for a coach.

I made breakfast and that included milk[1] and with Lenny's snores still ringing in my ears, I went off to school. It began to sprinkle. Rain harder, I prayed. Rain real hard and wash out our game.

I'd never before prayed for a rained-out game.

It only went on sprinkling, and when I got to school there were the usual soccer games going on. It had been a long time since I'd got to school early enough to take part in a soccer game. I wasn't very good at the sport. Sometimes I kicked a kid instead of the ball and sometimes the kid I kicked would get mad and want to scuffle. So we'd scuffle and word would get out that Jake Wrather was a dirty soccer player, when all I was was an awful soccer player. But I was pretty good at the scuffling part. Fact was: I liked the scuffling part.

Danny Kohl was in one of the games and he was fun to watch. Quick and agile, he anticipated the flow of the game. I watched him give a pass, and receive it right back and take it down the field to score. He was a natural athlete, good at any sport. I was good at only one sport: baseball. If I didn't make it in baseball, I was through.

The first bell rang and the game broke up. Ned Franks came up behind me.

"Hey, Jake, you're on time today."

"What's wrong with that?"

"Hey, don't get mad. I've never seen you on time." Ned looked up at the sky. "You think it'll rain harder than this?"

---

1. *School officials thought that Jake wasn't eating a proper breakfast and that Uncle Lenny wasn't a proper guardian.*

"I hope so."

"Me, too. Give us more time to find a coach."

I knew then that it would be on all the Print-Alls' minds.
Pray for rain and search for a coach.

Inside the school we met Jeff Bigler looking gloomy. Ned
slapped him hard on the back. That usually got Jeff sore,
but he was too sad to get sore. Jeff said: "The rules say you
got to show up with a full team even if it is raining. The
ump can call a postponement if it's raining, but if one team
doesn't have a coach and a team, he can also call it a forfeit."

"Is that right, Jake?"

I wasn't sure, but it was one of those things that sound so
stupid you know it's got to be right. And I could remember
the past two years we always showed up at ball diamonds
in the rain and the two coaches always shook hands and
discussed the weather situation with the umps. Only an
ump could call a game off. Though sometimes they
announced postponements over the local radio station. But
then it had to be raining real hard for hours ahead of time.
Not sprinkling like this.

"So you see," Jeff said, "even if it is raining, we got to get
ourselves a coach."

"What'll we do, Jake?" Ned asked as we walked down the
hall to our classroom. We stopped at his locker while he
put his lunch in it.

"I don't know. I'll think of something."

By the time Ned had put his lunch away and we were
almost at our room I thought of it. We'd get down to Vets
Park early and find some adult who'd pretend to be our
coach for a couple of minutes, just long enough to shake
hands with the Baer Machine coach and agree with the
umps that the game ought to be called. There had to be an
old guy down at Vets Park.

Ned brightened immediately when I told him my plan.

"Jake, I've seen lots of old guys hanging around the park shelter playing cards."

Good old Ned. He walked into the class whistling as if all our problems were over. I just shook my head. It was a good idea because it was the *only* idea, but old Ned was too thick to see that.

The morning dragged by. I knew old Atwell thought I was half-asleep again, but I was really just thinking about our coach problem, and looking out the window to see if it was still raining.

"What do you see out the window all the time, Jake?" she finally asked me.

"Rain," I said.

The class laughed.

"Haven't you ever seen rain before?"

"Yes, ma'am."

"Then please pay attention to what's happening in class."

I paid attention. We were doing a unit on explorers. De Soto, Henry Hudson, Champlain . . . . They were all good guys and tough, too. Not knowing where they were going. Having trouble with their own men, the Indians, sickness, the weather . . . .

The weather . . . . I looked outside. I thought it might be raining just a wee bit harder. But was it raining on the west side of town where Vets Park was?

"Jake!"

My head snapped around. I tried to pay attention but it was hard.

Lenny was humming a little tune when I got home for lunch. Usually a good sign.

"Hello, Jake."

I barely nodded at him. It had stopped raining. It was only sprinkling, I didn't feel hungry.

"Hey, man," he said cheerfully, "couldn't you have picked out a quieter alarm clock?"

"What do you want for three dollars?" I said grumpily.

His eyes opened wide. "What's the matter, kid?"

"Nothing."

I went into the kitchen and made myself a sandwich with cream cheese and poured myself a big old ugly glass of milk.

Lenny came in with coffee and sat down across the table from me.

"How was school?"

"Lousy."

"How come?"

"It's always lousy."

His eyes narrowed. "What'd you do bad this morning?"

"Nothing," I said.

He relaxed. "We're getting you back on the ball, so don't foul up. By the way . . ." He started examining me like I was something on a shelf in a bargain store.

"Now what?"

"That thing on your back."

"What thing?"

"That shirt you're wearing. How long you been wearing it?"

"A couple of days. Why?"

"A couple of weeks looks more like it."

"It fits good."

"Yeah, but it smells bad. How many shirts do you have, Jake?"

"I got plenty."

"You got nothing. This morning I got up early and began looking through your clothes. You're wearing all your last year's stuff."

"So what?"

"It looks terrible. People will think I don't take good care of you."

"Don't worry about it. I'll tell them you do."

Lenny laughed. "I'll pick you up in the parking lot right after school's out."

"I can't, Lenny. I got a ball game."

"What time's your ball game?"

"Five-thirty."

"I'll get you there by five-thirty."

"I got to be at Vets Park by four."

"Four? Listen, Jake, don't feed me a line. You're not a major leaguer yet. Nobody eleven years old has got to be at his ball game an hour and a half early. Besides, there won't even be a ball game this afternoon because the radio just said thundershowers."

"We still got to be there even if it's raining."

"Well, you'll be there."

"But I got to be there early enough to find us a coach."

"What are you talking about, Jake?"

I finally got it through Lenny's thick skull what our problem was and how we needed someone to pretend for five minutes he was our coach, shake hands with the Baer Machine coach, and agree with the umps to call off the game, and then he could take off.

Old Lenny listened to me carefully, nodded, and when I was done, he said: "OK, Jake. I'll be your patsy for those five minutes. I don't have to be in Detroit till seven-thirty. I can make it even if I leave by six-fifteen. For this rainout, I'm your coach, but first you go with me to buy some clothes."

I stuck out my hand. "You got a deal."

"And you got a coach," Lenny said.

"I'd rather have your uncle coaching us for five minutes than anyone else all season," Tony Parker said.

Ned said: "Will he hit some fly balls to us even if it's raining?"

"I'll ask him," I said.

But when I saw Lenny in the parking lot after school, I realized I could no more ask him to hit fly balls than ask the President of the United States to be a pinch hitter. Lenny was all duded up for Detroit. Pressed suit, fancy shirt and tie, and sunglasses, and calfskin shoes I'd never seen before.

I grinned. "That's no coach's uniform I ever saw. I hope you ain't gonna buy me stuff like that."

Lenny smiled. "You're not worthy to be duded up like this, Jake."

"Good thing, too," I said, and we both laughed.

By the time we got through with our shopping expedition it was after five and we had to hustle to get me changed and the two of us over to Vets Park which is on the west side of town. We also had to pick up the equipment bag at the Fultons' house. I was getting nervous; Lenny tried to relax me by assuring me no one could play in a drizzle like this. The rain was coming down harder and harder though I hadn't heard any thunderclaps yet. The windshield wipers on his car were going splat-splat.

"How do I know it's raining on the west side?" I asked.

Lenny laughed. "Jake, I never thought of you as a worrier before."

"I got to worry about my team."

"*Your* team?"

"Yeah. I run the team."

Lenny whistled. "Isn't that taking on a lot for eleven years old?"

"I'm not eleven. I'm thirty-five."

We both laughed. It was one of those stupid things we say to each other that always made us both laugh.

We hit the west side of town, which starts west of Main Street, and it was still raining, but not as hard, I didn't think, as on our side. When we got to the parking lot at Vets, I could see our guys huddled under a tree on the first base side of the diamond, and their bikes parked by the tree. The Baer Machine team was sitting in a couple of station wagons, making a lot of noise. That would be all they were good for. Last year we almost wiped them out in two innings, getting ten runs in the first inning. There's a rule in the ten-, eleven-, twelve-, and thirteen-year-old leagues that if you get twelve runs in two innings and the other team doesn't get any, you win right away. It's called a "wipe-out win." The Baer Machine team was the only one we'd ever come close to wiping out, but that was last year, and this year they had some new players who couldn't, I figured, be any worse than their last year's guys.

It didn't look like the umps had arrived. When I started to get out of the car, Lenny told me I was crazy. But I told him I was going to join my team. So he gave me the key to the trunk and I got out the equipment bag, hoisted it on my shoulders, tossed the keys back at him, and walked through the drizzle to the tree sheltering my guys. Ned came out to help me with the bag.

"That your uncle in the car, Jake?"

"Sure. Who'd you think it was?"

"I don't know. I've never seen him before. But I sure've heard about him. Will he coach us on Saturday, too?"

"He won't even coach us today. He's got more important things to do than coach a bunch of punks like us. All he does is shake hands with their coach, agree to postpone the game 'cause of rain, and take off for Detroit. Umps here yet?"

"I bet they don't even show up," Dick Williams said. We'd arrived under the tree.

"How much you want to bet?" Tony asked.

We all turned to look at the car coming into the lot. Two guys in dark blue. Umps. They got right out of their car, too, carrying their gear and a box with two new balls in it.

"They got to be kidding."

"Umps never joke."

"We ought to find an umbrella for them."

The arrival of the two umpires brought the Baer Machine clambering out of their station wagons, and their coaches and their parents. It seems every team but us has adult fans.

Only Lenny was left in his car and I knew he didn't want to get those fancy guitar-playing duds of his wet. But he got out, slowly, glaring at the sky like he was telling it to stop raining.

It didn't stop raining and Lenny put on a good sprint and arrived, all six-foot-three of him under the tree.

Everyone looked up at him. The umps, the Baer Machine team, and our guys, too. Mr. Phelps, the Baer Machine coach, came over to Lenny.

"Hello, Lenny. So they got you in the coaching business."

Lenny grinned. I could tell he didn't know who Mr. Phelps was. "Yeah," he said, "for a little while. How you been?"

"Fine. You still playing basketball?"

"No. I gave it up. I'm in the music racket now."

"So I hear. These kids of yours are good ball players, but they need a coach with a firm hand."

"I got the hands," Lenny said, with a laugh. "Don't I, Jake?"

I blushed. "Yeah."

My guys laughed.

"How's the weather look to you, Umps?" Lenny asked.

"Pretty bad, Mr. Johnson," one of the umps said.

"Guess we ought to call it."

"League rules say we got to wait till five forty-five to call it, unless the diamond looks unplayable."

"That third base looks bad."

"I could put some sand on it," the other ump said. "I brought a shovel with me."

"What about home plate?"

"A little sand would help that."

"Provided it stops raining," Lenny said.

"That's right. We've got to wait another five minutes."

Lenny grinned. "I can wait five minutes."

He started chatting with the Baer Machine coach, Mr. Phelps. As I look back on it now, Lenny could have made them call the game right then and there, but he said he could wait five minutes and so we waited that five minutes. The Baer Machine kids asked us about the game with the McLeod Builders. It seemed everyone in town had heard about it. Jerry and Andy were tossing a ball back and forth. So were Tony and Danny. Lenny and Mr. Phelps were chatting and I was telling the Baer Machine first baseman how they'd robbed us of the game the other day when all of a sudden, everyone became silent.

Everyone became silent because suddenly we couldn't hear the sounds of the rain falling on the tree.

We looked up. The rain had stopped.

I looked at Lenny. He was flabbergasted. He was watching the umps taking their bases out of their equipment bag.

"You don't mean you're gonna play this game?" Lenny asked.

"Got to," an ump said.

"But look at third."

"I'll fix that in two minutes with my shovel and some sand."

Mr. Phelps clapped his hands. "OK, Baer Machine, loosen up your arms. Lenny, do you want the infield first?"

Lenny was really in a state of shock. I couldn't blame him. I had sworn to him that all he had to do was shake hands and leave for Detroit. He had to go.

He looked over at me and I nodded. "It's OK," I said. "Go."

I looked at our guys. They were looking at me wonderingly, not knowing what was going on. I felt a little sick. Now it was our turn to forfeit, and this was one they wouldn't play over.

"What do you say, Lenny?" Mr. Phelps repeated. "Do you want the infield first, or us?"

Silence. Lenny's face was grim. "We'll take it first," he said. He turned to us. "What're you guys waiting for? A silver-plate invitation? Let's go. Git!"

With a gleeful shout, the Print-Alls took the field. I stayed behind trying to catch Lenny's eye, to ask him why, what about Detroit, his rehearsal. He hired that hall there by the hour. It was expensive.

"What's the matter with you, Wrather?" he snarled at me. "Didn't you hear me tell you to git?"

I got.

R ight away Lenny could do something I'd never seen any other coach in our league do. He could hit spinning fouls to the catcher on purpose, slicing under the ball with his bat. He could also hit mean twisting grounders that skidded in front of you; he could hit exasperating little pop flies that drove Danny Kohl at shortstop back on the grass for diving catches, and he sent sky-high fly balls that Andy Black circled under endlessly.

In five minutes of fielding practice on a wet field, we felt like we'd never known what fielding practice was before.

The Baer Machine kids were positively bug-eyed, and so were we, and all of this from a big husky guy in a fancy suit, shirt, and tie. It was too much.

Lenny called us in. "OK, guys," he said softly, "these are the facts. I didn't expect to be coaching here, but here I am. I got to be in Detroit in an hour and a half. Now I understand you got a rule in this league that any team ahead by twelve runs at the end of the second inning wins the game right then and there. Is that right?"

"Yes," we all said.

"Good." He grinned. "That's what you guys are going to do for me. You're gonna get twelve quick runs and I'm gonna get to Detroit just a couple of minutes late instead of not at all. You hear?"

We heard. We didn't quite believe, but we heard.

"Good. Now let's quick go over some basics. How do you get twelve runs fast? Put your hand down, first baseman. I'm gonna tell you. You get twelve quick runs by hitting every ball around the plate, hitting it hard, putting your head down and running. On any ball going out of the infield, I want the runner taking a big turn at second and if he thinks he's got a chance, he goes. I want everyone stealing second base."

"Even Fulton?" someone asked.

"Who's Fulton?"

John raised his hand reluctantly.

"What's the matter with you?"

"I'm slow," John said.

"You got rheumatism?"

"No. Just slow."

"Today you're fast."

"He stole two bases in our last game," I said.

That broke everyone up.

"No signals to steal," Lenny said. "Everyone goes on his own. Everyone swings at every pitch around the plate."

"Even at three and 0?" Bigler asked.

"Especially at three and 0." Lenny said. "I want home runs, first baseman, not walks or singles. I got to be in Detroit by seven-thirty. This is going to be a two–inning ball game or I'm gonna stomp every one of you into the ground."

He looked pretty fierce when he said it, and no one said a thing. Finally, Jerry Jones, grinning, asked: "What about bunts, Lenny?"

"No bunts, especially from a big strong guy like you. You hit home runs or don't bother to come back to the bench. You're the pitcher, aren't you?"

"Sometimes," Jerry said.

"Well, go and warm up and throw strikes. What's your batting order, Jake?"

"Kohl, Parker, Wrather, Black, Jones, Bigler, Fulton, Williams, Franks."

"OK, guys, I don't know your names but I know your faces and I'm holding each one of you personally responsible if I don't get to Detroit on time. Twelve runs in two innings, that's an order."

It was the craziest pep talk we'd ever got in our lives, and from the strangest-looking coach anyone had ever seen. My Uncle Lenny, six-foot-three inches and dressed to kill.

The ump called batter up. The rain had completely stopped, though it was still cloudy and dark. Third base looked peculiar, full of mud and sand. The grass was wet. I had the eerie feeling we could lose twelve to nothing just as easily as win.

Only a few fans—parents of Baer Machine—had come to watch. It wasn't a baseball kind of day. It wasn't any kind of day at all.

Danny Kohl stepped in there. Lenny cupped his hands over his mouth and called out: "Get me to Detroit on time."

It was to be one of two rallying cries during the game. I don't know what the Baer Machine team thought of it.

The pitcher came down with his first pitch and Danny stepped into it and cracked it on a line over the third baseman's head.

"Wahoo," Lenny shouted gleefully. Danny took a big turn at first and then hustled back to the bag as their left fielder showed us a good arm, rifling the ball to second on one bounce. They were a well-coached team, but as I remembered from last year, they didn't have many hitters. Their pitcher had good control and a medium fast ball, but we'd hit him plenty last year, and on the basis of that one pitch to Danny, it looked like we'd hit him this year.

"Get me to Detroit on time, baby," Lenny called out.

"Twelve in two," Ned shouted at Tony, who, grinning from ear to ear, stepped in there.

Twelve in two became the other rallying cry.

Tony was first pitch swinging, too. The pitch was wide, but Tony reached across the plate and poked it into right field. Danny sped around second never hesitating and headed toward third. Foolishly their right fielder tried to get him. The right fielder lobbed high in the air, and Tony took second on the silly throw. Two balls pitched, two men on. Even a hurry-up musician couldn't ask for more action than that. But Lenny did.

"Get me to Detroit on time, Jake," he shouted.

"Twelve in two," Ned shouted.

"I want a homer, Jake," Lenny shouted. "Nothing less or I'll stomp you right into the ground."

I tried to ignore him and concentrate on the pitcher. Baseball was my game, not Lenny's. I didn't need him coaching me, distracting me. If he wanted to get to Detroit on time, he ought to shut up a little.

The next pitch, I had the idea, was not going to be around the plate. They would be getting the idea we were first pitching swinging, so he'd probably throw me a bad one.

I was right. The pitch came in waist high but way outside. The catcher made a good stop on it. The second pitch was low around my ankles. I don't think he wanted to throw two balls in a row, but once you let up it isn't always so easy to get in the groove again. Also the ball was wet. It wasn't raining, but the grass was wet, the infield was wet, and the air was humid.

The two and 0 pitch came in . . . high. I checked my swing.

"Three balls and no strikes," the ump called out.

Lenny shouted down at me, loud enough for the whole world to hear: "If you take this pitch, Wrather, you won't be able to sit down for a week."

I heard Andy Black, on deck behind me, start laughing. I'm sure the Baer Machine pitcher thought Lenny was kidding because he grooved the next pitch. I waited on it.

That's the big thing on those slow easy pitches. Don't get anxious to kill it. Don't get out in front of it. Wait till the very last second when it's sitting there in front of you, then whip that old bat around, snap those wrists, listen to that solid sound, and watch the old white ball disappear in the mists of the outfield.

I got good wood on it and the ball took off. It went behind the left fielder and the center fielder, and the poor kid in center fell on the wet grass trying to catch up with it. That turned it into an easy home run for me.

"Step on those bags, Wrather," Lenny shouted at me. "Git your foot into those bags."

As I came around third, he said: "Git, Wrather, git."

The ball was still in the outfield, but I put on the steam and gave home plate a solid plunk with my spikes.

Andy and I slapped hands, and Jerry, and Dick, and there was the whole gang pounding me, shouting: "Twelve in two. Twelve in two."

Bigler nudged me. "Look who just arrived."

I followed his look over to the wooden stands behind first. There was Mr. Fredericks, the league president, sitting alone.

"How long's he been here?"

"Just got here. I bet he came to check on us."

"Let him check."

Mr. Fredericks was looking at Lenny as though he'd never seen a baseball coach in a fancy suit, shirt, and tie and wearing sunglasses on a cloudy dark afternoon. I had to laugh. Now Mr. Fredericks would probably make a rule about what the well-dressed coach is supposed to wear.

"C'mon, number four," Lenny called down, "be a hitter up there."

Old Andy wanted to do right by Lenny so he swung at the first pitch which was over his head and missed it by a mile.

"I never knew a number-four hitter who could hit bad pitches yet," Lenny called out. It was his way of calming Andy down.

Andy dug in. Big shouldered, narrow-waisted, he was going to be a great fullback some day. He could muscle a baseball better than anyone I knew.

The Baer Machine pitcher cleverly threw him another bad ball, hoping old Andy would go fishing again. Andy did.

"Strike two!"

"How about waiting for one in the strike zone, big guy?" Lenny called out. One big jock getting on another one.

Andy was rattled up there. I could tell; even though his broad face revealed nothing. I could see him deciding not to swing at the next one. He didn't.

It was in there.

"You're out," the ump said.

Andy walked back to the bench without looking at anyone. He sat down beside me and buried his face in his hands.

"Hey, man, cut it out. Everyone strikes out now and then."

"Yeah, but we got to get your uncle to Detroit on time."

"Nuts to him. We're playing baseball. You got to stop listening to him. Play your game, hit your pitches. Forget about him." I clapped him on the shoulder.

"You'll get another crack at that pitcher."

What I didn't realize was how soon Andy would get another crack. Here we were, in the first inning, 3-0, one out, and Jerry was up. From that moment on, mayhem broke loose.

Jerry sent a high fly into center field. The center fielder started forward, then had to reverse himself and get back. He slipped again on the grass, and the ball fell behind him. Jerry ended up on third. He wasn't there long when John Fulton slapped a sizzling ground ball that bounced off the pitcher's knees. Jerry scored and John got to first safely. Bigler laid down his usual bunt and got on. Then Dick Williams who was a streak hitter but usually started his streaks the end of July just before the season ended, hit a fly ball down the line in right field. John scored, and so did Bigler who almost overtook John coming into home. Baer Machine changed pitchers, bringing in their first baseman to pitch, but it didn't do them any good. Danny Kohl got his second hit of the inning, an infield single to deep short. Tony Parker chopped down on a pitch and by the time the pitcher caught it, he was on and Danny was on second. I was up for the second time. I took one pitch for a strike, just to see what this new pitcher looked like. Then when he threw the pitch in the same place again, I laced it into right center for an easy double. Two more runs scored. Six runs batted in in one inning for me. It was a little scary. I didn't dare look at Lenny. I mean, all these years I'd been telling him how good I am, and in the first inning I knock in six runs. It's enough to make a guy real humble.

But if Lenny was satisfied, he didn't show it. He kept shouting: "Get me to Detroit on time, fellas. Twelve in two. Twelve in two."

We already had nine, and three more didn't seem too hard. Baer Machine was falling apart right in front of us. No chatter, no hustle, they kept looking up at the sky.

It was getting darker, and once in a while you could feel tiny drops of rain. Now we were rooting for it not to rain.

They decided to change pitchers again, bringing in their catcher. All this used up time because the catcher had to take off his equipment. He took his shin guards off very, very slowly.

"They're stalling, Ump," Bigler shouted, reminding me of Mr. McLeod in the last game.

The ump smiled. He knew what we wanted, but there wasn't any way to make their catcher go faster.

The drops fell a little faster. But it still wasn't bad. We could play. Finally their catcher had his equipment off and he went out to the mound to warm up.

"He only gets six pitches," Bigler shouted.

"Shut up, Bigler," I said.

We waited while their catcher warmed up. He couldn't throw any better than the other two guys, but he took a lot longer between warm-ups. And meanwhile, their first baseman was having a hard time making the shin guards fit. John Fulton offered his help, but the kid declined it.

"Batter up," Bigler shouted.

They finally got all set, and Andy Black stepped in. I took a big lead off second.

"Give it a ride, Andy," I shouted.

Andy obliged. He belted the ball way over the left fielder's head for a two-run homer. I waited at the plate to congratulate him. As he came around third, Lenny stepped over and swatted him on the behind. "I always knew you were my number-four hitter, man."

Andy had a big grin as he came across home plate.

Eleven runs in the first inning. One more, and then all we had to do was strike out as fast as we could, and then strike them out as fast as we could, and the game would be over.

Jerry was up next. Trying to duplicate Andy's feat he popped up. Never try to hit a home run. They just come when you're swinging in a groove. Two out. John Fulton was up next. He hit a grounder right at the third baseman who backed up, grabbed it, and threw John out.

We'd finished our licks one run short. All we had to do now was hold them, get one more run in the top of the second, and wipe them out in their bottom half.

Lenny stopped Jerry on his way to the mound. "No fooling around out there, Pitch. Just chuck that old fast one in there and mow those boys down. You hear?"

"I hear, man," Jerry said.

It was raining a little harder, but still OK. I got a knot in my stomach just thinking about it.

Jerry took two pitches and Lenny called out: "My man's all warmed up. Let's move this old ball game along."

"Batter up," the ump said promptly. He didn't like getting wet either.

But their batter took his own sweet time moving into the box. First he had a conference with his coach. We all shouted "stalling" but it didn't hurry them.

Finally though he got in there. Jerry was so anxious to strike him out that he poured his fast ball in there about five feet high. John just let it go.

Jerry's second pitch was a shovel ball and John scooped it out of the mud.

"Time," Lenny said, and he trotted out to the mound in his fancy white suit, avoiding the wet spots, making Jerry come off the muddy mound to talk with him on the grass.

"What're you trying to do, Pitch? Make me late for my rehearsal?"

Jerry giggled. I was annoyed. This was no time for a comedy act. I kicked the dirt.

Lenny kicked his leg in the air. "Get your left leg out there. I know it's slippery, but make a hole right there . . . no back there. OK . . . now that's where your left foot should go. Then you swing around with your pitch and follow through. You got a whole body on you to help that big arm of yours. You get as much control from your hips as from your arm. Now try it."

Right then and there, he gave Jerry a pitching lesson. I didn't even know Lenny knew anything about pitching. He'd played first in high school and in semipro ball.

Jerry went through the motions. "I got it."

"OK. Now no fancy stuff. Just get that left leg out, and follow it with your body and throw that ball into the catcher's glove. They'll never see it."

Lenny went back to the bench. It was an amazing performance. Nobody had ever told Jerry anything about pitching before. We all assumed he was so good because he was natural. But I learned you can make the natural more effective with good coaching.

Jerry got his left foot way out there, followed it around, and the pitch smoked across the plate for a strike.

"Now you got it," Lenny called out.

That did it for Baer Machine right then and there. Jerry's left foot came out and the Baer Machine batters went down one, two, three. They never even saw the ball.

"Hustle in, boys," Lenny called out.

The rain was coming down a little harder now. Only a few fans were left, and they were under umbrellas. Most of the others had gone to their cars and were watching from the parking lot.

Mr. Phelps, the Baer Machine coach, had gone over to the stands and was talking with Mr. Fredericks. I had a good idea what they were talking about. When to call a game.

"Let's go, guys," I shouted. "Let's get a batter in there. Bigler, get in there. Forget about the doughnut. Get in there and bunt the ball."

"Batter up," Ned shouted.

But the Baer Machine pitcher went on taking his warm-up pitches.

Mr. Phelps came back from his conference. "Lenny, don't you think it's getting a little wet to play ball?"

"Depends on who's winning," Lenny said, with a grin. "Me, I've never been drier in my life. Let's keep going."

Mr. Phelps hesitated, shrugged, and nodded to the umps.

Bigler stepped in. The pitcher took his time, wiped his face. The drizzle was harder now.

"Step into it, First Baseman," Lenny called out. "All we need is a little old homer."

Lenny didn't know that all Jeff did was bunt. But Jeff, listening to Lenny, knew he had to swing on the first pitch. He swung on a bad ball and popped it up. Their third baseman grabbed it.

That brought up Dick Williams. Dick had got a lucky hit in the first inning, down the right field line. I could see him thinking he could do it again. He swung on the first pitch, too, and popped it up to the first baseman.

"C'mon, guys," I shouted, "forget about the rain. Wait on your pitches. You hear? Wait on your pitches."

"Hit it out of here, Ned."

"No pitcher in there, Neddy."

I looked at Ned up there and my heart sank. Our last chance to win this game in two innings. Ned was strong but fat. He'd had to hit that ball three miles to hit a home run. Still, if he got a double, then Danny . . .

The first pitch was way high, and Ned let it go by.

"That's the eye, Ned."

"We got to swing, Jake," Tony said.

"Not at bad pitches. Never at bad pitches."

The next pitch was in there and Ned really walloped it. It went into left field on the line. The left fielder charged it, trying to make a shoestring catch. He didn't. The ball skidded in front of him and went right through his legs. And there was fat old Ned legging and puffing and chugging away, and all of us up and screaming at him. The left fielder had reached the ball. He had that good arm. Lenny was coaching at third. Ned was around second and coming toward third. It was up to Lenny. Ned would never make it home against a good throw. Lenny was the one who needed this twelfth run so badly. Ned was too slow to leg it home safely. It was up to Lenny to hold him. Hold him, Lenny, I prayed. Play baseball.

Lenny held up his hands. "Hold it," he shouted.

But either Ned couldn't or wouldn't hear him. With the rain coming down, everyone screaming, third base a slippery shifting sea of mud, that fat old Ned Franks hit the inside of the bag, made a wide turn and kept going for home. He couldn't have stopped even if he wanted to.

"Oh, no," we groaned.

"That's it."

We watched and waited. The left fielder threw. A beautiful throw, low and accurate right on the plate. Ned would be out by ten feet. The only thing he could do was crash into the catcher and make him drop the ball. It was a substitute catcher.

"Hit him, Ned," I shouted.

"Hit him."

Ned hit him. He rumbled into him like a big old express train, and the kid and Ned tumbled together into the mud.

"Out," the ump shouted. "No, safe!"

The ball trickled out of their embrace and rolled to a resting stop in the mud.

Safe!

We'd made it.

Twelve to zip. We ran screaming to Ned and began pounding him, kissing him, hugging him, trying to hoist him onto our shoulders, collapsing under his weight, and while we were doing this, the rain came down.

The rain came down from the skies.

It emptied out of the skies.

The fattest rain you ever saw, great globs of it, pouring, pelting, turning the field into a quagmire, making everyone run for trees, cars, umbrellas. Our guys didn't run though, they just kept jumping up and down screaming hysterically: "Twelve in two, twelve in two—we made it!"

But they were wrong. It wasn't twelve in two at all. It was twelve in one and one half innings. We had to give Baer Machine their bats, and no one could bat in this rain, no one could play on this diamond for another twenty-four hours.

The thunder started then, and lightning. I wanted to cry. If there wasn't so much water around already, I would have cried.

I stood with Lenny under the tree. And the guys stood there, too, and slowly it dawned on them, from our two faces, that something was wrong, and so I told them what was wrong. As the umpires pulled the base stakes out and ran for their car, I told the Print-Alls we'd just wasted twelve runs and that the game would have to be played over again.

It was like air going out of a balloon . . . . No one said a thing. We were getting soaked, but no one moved.

Mr. Phelps, wet to his skin, came over to us. "That's tough luck, boys. I'm sorry."

I think he meant it, too. He turned to Lenny. "I don't know what your coaching tricks are, Lenny, but you sure fired your team up. Do you want me to call you to arrange the make-up game or do you want to call me?"

He thought Lenny was our real coach. Lenny stood there, his face wet, his white suit soaked through, his purple shirt and yellow tie a mess . . . .

"We'll arrange it, Coach," he said. "I'll have one of the boys get in touch with you."

They shook hands.

Although the rain was pouring through the shelter of our tree, Lenny didn't move. We didn't either. He turned to Ned. "Didn't you hear me tell you to wait up?"

Ned shook his head, "I remember you said: Keep running. Go on your own."

Lenny had to smile. "You were on your own all right. Out by ten feet." He slapped Ned on the back. "Good going."

He turned to us.

"I know it's wet, but I want to say something to you boys. You made me real proud." His voice was soft, he kept wiping his face with a handkerchief. "You hit, you hustled, you played like a bunch of major leaguers. You did everything I asked you to. You got the twelve runs and I'm gonna get to Detroit on time—a little wet, but on time." He smiled crookedly. "You didn't win it, and I know that hurts. But for me," he leaned forward, "you're one bunch of gutsy winners."

He looked at me. "Jake, how are you gonna get home?"

"I'll ride with Andy on his bike."

"Say, Mr. Johnson," Danny Kohl said.

"Lenny's my name, Mister Shortstop."

"Lenny . . . will you coach us again?"

Lenny smiled. Like he knew it was coming and what was he going to do? Duck, get hit by the pitch, or hit it.

He hit it. Honestly but sadly.

"Can't do it, Mister Shortstop. Much as I'd like to because you boys are one sweet team. But I got to make my music rehearsals in Detroit, and that's the size of it. Jake, you and Andy hustle the equipment to the car. I'll open the trunk for you. See you guys. You were beautiful."

With that Lenny took off into the rain with those long basketball strides of his. Andy and I walked slowly, sharing the load of the equipment bag. Lenny threw the key out the window to me. I caught it, put the bag in, locked the trunk, and gave him the key back.

"Change into dry clothes when you get home, Jake, and heat up some pea soup. And get to bed early."

I nodded. Just before he closed his car window I said something I don't usually say to that big galoot of an uncle of mine: "Thanks."

He winked at me, and took off in a squeal of tires. We stood in the rain and watched him go. The others came around.

"Boy, he's something else," Jerry said.

"You got a great uncle," Bigler said.

"I wish I had an uncle like that," Tony said.

"Jake, you're lucky, you know that."

I couldn't believe my ears. There we were, standing in the rain having had another victory taken away from us— the second in a row—and they were telling me how lucky I was to be living with Lenny and then how great it would be if we could find a place in Arborville where Lenny and his rock band could rehearse and maybe then he could stay and coach us . . . and on and on they went, wet to the skin, water running down their faces, looking like they were standing at the bottom of the ocean. And happy. Crazy happy.

"You guys are nuts," I said. "Let's get home."

It was a long wet bicycle ride home, but it didn't stop

40

them from making all kinds of stupid plans about finding a place for Lenny's band in Arborville. After a while I got so wet I didn't hear a thing and didn't care either.

Jake and his friends eventually find a place for Lenny's band to practice in Arborville—but Jake has to break one of his legs to do it. Jake has to give up baseball for the season. How do you think he feels about it? You will be surprised. The rest of the novel tells how Jake learns something important from this accident.

Meet the Author: **Alfred Slote**

Alfred Slote says, "Not all readers become authors but all authors are readers. You can't get there any other way." Slote writes every day because, as he says, "If I didn't, I'd feel bad. Icky. It would be like not brushing my teeth. So I write whether I feel like writing or not. I don't wait for inspiration, I just get going every morning."

Slote has had twenty-seven books published, six for adults and twenty-one for young people. *Jake* is one of his favorites. Slote describes it as the story of a boy, a young, tough, but spunky loner who is looking for a father at the same time his team is looking for a coach. Along the way, the team finds a coach—someone very close to Jake—and Jake learns two great lessons: that he can receive without taking, and that he doesn't have to be so tough all the time.

For Alfred Slote, reading is one of the most important things a young person can do. "If you don't read," he says, "you're limiting yourself. All you'll know is what your eyes see and your ears hear. That's good knowledge but it's not enough. Reading will take you beyond and let you meet people you'd otherwise never meet, and travel to worlds you never knew existed."

Responding to Literature

1. A sports story could have a predictable plot, a long and dull description of a game, and very little character development. Do you think this description fits *Jake?* Explain your answer.

2. Jake's day begins as he awakens from his dream and ends with him riding his bike home after the game. Imagine that Jake keeps a journal and goes home to record the important events of his day. What would he write?

3. Alfred Slote, the author of *Jake*, creates suspense in the story through a series of complications in the plot. When Jake and his friends think they have solved one of their problems, something happens, and they realize they haven't solved it at all. Find two examples which show how they think they've solved a problem when another one arises.

4. Jake seems to admire the explorers he is reading about in school. In what ways might Jake think of himself as being like them?

5. Jake jokes with Lenny and says, "I'm not eleven. I'm thirty-five." Give one example from the story that shows how Jake acts like an eleven-year-old and one example that shows how Jake acts like an adult.

6. Think about how Jake gets along in life—at home, at school, and on the baseball field. Would you say he gets along well in all he does? Explain your answer.

JIM

There never was a nicer boy
Than Mrs. Jackson's Jim.
The sun should drop its greatest gold
On him.

Because, when Mother-dear was sick,
He brought her cocoa in.
And brought her broth, and brought her bread.
And brought her medicine.

And, tipping, tidied up her room.
And would not let her see
He missed his game of baseball
Terribly.

Gwendolyn Brooks

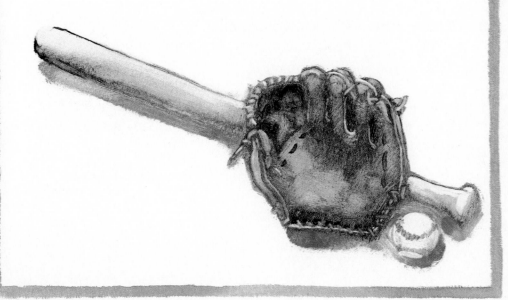

Appreciating Author's Craft

Thinking About Plot Complications

Jake faces a big problem in the beginning of the story— finding a coach for his team. Jake does get a coach for five minutes, but then the author introduces complications in the plot that keep you in suspense as to what will happen next. Plot is a series of important and related events—in this case, the events that lead to Lenny being the temporary coach and the events that lead to the outcome of the game.

Complications are important in the story of Jake. They make you want to keep reading to find out how things will turn out. For example, Jake says on the day of the game: "I made breakfast and that included milk and with Lenny's snores still ringing in my ears, I went off to school. It began to sprinkle. Rain harder, I prayed. Rain real hard and wash out our game."

Authors also help you understand the characters by showing you how they react to unexpected problems.

Writing About Plot Complications

You will be writing a narrative paragraph for your classmates.

Prewriting   The chart below shows two events that the Print-Alls planned and what happened instead. Copy the chart and add two more examples.

What the Print-Alls Planned	What Happened
Lenny would stay for 5 minutes	Lenny has to coach 1½ innings.
Game was to last two innings.	Game lasted 1½ innings.

Now, with a partner, brainstorm three unexpected events that could lead to writing a narrative paragraph about a make-believe Print-Alls game. For example, Jake swallows a bug when he opens his mouth to yell at the umpire.

Writing   Use the three unexpected events to write the narrative paragraph. Remember that a good narrative paragraph includes clue words such as *at first, then, after a while*, and so on. (For more ideas about writing, look at The Writer's Handbook.)

Revising   Go over your draft and underline the clue words you used. Then read your draft to your partner. Between the two of you, see how well the clue words keep the events in order. Then revise your draft. Have your partner check to see that the sentences read smoothly from action to action. Then write your final copy.

Presenting   Now imagine that your paragraph will be on the radio. Practice reading it aloud with a partner so you will be able to read it smoothly. Present your "on the air" broadcast to the class, introducing yourself as the sports announcer and signing off at the end.

Extending Your Reading

Expressing Yourself
Choose one or more of these activities:

Getting to Know You Pretend you are a TV sportscaster and are interviewing Jake, Lenny, and Mr. Phelps for the 6:00 P.M. news. You are doing an in-depth interview. Choose a classmate for each role.

Create a Logo Suppose that Jake and the Print-Alls decide to have a T-shirt for each member of their team. The T-shirt will be decorated with a logo (a symbol or trademark) to identify the team. Design a logo for the team.

Rally Cry "Twelve in two" became one of the rallying cries of the game between the Print-Alls and the Baer Machine team. Make up a rallying cry for one of your school teams or for your favorite professional sports team.

What Do You Think? The poem on page 43 is about a boy who gives up a baseball game to take care of his ailing mother. Do you think Jake would do this if Lenny were sick? Would Lenny miss his rehearsal to take care of Jake? What do you think?

More Books About Getting Along with Others

S.O.R. Losers by Avi. Avon. A group of boys who are not athletically inclined is expected to play on a school soccer team with some surprising and highly amusing results.

The Eighteenth Emergency by Betsy Byars. Penguin. Benjie Fawley is usually an encyclopedia of solutions for emergencies. One problem, though, has Benjie worried—the school bully, Marv Hammerman, is searching for him, and he's good and mad at Benjie.

The Secret Life of Dilly McBean by Dorothy Haas. Bradbury. Dilloway McBean, a wealthy orphan and the hero of this modern science-fiction story, has more than money to his name: he has magnetism. When his guardians move him to a small town, he at last finds some friends. He also begins to learn about his talents and so does a mad computer scientist who is on a suspicious sabbatical.

The Way to Sattin Shore by Philippa Pearce. Penguin. Kate has always believed that her father died the same day she was born. Slowly the jigsaw pieces of the present and past begin to fit together in Kate's mind. Real life turns out to be much more surprising than the family story.

Keep Stompin' Till the Music Stops by Stella Pevsner. Houghton Mifflin. Because of his learning disability, Richard spends a lot of his time just keeping up. Then his family faces a more pressing problem—how to care for his grandfather. Richard learns that what he thinks and does about it really does matter.

Rebecca
of
Sunnybrook Farm

Kate Douglas Wiggin

Introducing

Rebecca
of
Sunnybrook Farm

Rebecca, a lively and high-spirited young girl, is always on the lookout for new adventures. She is sent to live with her aunts Miranda and Jane in Riverboro. Her aunts, especially the stern and proper Miranda, expect her to be well-behaved and ladylike at all times. Rebecca has trouble holding back her enthusiasm, and this makes life in Riverboro a sometimes difficult and challenging experience for her.

Life Long Ago

The story of Rebecca's adventures is set a long time ago. Imagine walking a mile or more, rain or shine, to a one-room schoolhouse. The boys and girls use separate entrances. Once inside they sit at their desks on wooden benches and do their written work on hand-held slates. The room is only heated by a woodburning stove, and the warmest seats are those nearest to it. Instead of jeans, students wear clothes made of other types of cotton called calico and gingham, and the girls' dresses are trimmed with frills called furbelows (fėr′bə lōz′). If it is a Friday afternoon, pupils are expected to recite a poem or story or act out a dialogue with another student for the class and invited guests.

Going home is another long walk. People travel greater distances in stagecoaches and "carryalls." At home children are expected to enter the house through the kitchen door and go up to their rooms by using the back stairs. The front parlor and front stairs are reserved for company and other special occasions.

Why is *Rebecca of Sunnybrook Farm* a Classic?

In spite of these differences in setting and manners, you'll find that if you put Rebecca, her family, or her friends in modern clothes and a modern setting, they might be like people you know. Stories such as *Rebecca of Sunnybrook Farm* that appeal to people in many different time periods are called classics.

Classics last for generations, but the way people write changes. Reading this story, you will find that it is written in a style that is different from today's writing. Kate Douglas Wiggin, the author of *Rebecca of Sunnybrook Farm,* uses longer and more descriptive sentences, and as she tells the story, she sometimes makes comments about the characters and events.

Thinking About Theme

"What happens?" is a question about a story's plot. "What does it all mean?" is a question about a story's theme. Wiggin expresses ideas about life through Rebecca's adventures. These ideas that she expresses are the story's themes.

As you're reading this excerpt on your own, find out how Rebecca learns to deal directly with her problems rather than running away from them.

Rebecca
of
Sunnybrook Farm

CLASSIC

"It is a journey when you carry a nightgown," Rebecca Rowena Randall *tells her mother as she cheerfully climbs into Mr. Cobb's stagecoach. Rebecca is going to live with her aunts Miranda and Jane in Riverboro. Now that her father is dead, her poor mother is having difficulty making ends meet with six other children to care for at Sunnybrook Farm.*

When Miranda learns that Rebecca is coming to stay, she is upset because she had asked for Rebecca's sister Hannah, a quiet girl. "It's just like Aurelia to palm off that wild young one on someone else!" Miranda said.

Rebecca is not much happier with the situation. She writes to her mother that "the parlor is splendid and gives you the creeps and chills . . . there are no good sitting down places except in the kitchen . . . the cat is too old to play with."

About her aunts she writes that "If Aunt Miranda would run away, I think I should like to live with Aunt J. She does not hate me as bad as Aunt M. does."

Rebecca's only escape from this cold, lonely house is at school where she is popular with the other students because of her great enthusiasm and imagination.

COLOR OF ROSE

There were great doings in the little schoolhouse on the hill. Friday afternoon was always the time chosen for dialogues, songs, and recitations, but it cannot be stated that it was a gala day in any true sense of the word. Most of the children hated "speaking pieces," hated the burden of learning them, dreaded the danger of breaking down in them. Miss Dearborn commonly went home with a head-ache and never left her bed during the rest of the afternoon or evening, and the casual female parent who attended the exercises sat on a front bench with beads of cold sweat on her forehead, listening to the all-too-familiar halts and stammers. Sometimes a bellowing infant who had clean forgotten his verse would cast himself bodily on the maternal bosom and be borne out into the open air, where he was sometimes kissed and occasionally spanked, but in any case the failure added an extra dash of gloom and dread to the occasion. The advent of Rebecca had somehow infused a new spirit into these hitherto terrible afternoons. She had taught Elijah and Elisha Simp-son so that they recited three verses of something with such comical effect that they delighted themselves, the teacher, and the school, while Susan, who lisped, had been provided with a humorous poem in which she impersonated a lisping child. Emma Jane and Rebecca had a dialogue, and the sense of companionship buoyed up Emma Jane and gave her self-reliance. In fact, Miss Dearborn announced on this particular Friday morning that the exercises promised to be so interesting that she had invited the doctor's wife, the minister's wife, two members of the school committee, and a few mothers. Living Perkins was asked to decorate one of the blackboards and Rebecca the other. Living, who was the star artist of the school, chose the map of

North America. Rebecca liked better to draw things less realistic, and speedily, before the eyes of the enchanted multitude, there grew under her skillful fingers an American flag done in red, white, and blue chalk, every star in its right place, every stripe fluttering in the breeze. Beside this appeared a figure of Columbia, copied from the top of the cigar box that held the crayons.

Miss Dearborn was delighted. "I propose we give Rebecca a good handclapping for such a beautiful picture—one that the whole school may well be proud of!"

The scholars clapped heartily, and Dick Carter, leaping to his feet, waved his hand and gave a rousing cheer.

Rebecca's heart leaped for joy, and to her confusion she felt the tears rising in her eyes. She could hardly see the way back to her seat, for in her ignorant, lonely little life she had never been singled out for applause, never lauded or crowned, as in this wonderful, dazzling moment. If "nobleness enkindleth nobleness," so does enthusiasm beget enthusiasm, and so do wit and talent enkindle wit and talent. Alice Robinson proposed that the school should sing "Three Cheers for the Red, White, and Blue!" and, when they came to the chorus, all point to Rebecca's flag. Dick Carter suggested that Living Perkins and Rebecca Randall should sign their names to their pictures, so that the visitors would know who drew them. Huldah Meserve asked permission to cover the largest holes in the plastered walls with boughs and fill the water pail with wildflowers. Rebecca's mood was above and beyond all practical details. She sat silent, her heart so full of grateful joy that she could hardly remember the words of her dialogue. At recess she bore herself modestly, notwithstanding her great triumph, while in the general atmosphere of goodwill the Smellie-Randall hatchet was buried[1] and Minnie gathered maple boughs and covered the ugly stove with them, under Rebecca's direction.

Miss Dearborn dismissed the morning session at quarter to twelve,

---

1. Minnie was mean to the Simpson children and Rebecca scolded her for this.

so that those who lived near enough could go home for a change of dress. Emma Jane and Rebecca ran nearly every step of the way, from sheer excitement, only stopping to breathe at the stiles.

"Will your Aunt Mirandy let you wear your best or only your buff calico?" asked Emma Jane.

"I think I'll ask Aunt Jane," Rebecca replied. "Oh, if my pink was only finished! I left Aunt Jane making the buttonholes!"

"I'm going to ask my mother to let me wear her garnet ring," said Emma Jane. "It would look perfectly elegant flashing in the sun when I point to the flag. Good-bye; don't wait for me going back; I may get a ride."

Rebecca found the side door locked, but she knew that the key was under the step, and so, of course, did everybody else in Riverboro, for they all did about the same thing with it. She unlocked the door and went into the dining room to find her lunch laid on the table and a note from Aunt Jane saying that they had gone to Moderation with Mrs. Robinson in her carryall. Rebecca swallowed a piece of bread and butter and flew up the front stairs to her bedroom. On the bed lay the pink gingham dress finished by Aunt Jane's kind hands. Could she, dare she, wear it without asking? Did the occasion justify a new costume, or would her aunts think she ought to keep it for the concert?

I'll wear it, thought Rebecca. *They're not here to ask, and maybe they wouldn't mind a bit; it's only gingham after all and wouldn't be so grand if it wasn't new, and hadn't tape trimming on it, and wasn't pink.*

She unbraided her two pigtails, combed out the waves of her hair and tied them back with a ribbon, changed her shoes, and then slipped on the pretty frock, managing to fasten all but the three middle buttons, which she reserved for Emma Jane.

Then her eyes fell on her cherished pink sunshade, the exact match, and the girls had never seen it. It wasn't quite appropriate for school, but she needn't take it into the room; she would wrap it in a piece of paper, just show it, and carry it coming home. She glanced in the parlor looking glass downstairs and was electrified at the vision. It

seemed almost as if beauty of apparel could go no further than that heavenly pink gingham dress! The sparkle of her eyes, glow of her cheeks, sheen of her falling hair, passed unnoticed in the all-conquering charm of the rose-colored garment. Goodness! It was twenty minutes to one, and she would be late. She danced out the side door, pulled a pink rose from a bush at the gate, and covered the mile between the brick house and the seat of learning in an incredibly short time, meeting Emma Jane, also breathless and resplendent, at the entrance.

"Rebecca Randall!" exclaimed Emma Jane. "You're handsome as a picture!"

"I?" laughed Rebecca. "Nonsense! It's only the pink gingham."

"You're not good-looking every day," insisted Emma Jane, "but you're different somehow. See my garnet ring; Mother scrubbed it in soap and water. How on earth did your Aunt Mirandy let you put on your bran'-new dress?"

"They were both away, and I didn't ask," Rebecca responded anxiously. "Why? Do you think they'd have said no?"

"Miss Mirandy always says no, doesn't she?" asked Emma Jane.

"Ye-es; but this afternoon is very special—almost like a Sunday school concert."

"Yes," assented Emma Jane, "it is, of course, with your name on the board, and our pointing to your flag, and our elegant dialogue, and all that."

That afternoon was one succession of solid triumphs for everybody concerned. There were no real failures at all, no tears, no parents ashamed of their offspring. Miss Dearborn heard many admiring remarks passed upon her ability and wondered whether they belonged to her or partly, at least, to Rebecca. The child had no more to do than several others, but she was somehow in the foreground. It transpired afterwards at various village entertainments that Rebecca couldn't be kept in the background; it positively refused to hold her. Her worst enemy could not have called her pushing. She was ready and willing and never shy, but she sought for no chances of display

She saw her Aunt Miranda standing in the open doorway.

and was, indeed, remarkably lacking in self-consciousness, as well as eager to bring others into whatever fun or entertainment there was. If wherever the MacGregor sat was the head of the table,[2] so in the same way wherever Rebecca stood was the center of the stage. Her clear, high treble soared above all the rest in the choruses, and somehow everybody watched her, took note of her gestures, her whole-souled singing, her irrepressible enthusiasm.

Finally it was all over, and it seemed to Rebecca as if she should never be cool and calm again, as she loitered on the homeward path. There would be no lessons to learn tonight, and the vision of helping with the preserves on the morrow had no terrors for her—fears could not draw breath in the radiance that flooded her soul. There were thick gathering clouds in the sky, but she took no note of them save to be glad that she could raise her sunshade. She did not tread the solid ground at all, or have any sense of belonging to the common human family, until she entered the side yard of the brick house and saw her Aunt Miranda standing in the open doorway. Then with a rush she came back to earth.

2. A saying that means wherever a certain individual is, that person is the center of attention.

ASHES OF ROSES

"There she is, over an hour late; a little more, an' she'da been caught in a thundershower, but she'd never look ahead," said Miranda to Jane, "and added to all her other iniquities, if she aint' rigged out in that new dress, steppin' along with her father's dancin' school steps, and swingin' her parasol for all the world as if she was playactin'. Now I'm the oldest, Jane, an' I intend to have my say out; if you don't like it, you can go into the kitchen till it's over. Step right in here, Rebecca; I want to talk to you. What did you put on that good new dress for, on a school day, without permission?"

"I had intended to ask you at noontime, but you weren't at home, so I couldn't," began Rebecca.

"You did no such a thing; you put it on because you was left alone, though you knew well enough I wouldn't have let you."

"If I'd been *certain* you wouldn't have let me, I'd never have done it," said Rebecca, trying to be truthful, "but I wasn't *certain*, and it was worth risking. I thought perhaps you might, if you knew it was almost a real exhibition at school."

"Exhibition!" exclaimed Miranda scornfully. "You are exhibition enough by yourself, I should say. Was you exhibitin' your parasol?"

"The parasol *was* silly," confessed Rebecca, hanging her head, "but it's the only time in my whole life when I had anything to match it, and it looked so beautiful with the pink dress! Emma Jane and I spoke a dialogue about a city girl and a country girl, and it came to me just the minute before I started how nice it would come in for the city girl, and it did. I haven't hurt my dress a mite, Aunt Mirandy."

"It's the craftiness and underhandedness of your actions that's the worst," said Miranda coldly. "And look at the other things you've done! It seems as if Satan possessed you! You went up the front stairs to your room, but you didn't hide your tracks, for you dropped your handkerchief on the way up. You left the screen out of your bedroom

59

window for the flies to come in all over the house. You never cleared away your lunch nor set away a dish, and *you left the side door unlocked* from half past twelve to three o'clock, so't anybody coulda come in and stolen what they liked!"

Rebecca sat down heavily in her chair as she heard the list of her transgressions. How could she have been so careless? The tears began to flow now as she attempted to explain sins that never could be explained or justified.

"Oh, I'm so sorry!" she faltered. "I was trimming the schoolroom, and got belated, and ran all the way home. It was hard getting into my dress alone, and I hadn't time to eat but a mouthful, and just at the last minute, when I honestly—*honestly*—would have thought about clearing away and locking up, I looked at the clock and knew I could hardly get back to school in time to form in the line, and I thought how dreadful it would be to go in late and get my first black mark on a Friday afternoon, with the minister's wife and the doctor's wife and the school committee all there!"

"Don't wail and carry on now; it's no good cryin' over spilt milk," answered Miranda. "An ounce of good behavior is worth a pound of repentance. Instead of tryin' to see how little trouble you can make in a house that ain't your own home, it seems as if you tried to see how much you could put us out. Take that rose out o' your dress, and let me see the spot it's made on your yoke an' the rusty holes where the wet pin went in. No, it ain't, but it's more by luck than forethought. I ain't got any patience with your flowers and frizzled-out hair and furbelows an' airs an' graces, for all the world like your Miss Nancy[3] father."

Rebecca lifted her head in a flash. "Look here, Aunt Mirandy, I'll be as good as I know how to be. I'll mind quick when I'm spoken to and never leave the door unlocked again, but I won't have my father spoken about unkindly. He was a p-perfectly l-lovely father, that's

---

3. Miss Nancy: Aunt Miranda thinks that the interest of Rebecca's father in music and in dancing is more appropriate for a woman than a man.

what he was, and it's *mean* to call him Miss Nancy!"

"Don't you dare answer me back that imperdent way, Rebecca, tellin' me I'm mean; your father was a vain, foolish, shiftless man, an' you might as well hear it from me as anybody else; he spent your mother's money and left her with seven children to provide for."

"It's s-something to leave s-seven nice children," sobbed Rebecca.

"Not when other folks have to help feed, clothe, and educate 'em," responded Miranda. "Now you step upstairs, put on your nightgown, go to bed, and stay there till mornin'. You'll find a bowl o'crackers an' milk on your bureau, an' I don't want to hear a sound from you till breakfasttime. Jane, run an' take the dish towels off the line, and shut the shed doors; we're goin' to have a turrible shower."

"We've had it, I should think," said Jane quietly as she went to do her sister's bidding. "I don't often speak my mind, Mirandy, but you ought not to have said what you did about Lorenzo. He was what he was and can't be made any different, but he was Rebecca's father, and Aurelia always says he was a good husband."

Miranda . . . said grimly, "Yes, I've noticed that dead husbands are usually good ones; but the truth needs an airin' now and then, and that child will never amount to a hill o' beans till she gets some of her father trounced out of her. I'm glad I said just what I did."

"I daresay you are," remarked Jane, with what might be described as one of her annual bursts of courage, "but all the same, Mirandy, it wasn't good manners, and it wasn't good religion!"

The clap of thunder that shook the house just at that moment made no such peal in Miranda Sawyer's ears as Jane's remark made when it fell with a deafening roar on her conscience.

Perhaps, after all, it is just as well to speak only once a year and then speak to the purpose.

Rebecca mounted the back stairs wearily, closed the door of her bedroom, and took off the beloved pink gingham with trembling fingers. Her cotton handkerchief was rolled into a hard ball, and in the intervals of reaching the more difficult buttons that lay between her shoulder blades and her belt, she dabbed her wet eyes carefully, so

that they should not rain salt water on the finery that had been worn at such a price. She smoothed it out carefully, pinched up the white ruffle at the neck, and laid it away in a drawer with an extra little sob at the roughness of life. The withered pink rose fell on the floor. Rebecca looked at it and thought, *Just like my happy day!* Nothing could show more clearly the kind of child she was than the fact that she instantly perceived the symbolism of the rose and laid it in the drawer with the dress as if she were burying the whole episode with all its sad memories. It was a child's poetic instinct with a dawning hint of woman's sentiment in it.

She braided her hair in the two accustomed pigtails, took off her best shoes (which had happily escaped notice), with all the while a fixed resolve growing in her mind, that of leaving the brick house and going back to the farm. She would not be received there with open arms—there was no hope of that—but she would help her mother about the house and send Hannah to Riverboro in her place. *I hope she'll like it!* she thought in a momentary burst of vindictiveness. She sat by the window trying to make some sort of plan, watching the lightning play over the hilltop and the streams of rain chasing each other down the lightning rod. And this was the day that had dawned so joyfully! It had been a red sunrise, and she leaned on the windowsill, studying her lesson and thinking what a lovely world it was. And what a golden morning! The changing of the bare, ugly little schoolroom into a bower of beauty; Miss Dearborn's pleasure at her success with the Simpson twins' recitation; the privilege of decorating the blackboard; the happy thought of drawing Columbia from the cigar box; the intoxicating moment when the school clapped her! And what an afternoon! How it went on from glory to glory, beginning with Emma Jane's telling her, Rebecca Randall, that she was as "handsome as a picture."

She lived through the exercises again in memory, especially her dialogue with Emma Jane and her inspiration of using the bough-covered stove as a mossy bank where the country girl could sit and watch her flocks. This gave Emma Jane a feeling of such ease that she

never recited better, and how generous it was of her to lend the garnet ring to the city girl, fancying truly how it would flash as she furled her parasol and approached the awestricken shepherdess! She had thought Aunt Miranda might be pleased that the niece invited down from the farm had succeeded so well at school, but no, there was no hope of pleasing her in that or in any other way. She would go to Maplewood on the stage next day with Mr. Cobb and get home somehow from Cousin Ann's. On second thoughts her aunts might not allow it. Very well, she would slip away now and see if she could stay all night with the Cobbs and be off next morning before breakfast.

Rebecca never stopped long to think, more's the pity, so she put on her oldest dress and hat and jacket, then wrapped her nightdress, comb, and toothbrush in a bundle and dropped it softly out of the window. Her room was in the L, and her window at no very dangerous distance from the ground, though had it been, nothing could have stopped her at the moment. Somebody who had gone on the roof to clean out the gutters had left a cleat nailed to the side of the house about halfway between the window and the top of the back porch. Rebecca heard the sound of the sewing machine in the dining room and the chopping of meat in the kitchen, so knowing the whereabouts of both her aunts, she scrambled out of the window, caught hold of the lightning rod, slid down to the helpful cleat, jumped to the porch, used the woodbine trellis for a ladder, and was flying up the road in the storm before she had time to arrange any details of her future movements.

Jeremiah Cobb sat at his lonely supper at the table by the kitchen window. "Mother," as he with his old-fashioned habits was in the habit of calling his wife, was nursing a sick neighbor. Mrs. Cobb was mother only to a little headstone in the churchyard, where reposed "Sarah Ann, beloved daughter of Jeremiah and Sarah Cobb aged seventeen months," but the name of Mother was better than nothing and served at any rate as a reminder of her woman's crown of blessedness.

Rebecca slid down the lightning rod.

The rain still fell, and the heavens were dark, though it was scarcely five o'clock. Looking up from his "dish of tea," the old man saw at the open door a very figure of woe. Rebecca's face was so swollen with tears and so sharp with misery that for a moment he scarcely recognized her. Then, when he heard her voice asking, "Please may I come in, Mr. Cobb?" he cried, "Well, I vow! It's my little lady passenger! Come to call on old Uncle Jerry and pass the time o' day, hev ye? Why, you're wet as sops. Draw up to the stove. I made a fire, hot as it was, thinkin' I wanted somethin' warm for my supper, bein' kind o' lonesome without Mother. She's settin' up with Seth Strout tonight. There, we'll hang your soppy hat on the nail, put your jacket over the chair rail, an' then you turn your back to the stove an' dry yourself good."

Uncle Jerry had never before said so many words at a time, but he had caught sight of the child's red eyes and tear-stained cheeks, and his big heart went out to her in her trouble, quite regardless of any circumstances that might have caused it.

Rebecca stood still for a moment until Uncle Jerry took his seat again at the table and then, unable to contain herself longer, cried, "Oh, Mr. Cobb, I've run away from the brick house, and I want to go back to the farm. Will you keep me tonight and take me up to Maplewood in the stage? I haven't got any money for my fare, but I'll earn it somehow afterwards."

"Well, I guess we won't quarrel 'bout money, you and me," said the old man, "and we've never had our ride together, anyway, though we allers meant to go downriver, not up."

"I shall never see Milltown now!" sobbed Rebecca.

"Come over here side o' me an' tell me all about it," coaxed Uncle Jerry. "Jest set down on that there wooden cricket an' out with the whole story."

Rebecca leaned her aching head against Mr. Cobb's homespun knee and recounted the history of her trouble. Tragic as that history seemed to her passionate and undisciplined mind, she told it truthfully and without exaggeration.

RAINBOW BRIDGES

Uncle Jerry coughed and stirred in his chair a good deal during Rebecca's recital, but he carefully concealed any undue feeling of sympathy, just muttering, "Poor little soul! We'll see what we can do for her!"

"You will take me to Maplewood, won't you, Mr. Cobb?" begged Rebecca piteously.

"Don't you fret a mite," he answered, with a crafty little notion at the back of his mind. "I'll see the lady passsenger through somehow. Now take a bite o' somethin' to eat, child. Spread some o' that tomato preserve on your bread; draw up to the table. How'd you like to set in Mother's place an' pour me out another cup o' hot tea?"

Mr. Jeremiah Cobb's mental machinery was simple and did not move very smoothly save when propelled by his affection or sympathy. In the present case these were both employed to his advantage, and mourning his stupidity and praying for some flash of inspiration to light his path, he blundered along, trusting to Providence.

Rebecca, comforted by the old man's tone and timidly enjoying the dignity of sitting in Mrs. Cobb's seat and lifting the blue china teapot, smiled faintly, smoothed her hair, and dried her eyes.

"I suppose your mother'll be turrible glad to see you back again?" queried Mr. Cobb.

A tiny fear—just a baby thing—in the bottom of Rebecca's heart stirred and grew larger the moment it was touched with a question.

"She won't like it that I ran away, I s'pose, and she'll be sorry that I couldn't please Aunt Mirandy; but I'll make her understand, just as I did you."

"I s'pose she was thinkin' o' your schoolin', lettin' you come down here, but land, you can go to school in Temperance, I s'pose?"

"There's only two months' school now in Temperance, and the farm's too far from all the other schools."

"Oh, well, there's other things in the world beside edjercation," responded Uncle Jerry, attacking a piece of apple pie.

"Ye-es, though Mother thought that was going to be the making of me," returned Rebecca sadly, giving a dry little sob as she tried to drink her tea.

"It'll be nice for you to be all together again at the farm—such a house full o' children!" remarked the dear old deceiver, who longed for nothing so much as to cuddle and comfort the poor little creature.

"It's too full—that's the trouble. But I'll make Hannah come to Riverboro in my place."

"S'pose Mirandy 'n' Jane'll have her? I should be 'most afraid they wouldn't. They'll be kind o' mad at your goin' home, you know, and you can't hardly blame 'em."

This was quite a new thought—that the brick house might be closed to Hannah since she, Rebecca, had turned her back upon its cold hospitality.

"How is this school down here in Riverboro—pretty good?" inquired Uncle Jerry, whose brain was working with an altogether unaccustomed rapidity—so much so that it almost terrified him.

"Oh, it's a splendid school! And Miss Dearborn is a splendid teacher!"

"You like her, do you? Well, you'd better believe she returns the compliment. Mother was down to the store this afternoon buyin' liniment for Seth Strout, an' she met Miss Dearborn on the bridge. They got to talkin' 'bout school, for Mother has summer-boarded a lot o' the schoolmarms an' likes 'em. 'How does the little Temperance

67

girl git along?' asks Mother. 'Oh, she's the best scholar I have!' says Miss Dearborn. 'I could teach school from sunup to sundown if scholars were all like Rebecca Randall,' says she."

"Oh, Mr. Cobb, *did* she say that?" glowed Rebecca, her face sparkling and dimpling in an instant. "I've tried hard all the time, but I'll study the covers right off the books now."

"You mean you would if you'd ben goin' to stay here," interposed Uncle Jerry. "Now ain't it too bad you've jest got to give it all up on account o' your aunt Mirandy? Well, I can't hardly blame ye. She's cranky an' she's sour; I should think she'd ben nussed on a bonnyclabber[4] an' green apples. She needs bearin' with, an' I guess you ain't much on patience, be ye?"

"Not very much," replied Rebecca dolefully.

"If I'd had this talk with ye yesterday," pursued Mr. Cobb, "I believe I'd have advised ye different. It's too late now, an' I don't feel to say you've ben all in the wrong; but if 'twas to do over again, I'd say, well, your aunt Mirandy gives you clothes and board and schoolin' and is goin' to send you to Wareham at a big expense. She's turrible hard to get along with an' kind o' heaves benefits at your head, same's she would bricks; but they're benefits jest the same, an' mebbe it's your job to kind o' pay for 'em in good behavior. Jane's a leetle bit more easygoin' than Mirandy, ain't she, or is she jest as hard to please?"

"Oh, Aunt Jane and I get along splendidly," exclaimed Rebecca; "she's just as good and kind as she can be, and I like her better all the time. I think she kind of likes me, too; she smoothed my hair once. I'd let her scold me all day long, for she understands, but she can't stand up for me against Aunt Mirandy; she's about as afraid of her as I am."

"Jane'll be real sorry tomorrow to find you've gone away, I guess, but never mind, it can't be helped. If she has a kind of a dull time with

---

4. bonnyclabber: Sour, thick milk.

Mirandy, on account o' her bein' so sharp, why, of course, she'd set great store by your comp'ny. Mother was talkin' with her after prayer meetin' the other night. 'You wouldn't know the brick house, Sarah,' says Jane. 'I'm keepin' a sewin' school, an' my scholar has made three dresses. Wat do you think o' that?' says she. 'I've taken a class in Sunday school,' says Jane, 'an' think of renewin' my youth an' goin' to the picnic with Rebecca,' says she, an' Mother declares she never seen her look so young 'n happy."

There was a silence that could be felt in the little kitchen, a silence only broken by the ticking of the tall clock and the beating of Rebecca's heart, which, it seemed to her, almost drowned the voice of the clock. The rain ceased, a sudden rosy light filled the room and through the window a rainbow arch could be seen spanning the heavens like a radiant bridge. Bridges took one across difficult places, thought Rebecca, and Uncle Jerry seemed to have built one over her troubles and given her strength to walk.

"The shower's over," said the old man, filling his pipe; "it's cleared the air, washed the face o' the airth nice an' clean, an' everything tomorrer will shine like a new pin—when you an' I are drivin' upriver."

Rebecca pushed her cup away, rose from the table, and put on her hat and jacket quietly. "I'm not going to drive upriver, Mr. Cobb," she said. "I'm going to stay here and—catch bricks, catch 'em without throwing 'em back, too. I don't know as Aunt Mirandy will take me in after I've run away, but I'm going back now while I have the courage. You wouldn't be so good as to go with me, would you, Mr. Cobb?"

"You'd better b'lieve your Uncle Jerry don't propose to leave till he gits this thing fixed up," cried the old man delightedly. "Now you've had all you can stan' tonight, poor little soul, without gettin' a fit o' sickness, an' Mirandy'll be sore an' cross an' in no condition for argument, so my plan is jest this: to drive you over to the brick house in my top buggy; to have you set back in the corner, an' I git out an'

go to the side door; an' when I git your aunt Mirandy 'n' aunt Jane out int' the shed to plan for a load o' wood I'm goin' to have hauled there this week, you'll slip out o' the buggy and go upstairs to bed. The front door won't be locked, will it?"

"Not this time of night," Rebecca answered, "not till Aunt Mirandy goes to bed, but oh, what if it should be?"

"Well, it won't, an' if 'tis, why we'll have to face it out, though in my opinion there's things that won't bear facin' out an' had better be settled comfortable an' quiet. You see you ain't run away yet; you've only come over here to consult me 'bout runnin' away, an' we've concluded it ain't wuth the trouble. The only real sin you've committed, as I figger it out, was in comin' here by the winder when you'd ben sent to bed. That ain't so very black, an' you can tell your aunt Jane 'bout it come Sunday, when she's chock-full o' religion, an' she can advise you when you'd better tell your aunt Mirandy. I don't believe in deceivin' folks, but if you've hed hard thoughts, you ain't obleeged to own 'em up; take 'em to the Lord in prayer, as the hymn says, and then don't go on hevin' 'em. Now come on; I'm all hitched up to go over to the post office; don't forget your bundle; 'it's always a journey, Mother, when you carry a nightgown'; them's the first words your Uncle Jerry ever heard you say! He didn't think you'd be bringin' your nightgown over to his house. Step in an' curl up in the corner; we ain't goin' to let folks see little runaway gals, 'cause they're goin' back to begin all over ag'in!"

When Rebecca crept upstairs and, undressing in the dark, finally found herself in her bed that night, though she was aching and throbbing in every nerve, she felt a kind of peace stealing over her. She had been saved from foolishness and error, kept from troubling her poor mother, prevented from angering and mortifying her aunts.

Her heart was melted now, and she determined to win Aunt Miranda's approval by some desperate means and to try and forget the one thing that rankled worst, the scornful mention of her father, of

"Step in an' curl up in the corner," said Mr. Cobb.

whom she thought with the greatest admiration and whom she had not yet heard criticized, for such sorrows and disappointments as Aurelia Randall had suffered had never been communicated to her children.

It would have been some comfort to the bruised, unhappy little spirit to know that Miranda Sawyer was passing an uncomfortable night and that she tacitly regretted her harshness, partly because Jane had taken such a lofty and virtuous position in the matter. She could not endure Jane's disapproval, although she would never have confessed to such a weakness.

As Uncle Jerry drove homeward under the stars, well content with his attempts at keeping the peace, he thought wistfully of the touch of Rebecca's head on his knee and the rain of her tears on his hand; of the sweet reasonableness of her mind when she had the matter put rightly before her; of her quick decision when she had once seen the path of duty; of the touching hunger for love and understanding that were so characteristic in her. " . . . To hector and abuse a child like that one! 'Tain't *abuse* exactly, I know, or 'twouldn't be to some o' your elephant-hided young ones, but to that little tender will-o'-the-wisp a hard word's like a lash. Mirandy Sawyer would be a heap better woman if she had a little gravestun to remember, same's Mother 'n' I have."

"I never seen a child improve in her work as Rebecca has today," remarked Miranda Sawyer to Jane on Saturday evening. "That settin' down I gave her was probably just what she needed, and I daresay it'll last for a month."

"I'm glad you're pleased," returned Jane. "A cringing worm is what you want, not a bright, smiling child. Rebecca looks to me as if she'd been through the Seven Years' War. When she came downstairs this morning, it seemed to me she'd grown old in the night. If you follow my advice, which you seldom do, you'll let me take her and Emma Jane down beside the river tomorrow afternoon and bring Emma Jane home to a good Sunday supper. Then, if you'll let her go to Milltown

with the Cobbs on Wednesday, that'll hearten her up a little and coax back her appetite. Wednesday's a holiday on account of Miss Dearborn's going home to her sister's wedding, and the Cobbs and Perkinses want to go down to the Agricultural Fair."

Rebecca's trip to the Agricultural Fair is only the beginning of her further adventures in a wider world than Riverboro. As you will discover by reading the rest of the novel, whether Rebecca is becoming a poet, a soap peddler, or a scholar, or simply working out her ups and downs with Aunt Miranda her adventures are always worth sharing. Life with Rebecca is never dull.

Meet the Author: **Kate Douglas Wiggin**

Kate Douglas Wiggin, born in 1856, wrote several books for children, but *Rebecca of Sunnybrook Farm* is by far the most popular. *Rebecca* was a bestseller when it was first published in 1903 and has been read widely by young people ever since. Rebecca is such an irresistible heroine that film versions of the book have been made three times, in 1917, 1932, and 1938.

Kate Douglas Wiggin began writing in order to raise money for a California Kindergarten Training School. She was a pioneer in developing free kindergartens in the United States and set up the first free kindergarten west of the Rocky Mountains. However, Wiggin was so successful as an author that she eventually gave up her career in education and wrote full time. Kate Douglas Wiggin, like her heroine Rebecca, was a woman of spirit and independence.

Responding to Literature

1. "Yuck. *Rebecca of Sunnybrook Farm* . . . do I have to read it?" So said Paula Danziger, author of the popular *The Cat Ate My Gymsuit,* when asked to write about Kate Douglas Wiggin's novel. Later Danziger said, "Surprise . . . I *really* liked *Rebecca of Sunnybrook Farm.*" Do you feel the same way about *Rebecca?* Tell why.

2. Imagine that Rebecca goes to her room on Saturday evening to write a letter to her sister, Hannah. Begin with what happened at school Friday morning and explain the important events that took place during the rest of the day.

3. Rebecca seems very determined to run away when she arrives at Mr. Cobb's house. Why do you think she changes her mind? Give reasons for your answer.

4. What does Rebecca mean when she tells Mr. Cobb that she is going to ". . . catch bricks . . . without throwing them back . . ."?

5. Rebecca makes her decision to leave her aunts' house without thinking about whom, other than herself, it might affect. What does her visit with Mr. Cobb help her to discover about the effect of her decision on other people in Riverboro and at Sunnybrook Farm?

Protest

How can I show them
    when they say I must
    that I don't want to?
Why can't they see
    that I just can't
    and what's more shan't?
How can I tell them
    that what *they* want
    I do not?
I cannot.
So I say
Okay.

Felice Holman

Truly My Own

I think if I searched a thousand lands
and twice the number in rainbows,
I'd never find one human being
who chose the things that I chose
a person who wanted the things I wanted
or sought what I sought to be

I'd never find one human being
like or comparison to me
and if I traveled seven seas
I still would be alone
for there is no one who thinks like me
for my dreams are truly my own.

Vanessa Howard, Age 13

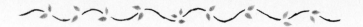

Appreciating Author's Craft

Thinking About Theme

"What happens in *Rebecca of Sunnybrook Farm?*" You might summarize the plot this way: Rebecca is criticized by her aunt because she did not receive permission to wear a new dress to the school recital. Rebecca decides to run away but then changes her mind.

"What does the story mean?" To find out what the author means, think about the underlying meaning, or theme, of the story. The **theme** is the meaning behind things that happen. A story may have one theme or several. A good author leads you to discover connections between your life and the lives of the characters of the story. The theme helps you make that connection. Wiggin has provided several themes in *Rebecca,* one of which is that friends can help us see our way through problems. Think about how Uncle Jerry helps Rebecca get herself out of a terrible mess.

Writing About Theme

Some of the themes in *Rebecca* might fit the life of someone you know. You will write about one of these themes in a personal narrative paragraph to share with your friends.

Prewriting The list on the next page gives two other possible themes. Copy the list, and add examples from the story that give support to these themes.

Possible Themes	Events and Reasons
1. Dealing with problems is better than running away from them. 2. Changes can be both good and bad	

Writing Choose one of the themes on your list. Select an event or series of events from the life of someone you know to illustrate the theme. Don't state your theme directly—let the events show the theme. Put the events that illustrate your theme in the order they occurred. (For ideas about writing, look at The Writer's Handbook.)

Revising Read your draft to a partner and discuss how well the theme is developed. Then revise your draft. Make any changes you need so the events are in order and the theme is strong, but not stated. Now proofread for errors. Then write your final copy.

Presenting Ask your classmates to listen carefully as you read your narrative paragraph to see if they can discover the theme.

Extending Your Reading

Expressing Yourself
Choose one or more of these activities:

Draw Rebecca's Flag Re-create the
American flag that Rebecca drew on the
blackboard. You will need to go to the library
to find a picture of the flag as it appeared in
1903 when this story was first published.

Recite a Poem Imagine that it is Friday afternoon recital time
and you are one of the students in Rebecca's class. Find a
short poem and practice reciting it to a partner as one of the
following characters: Rebecca, Emma Jane, Susan Simpson,
Living Perkins, or Samuel Simpson. Recite the poem for the
entire class, and see if they can guess which character you
are.

Picturesque Titles The author uses symbolism a number of
times in this excerpt. (See Student's Handbook of Literary
Terms for an explanation of symbolism.) The author entitles
the chapter in which Rebecca has her triumph at school,
"Color of Rose." The next chapter where her aunt is angry
with Rebecca is called "Ashes of Roses." The last chapter in
which Rebecca runs away to Uncle Jerry is entitled "Rainbow
Bridge." Explain how these titles hint at the action in each
chapter.

Author of Poem The poem "Protest" on page 75 is by Felice
Holman. Do you think Rebecca could have written a poem
similar to this? Why or why not?

More Books About Turning Points

Queen of Hearts by Vera and Bill Cleaver. Lippincott. Wilma is sure that her grandmother, a tough, independent old woman, doesn't like her. When Granny chooses Wilma to take care of her while she's sick, Wilma finds ways of making things work that no one else can.

The Night Journey by Kathryn Lasky. Viking. Rachel has been told not to upset her great-grandmother by encouraging her to think about the past. But the old woman's secrets are too fascinating to be forgotten. Bit by bit, she tells the story of her amazing childhood escape from Russia in 1900.

Night of the Twisters by Ivy Ruckman. Harper. Based on an actual event which took place in 1980, this story is told by young Dan Hatch, whose town is suddenly destroyed and thrown into confusion by a series of tornadoes. Dan manages to rescue his baby brother in the first moments of disaster. Still more unexpected challenges await him, and the life of his town will never be the same.

Maggie Marmelstein for President by Marjorie Weinman Sharmat. Harper. When Maggie decides to run for president of her sixth-grade class, she starts out full of zest and optimism. After all, thinks Maggie, she can easily beat Thad Smith, her opponent and sometime friend. But nothing about the election seems to go just as planned.

Buffalo Moon by G. Clifton Wisler. Lodestar. Fourteen-year-old Willie Delamer is already a first-rate rancher when his parents decide to send him away to the city to be educated. Willie runs away and finds courage in his choice to stay in his native territory by living with the Comanches and learning their ways.

MYTHS

Stories That Explain Why

MYTHS

Stories That Explain Why

The beautiful colors of a flower, the graceful flight of a bird, the majestic streak of lightning across a stormy sky are all almost magical examples of nature's work. People have observed these wonders for as long as human beings have lived on this planet. For as long as people have been here, they've tried to understand and explain the wonders of nature.

Trying to Understand It All

Myths are stories told by people all over the world to explain what they observed. Sometimes myths explain the origins of things. These myths fall into a category known as *pourquoi* (pür kwä') tales. *Pourquoi* is the French word for *why* and it perfectly describes this category. These tales explain why a woodpecker's head is red, why a rose has thorns, or why thunder crashes. Of course, when these stories began, the scientific explanation for the workings of nature was unknown. Today, even though scientists may know about atoms, cells, and laser beams, the *pourquoi* tales explain the world in a fresh and imaginative way. Other types of myths are creation myths and hero myths. (For more about myths, see Handbook of Literary Terms.)

Myths from Around the World

Each culture has had its own myths to explain the natural world. Most cultures have sun myths, for example, but many myths deal with phenomena characteristic of a specific locale. In the Hawaiian Islands, the Polynesians made up stories to explain the things they saw, such as the eruption of volcanoes, the mighty surf, and man-eating sharks. In Puerto Rico, Pura Belpré heard stories about Royal Palm trees and hummingbirds. As a child she heard these tales told aloud at quiet siesta time or while seated under almond trees in little villages. Because myths were passed on by word of mouth, there are often several different versions of the same story.

What to Look for in Myths

People today now understand the world in a much different way than did the ancient people who created these myths, but the myths have survived thousands of years because they are such good stories. They have action, suspense, and basic conflict. The characters sometimes have supernatural powers, but often have feelings that are very human and easy to understand. The three nature myths that follow are still told today because the characters have real feelings and there is action in the stories.

As you're reading these myths on your own, find out how each myth explains a part of nature.

Narcissus and Echo

A Greek myth retold by Bernard Evslin

Of all the nymphs[1] of river and wood, a dryad[2] named
Echo was the best beloved. She was not only very
beautiful and very kind, but had a haunting musical voice.
The other dryads and naiads[3] and creatures of the wood
begged her to sing to them and tell them stories—and she
did. She was a great favorite of Aphrodite, who used to
come all the way from Olympus to chat with Echo and
listen to her tales. Being goddess of love, she was
especially concerned with gossip—which is mostly about

---

1. nymph (nimf), a lesser goddess of nature, found in seas, rivers,
   fountains, hills, woods, or trees
2. dryad (drī′əd), a nymph that lives in a tree
3. naiad (nā′ad), a nymph guarding a stream or spring

who loves whom and what they are doing about it. And Echo kept her entertained as no one else could.

Aphrodite said, "All the world asks me for favors, Echo. But not you. Tell me, is there not someone you would wish to love you? Some man, boy, god? Just name him, and I will send my son Eros, who will shoot him with his arrow and make him fall madly in love with you."

But Echo laughed and said, "Alas, sweet Aphrodite, I have seen no man who pleases me. And gods are too fickle. Man and boy—I look at them all very carefully— but none seem beautiful enough to match my secret dream. When the time comes, I shall ask your help—if it ever comes."

"Well, you are lovely enough to demand the best," said Aphrodite. "On the other hand, the best happens only once. And who can wait so long? However, I am always at your service."

Now Echo did not know this, but at that moment the most beautiful boy in the whole world was lost in that very wood, trying to find his way out. His name was Narcissus, and he was so handsome that he had never been able to speak to any woman except his mother. For any girl who saw him immediately fainted. Of course this also gave him a very high opinion of himself. And as he went through the woods, he thought:

"Oh, how I wish I could find someone as beautiful as I. I will not be friends with anyone less perfect in face or form. Why should I? This leaves me lonely, true, but it's better than lowering myself."

So he walked along the path, but he was going the wrong way, getting more and more lost. In the other part of the wood Echo had just said farewell to Aphrodite, and was coming back to the hollow tree in which she lived. She came to a glade in the forest and there saw something that made her stop in astonishment and hide behind a tree. For whom did she see but Zeus himself—king of the gods, lord of the sky. He was leaning on his volt-blue lightning shaft, holding a river nymph by the shoulder, and she was smiling up at him.

"Well," said Echo. "He's at it again. Won't Aphrodite enjoy hearing about *this!*"

But then her attention was caught by something else. She turned to see a tall purple-clad figure moving through the trees toward the glade. She recognized Hera, queen of the gods, jealous wife of Zeus, and she realized that Hera must have heard of what Zeus was doing, and was coming to catch him. And so the kind-hearted nymph hurried forward and curtsied low before Hera, saying, "Greetings, great queen. Welcome to the wood."

"Hush, fool!" whispered Hera. "Don't say a word! I am trying to take someone by surprise."

"This is a proud day for us," said Echo, thinking swiftly, "to be visited by so many gods. Just two minutes ago, Zeus was here looking for you."

"Zeus? Looking for *me?* Are you sure?"

"The great Zeus. Your husband. He asked me whether I had seen you. Said he had heard you were coming this way, and he wished very much to meet you. When I told him I had not seen you, he flew off looking very disappointed."

"Really? Can it be so? Zeus looking for me? Disappointed? Well—miracles never cease. Which way did he go?"

"Oh—toward Olympus."

"Thank you, child," said Hera. "I'll be going too."

And she disappeared.

In the meantime Zeus, hearing voices, had hidden himself and the river nymph in the underbrush. When Hera left, he came out, and to thank Echo he gave her a shining blue sapphire ring from his own finger.

Hera, having returned to Olympus, found that Zeus was not there. She realized that something was wrong and sped back to the forest. The first thing she saw was Echo admiring a large sapphire ring that burned on her finger like a fallen star. Hera recognized the ring and immediately understood that the nymph had tricked her in some way and had been given the ring as a reward.

"Wretched creature!" she cried. "I know what you have done. I see the gift you have been given. And I would not have it said that my husband is more generous than I. So I too shall reward you for what you have done. Because you have used your voice for lying, you shall never be able to say anything to anyone again—except the last words that have been said to you. Now try lying."

"Try lying," said Echo.

"No more shall you meddle in high concerns—no more shall you gossip and tell stories and sing songs—but endure this punishment evermore . . ."

"Evermore . . ." said Echo, sobbing.

And Hera went away to search for Zeus. And the nymph, weeping, rushed toward her home in the hollow tree. As she was going she saw once again the dazzling brightness that was the face of a god and she stopped to see. It was no god, but a lad about her own age, with black hair and eyes the color of the sapphire Zeus had given her. When she saw him, all the grief of her punishment dissolved and she was full of a great laughing joy. For here was the boy she had been looking for all her life, as beautiful as her secret dream—a boy she could love.

She danced toward him. He stopped and said, "Pardon me, but can you show me the path out of the wood?"

"Out of the wood . . ." said Echo.

"Yes," he said. "I'm lost. I've been wandering here for hours, and I can't seem to find my way out of the wood."

"Out of the wood . . ."

"Yes. I've told you twice. I'm lost. Can you help find the way?"

"The way . . ."

"Are you deaf, perhaps? Why must I repeat everything?"

"Repeat everything . . ."

"No, I will not! It's a bore! I won't do it!"

"Do it . . ."

"Look, I can't stand here arguing with you. If you don't want to show me the way, well then, I'll just try to find someone who can."

"Who can . . ."

Narcissus glared at her and started away. But she came to him and put her arms around him and tried to kiss his face.

"Oh, no—none of that!" said Narcissus, shoving her away. "You're just like all the rest of them, aren't you? They faint, and you say stupid things. Stop it! You can't kiss me."

"Kiss me . . ."

"No!"

"No . . ."

And she tried to kiss him again. Again he pushed her aside. She fell on her knees on the path and hugged his legs and lifted her lovely tear-streaked face to his, trying to speak. But she could not.

"No!" he said. "Let go! You can't hold me here. I will not love you."

"Love you . . ."

He tore himself from her grip and strode away. "Farewell," he called.

"Farewell . . ."

She looked after him until he disappeared. And when he was gone, she felt such sadness, such terrible tearing grief, such pain in every part of her, that it seemed she was being torn apart by white-hot little pincers, torn flesh from bone.

And since she could not speak, she said this prayer to herself:

"Oh, Aphrodite, fair goddess, you promised me a favor. Do me one now. Hear me though I am voiceless. My love has disappeared, and I must disappear too, for I cannot bear the pain."

And Aphrodite, in the garden on Olympus, heard this prayer—for prayers do not have to be spoken to be heard. She looked down upon the grieving nymph and pitied her and made her disappear. Her body melted into thin cool air, so that the pain was gone. All was gone . . . except her voice, for Aphrodite could not bear to lose the sound of that lovely story-telling voice. The goddess said, "I grant you your wish—and one thing more. You have not asked vengeance upon the love that has betrayed you. You are too sweet and kind. But *I* shall take vengeance, nevertheless. I decree now that whoever has caused you this pain will know the same terrible longing. He will fall in love with someone who cannot return his love—and will forever desire and never achieve."

But Narcissus knew nothing of this—of Echo's grief nor Aphrodite's vow. He wandered the forest path, thinking. "All these girls who love me on sight—it's too bad I cannot find one as beautiful as I. For until I do, I shall not love. And all their loving will be only vexation to me."

He sat down on the bank of a river to rest. Not a river really, but a finger of the river—a clear little stream moving slowly through rocks. The sun shone on it; it became a mirror, holding the trees and the sky upside down, and a small silver trembling sun. And Narcissus, looking into the stream, saw a face.

He blinked his eyes and looked again. It was still there—the most beautiful face he had ever seen. As beautiful, he knew, as his own, but with a nimbus of light behind it so that the hair was blurred and looked long— like a girl's. He gazed and gazed and could not have enough of it. He knew that he could look upon this face forever and still not be satisfied. He put out his hand to touch her. The water trembled and she disappeared.

"A water nymph," he thought. "A lovely dryad— daughter of the river god, no doubt. The loveliest of his daughters. She is shy. Like me, she can't bear to be touched. Ah—here she is again."

The face looked at him out of the stream. Again, very timidly, he reached his hand. Again the water trembled and the face disappeared.

"I will stay here until she loves me," he said to himself. "She may hide now, but presently she will recognize me too. And come out." And he said aloud: "Come out, lovely one."

And the voice of Echo, who had followed him to the stream, said, "Lovely one . . ."

"Hear that, hear that!" cried Narcissus, overjoyed. "She cares for me too. You do, don't you? You love me."

"Love me . . ."

"I do—I do—Finally I have found someone to love. Come out, come out—Oh, will you never come out?"

"Never come out . . ." said Echo.

"Don't say that, please don't say that. Because I will stay here till you do. This, I vow."

"I vow . . ."

"Your voice is as beautiful as your face. And I will stay here, adoring you forever."

"Forever . . ."

And Narcissus stayed there, leaning over the stream, watching the face in the water, watching, watching . . . sometimes pleading with it to come out, hearing its voice answer. Coaxing, begging, looking. . . . Day after day he stayed there, night after night, never moving, never eating, never looking away from the face. He stayed there so long that his legs grew into the bank of the river and became roots. His hair grew long, tangled, leafy. And his pale face and blue eyes became delicate blue and white petals—the flower Narcissus, which lives on the riverbanks and leans over watching its reflection in the water.

And there you can find it till this day. And in the woods too, when all is still, you will sometimes come upon Echo. And if you call to her in a certain way, she will answer your call.

Responding to Literature

1. Anne Terry White, author of *The Golden Treasury of Myths and Legends,* writes that the Greek gods "cannot die because the Greeks invented such wonderful myths about them." Now that you've read the myth of Narcissus and Echo, do you agree with the author's opinion of Greek myths? Tell why or why not.

2. The story begins by introducing Echo, a beloved dryad, and Narcissus, the most handsome boy in the world. At the end, Narcissus is a flower on the riverbank, and only Echo's haunting voice remains. Retell the important events that caused these amazing changes to take place.

3. Imagine that Echo is not punished by Hera and does not repeat her words when she meets Narcissus. Write a conversation Echo and Narcissus might have had.

4. Echo was punished by Hera for lying. Narcissus was punished by Aphrodite for causing Echo such grief. For which character do you feel more sorry? Tell why.

Light and Water

The light above—golden, orange, green—
among the misty clouds.

Oh, trees without leaves,
rooted in water,
branching in the light!—

Below, the water—green, orange, golden—
among the misty vapors.

Among the misty vapors, among the misty clouds,
light and water—what magics!—vanish.

Juan Ramón Jiménez

Luz y Aqua

La luz arriba—oro, naranja, verde—,
entre las nubes vagas.

¡Ay, árboles sin hojas;
raíces en el agua,
ramajes en la luz!—

Abajo, el agua—verde, naranja, oro—,
entre la vaga bruma.

Entre la bruma vaga, entre las vagas nubes,
luz y agua—; ¡qué májicas!—se van.

Juan Ramón Jiménez

The Legend of the Hummingbird

A Puerto Rican folk tale retold
by Pura Belpré

Between the towns of Cayey and Cidra, far up in the hills, there was once a small pool fed by a waterfall that tumbled down the side of the mountain. The pool was surrounded by pomarosa trees, and the Indians used to call it Pomarosa Pool. It was the favorite place of Alida, the daughter of an Indian chief, a man of power and wealth among the people of the hill.

One day, when Alida had come to the pool to rest after a long walk, a young Indian came there to pick some fruit from the trees. Alida was surprised, for he was not of her tribe. Yet he said he was no stranger to the pool. This was where he had first seen Alida, and he had often returned since then to pick fruit, hoping to see her again.

He told her about himself to make her feel at home. He confessed, with honesty and frankness, that he was a

member of the dreaded Carib tribe that had so often
attacked the island of Borinquen.[1] As a young boy, he had
been left behind after one of those raids, and he had stayed
on the island ever since.

Alida listened closely to his story, and the two became
friends. They met again in the days that followed, and
their friendship grew stronger. Alida admired the young
man's courage in living among his enemies. She learned to
call him by his Carib name, Taroo, and he called her Alida,
just as her own people did. Before long, their friendship
had turned into love.

Their meetings by the pool were always brief. Alida was
afraid their secret might be discovered, and careful though
she was, there came a day when someone saw them and
told her father. Alida was forbidden to visit the Pomarosa
Pool, and to put an end to her romance with the stranger,
her father decided to marry her to a man of his own
choosing. Preparations for the wedding started at once.

Alida was torn with grief, and one evening she cried out
to her god: "O Yukiyú, help me! Kill me or do what you
will with me, but do not let me marry this man whom I do
not love!"

And the great god Yukiyú took pity on her and changed
her into a delicate red flower.

Meanwhile Taroo, knowing nothing of Alida's sorrow,
still waited for her by the Pomarosa Pool. Day after day he
waited. Sometimes he stayed there until a mantle of stars
was spread across the sky.

One night the moon took pity on him. "Taroo," she called
from her place high above the stars. "O Taroo, wait no

---

1. Borinquen (bō rēn'ken), called Puerto Rico today

longer for Alida! Your secret was made known, and Alida was to be married to a man of her father's choosing. In her grief she called to her god, Yukiyú; he heard her plea for help and changed her into a red flower."

"Ahee, ahee!" cried Taroo. "O moon, what is the name of the red flower?"

"Only Yukiyú knows that," the moon replied.

Then Taroo called out: "O Yukiyú, god of my Alida, help me too! Help me to find her!"

And just as the great god had heard Alida's plea, he listened now to Taroo and decided to help him. There by the Pomarosa Pool, before the moon and the silent stars, the great god changed Taroo into a small many-colored bird.

"Fly, Colibrí,[2] and find your love among the flowers," he said.

Off went the Colibrí, flying swiftly, and as he flew his wings made a sweet humming sound.

In the morning the Indians saw a new bird darting about among the flowers, swift as an arrow and brilliant as a jewel. They heard the humming of its wings, and in amazement they saw it hover in the air over every blossom, kissing the petals of the flowers with its long slender bill. They liked the new bird with the music in its wings, and they called it Hummingbird.

Ever since then the little many-colored bird has hovered over every flower he finds, but returns most often to the flowers that are red. He is still looking, always looking, for the one red flower that will be his lost Alida. He has not found her yet.

––––––––––

2. Colibrí (kō lē brē'), hummingbird

Responding to Literature

1. For many years in many countries, young women had to marry whoever their parents picked out for them even though they often loved someone else. A great many famous stories and folktales concern this conflict. How would you feel if you had no say about who you were to marry?

2. Imagine a young Puerto Rican child seeing a hummingbird darting among the flowers for the first time. Now imagine you are that child's parent. Tell the important events of the myth to explain the hummingbird to your child.

3. Do you think the ending of this myth is happy or sad? Tell why.

4. If you could be changed into another living creature, what would it be? Explain your reasons.

Half Moon

The moon goes over the water.
How tranquil the sky is!
She goes scything slowly
the old shimmer from the river;
meanwhile a young frog
takes her for a little mirror.

Federico García Lorca

Media Luna

La luna va por el agua.
¡Cómo está el cielo tranquilo!
Va segando lentamente
el temblor viejo del río
mientras que una rana joven
la toma por espejito.

Federico García Lorca

Maui Traps Sun

A Hawaiian myth retold by Vivian L. Thompson

*On the Wailuku River, not far from Rainbow Falls, lived
the half-god, Maui. His mother, the goddess Hina, lived
behind the fall in the Cave-of-Mists. In those times the
days were short, but Maui found a way to lengthen
them . . .*

Maui was a young man of strength and courage. He had a
magic club, a magic spear, and a magic canoe paddle, all
given to him by his grandmother. In addition to these, he
had special powers because he was the son of a goddess.
He was very fond of his mother, Hina, and visited her
nearly every day; for his stepfather, Aikanaka-the-
Wanderer, was often away from home.

The goddess Hina was known throughout the islands for
her beauty and for the fine bark cloth she made. From the
time Sun came through the eastern gate until he went

100

through the western gate, Hina worked at her tapa.[1] She gathered the bark herself from mulberry trees. She brought sea water in which to soak it. She pounded the wet bark on her tapa log.

One time when Maui was watching her, he said, "You spend all your days making tapa!"

Hina laid aside her wooden beater, smiling in a sad way. "For those who make tapa, the day is never long enough. This piece is ready to dry but already Sun turns toward the west. My tapa will still be damp when Evening Star hangs in the sky."

"This is Sun's fault. He travels too swiftly. I shall find him and tell him so!"

"O Maui, Sun is a god!"

"We are gods, too," Maui said.

"But small ones, with small power. And you are but a half-god," his mother reminded him. "Sun has great powers. No one has ever gone close to him and lived!"

"Then I shall be the first!" Maui boasted. "I shall catch Sun and make him promise to go more slowly."

Hina warned, "Take your magic club and paddle. You will surely need all the power you have."

First, Maui made snares. He gathered coconut fiber and twisted eight strong cords. At the end of each he tied a noose.

Then, as Evening Star appeared in the sky, he coiled his snares in his canoe, laid his magic club beside them, and picked up his magic paddle. One stroke carried him down

---

1. tapa (tä′pə), cloth made from bark

the river, a second stroke to the island where Sun made his home in the crater of a dead volcano.

Maui left his canoe, took his eight snares and his magic club, and started up to House-of-Sun.

Swiftly he climbed the grassy slope. Slowly he climbed the steep side of the volcano. At the top, in the crater, Sun lay fast asleep under a blanket of clouds. Silently, Maui laid his snares. Then he hid behind a lava rock and slept through the night.

Before daybreak, Maui woke. Clouds were just beginning to roll out of the crater. Soon over its rim came Sun's longest leg, his first glittering ray of sunrise. Down the slope it came and into the center of Maui's snare it stepped.

Maui drew the cord tight and fastened it to the rock.

"What is this?" roared Sun.

"You are my prisoner," said Maui.

"Let me go at once!" Sun commanded. "I have a long journey to make."

"You will journey nowhere until you promise to travel more slowly," said Maui.

"I go swiftly so my night's rest will be longer. Why should I promise such a thing?" Sun demanded.

Maui picked up his magic club before he answered. "Because my mother Hina needs more time to dry her tapa."

"Tapa! I have no time for such things!"

Maui said no more. He swung his magic club against Sun's longest leg, breaking off a piece.

Sun screamed in pain and anger. He scrambled to get three more legs over the rim of the crater. But Maui had laid his snares wisely, and each leg was caught fast. Sun thrashed about, blowing his fiery breath. Maui backed off and tied the three cords fast.

Four legs crawled over the crater's rim. Four more legs were caught. Now Sun was frightened. The more he struggled, the tighter the nooses became. One leg was broken and seven more tied fast. He began to bluster.

"You dare not kill me! Without my light, plants and trees would die! Without plants, your people would die!"

Maui looked up from the cord he was tying. "Sun, let us bargain. Promise to travel more slowly for part of the time and I shall let you go."

"Ae.² I promise," said Sun crossly.

With his magic club, Maui broke the cords. Sun hurried off across the sky, and Maui paddled back with the good news for Hina.

After that, for part of each year, Sun traveled at his usual speed. Days were short and darkness came early.

---

2. ae (ä'ē), yes.

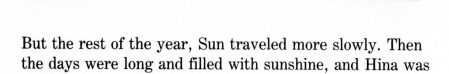

But the rest of the year, Sun traveled more slowly. Then the days were long and filled with sunshine, and Hina was able to dry her tapa.

Sun kept his promise. If there were times when he wanted to hurry, his broken ray reminded him of the strength and courage of the young half-god, Maui.

Meet the Authors

Bernard Evslin writes about Greek stories, "These were the first stories I ever heard. I was four years old, and my young uncle was practicing his Greek on me. He read me the *Iliad* and the *Odyssey*, translating as he went. The unknown words poured over me like dark music, and when he turned to English it was always a letdown . . . there seemed something missing, the golden hero voices, sea whispers . . .

"Later, modeling myself after my uncle, I studied Greek and Latin and read the stories the way (the ancient writers) told them . . . and knew the old enchantment. Then I went to them in most of their English versions, and again felt this terrible loss. So I began to tell them myself."

Pura Belpré began working in the New York Public Library as a librarian. She learned about the folklore of the world but, to her regret, could not find any folk tales from her native Puerto Rico. Later she was sent to library school for further training. There, in a storytelling class, the teacher asked the students to write a story. Belpré wrote a tale that her grandmother had told her. This was the beginning of Pura Belpré's career as a writer of folk tales.

Vivian L. Thompson, after many years spent on a sugar plantation, now lives in a town house in Hilo. Originally she went to Hawaii from the Mainland to attend a friend's wedding and spend two weeks. She remained to teach, to marry, and to write. Now, thirty-nine years and sixteen books later, she says it is beginning to look as though she might stay. Of those sixteen books, six are retellings of Hawaiian myths and legends, based on authentic source materials.

Responding to Literature

1. Myths helped explain why things happened in nature. But they also are good stories. Now that you've read three myths, choose the one you'd like best to tell, as a storyteller. Tell why.

2. At the end of the myth, Maui returns to tell his mother, Hina, the good news of his meeting with Sun. Explain what Maui tells Hina about the steps he took to get Sun to change.

3. Although he is only a half-god, Maui is one of the most popular characters in the myths of the Pacific Islands. What qualities does Maui have that make him a favorite?

4. The three myths help you find out why the narcissus, echo, and hummingbird exist and why the sun travels as it does. Explain briefly how these happenings occur in each myth.

5. If you could change or alter any event that occurs in nature, what would that be? Tell why.

The Sun Is a Golden Earring

Sayings collected by Natalia M. Belting

Some say the sun is a golden earring,
the earring of a beautiful girl.
A white bird took it from her
when she walked in the fields one day.
But it caught on a spider web
that stretches between the homes of men
and the homes of the gods.

—from India

The dark gray clouds,
the great gray clouds,
the black rolling clouds are elephants
going down to the sea for water.
They draw up the water in their trunks.
They march back again across the sky.
They spray the earth with the water,
and men say it is raining.

—from India

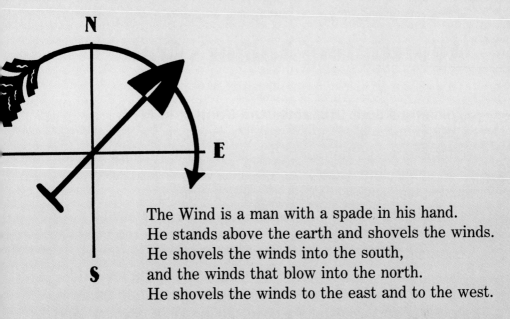

The Wind is a man with a spade in his hand.
He stands above the earth and shovels the winds.
He shovels the winds into the south,
and the winds that blow into the north.
He shovels the winds to the east and to the west.

—from Lapland

Once, when the sky was very near the earth,
a woman hoeing in her garden took off her necklace
and hung it in the sky.
The stars are her silver necklace.

—from the Hawaiian Islands

Appreciating Author's Craft

Thinking About Character and Conflict in Myth

Since there was such a specific purpose for a myth, the characters and the plot of the story had to be kept simple. The characters usually represented very few qualities; the action was usually limited to a few incidents.

Myths are filled with characters who have amazing powers. Even the gods act in a way that mere mortals can understand, and their characters and behavior are tied directly to the explanation of nature given in the myth. In the Hawaiian myth, for example, Sun is described as a powerful god, whose light gives life to plants, animals, and humans, yet Sun also sleeps in a crater, under a blanket of clouds. When Maui asks Sun to travel more slowly, Sun responds: "I go swiftly so my night's rest will be longer. Why should I promise such a thing?" Even the powerful Sun likes his own comforts. There is something both simple and satisfying about this explanation for why, during some seasons, the sun appears in our sky for a shorter time.

In order to be short and still explain a natural event, a myth must have action that is simple and direct. Usually the action is in the form of a conflict between gods or between gods and humans. How the characters resolve the conflict is what becomes the lesson we learn about nature.

Writing About Character and Conflict in Myth

What if Echo persuaded Hera to give Echo's voice back? Or what if Sun persuaded Maui to let him go? Imagine a sequel to one of the myths, one in which you write a paragraph that is so persuasive that you change the outcome of the myth.

Prewriting The chart below shows characters and the conflict situations. The last column gives an example of one character's persuasive statement. Copy the chart and use your imagination to complete the other examples.

Character	Conflict situation	Persuasive statement
Echo	Lies to Hera and loses her voice.	I want my voice back because . . .
Narcissus	Falls in love with his reflection.	
Alida	Father wants her to marry someone else.	
Maui	Captures Sun	

Review your chart and choose one character. Think of several reasons that will help your character win the argument.

Writing Now write your persuasive paragraph. You may use your persuasive statement from the chart as a basis for your topic sentence. (For ideas about writing, look at The Writer's Handbook.)

Revising Have a partner read your paper and comment on the persuasiveness of your argument. Make changes so that your argument is clearly stated, and you have good reasons to back it up.

Presenting Try to win your argument in a role-playing scene. Choose another partner to be the other character. Your partner may give reasons for not being persuaded.

Extending Your Reading

Expressing Yourself
Choose one or more of these activities:

Do a Dramatic Reading Turn to pages 91, 92 to find the scene where Narcissus speaks to his reflection. Practice Narcissus's and Echo's lines with a partner. Then present your reading to the class, having Echo seated where she cannot be seen by the class as she says her lines.

Research Myths Go to the library to find myths from the country or continent of your ancestors. Find one that you particularly like and share it with the class. Since myths were passed on by word of mouth, perhaps you could read the myth aloud, or tell it using some of your own words.

Paint a Poem Read Jiménez's poem "Light and Water" on page 94 and Lorca's poem "Half Moon" on page 99. Choose one of these poems to illustrate, using the images as a basis for a watercolor. Perhaps you could include one of the mythical characters in your watercolor.

Create Your Own Myth Carefully read the poem with the line "The stars are her silver necklace" on page 107. Use your imagination to make up your own myth about this event. You may want to give details about the woman, the necklace, and how and why the sky moved.

More Books About Myths

Words from the Myths by Isaac Asimov. Houghton Mifflin. Many of the words that we use in our daily language have their roots in the Greek myths. Did you know, for example, that the word *cereal* is derived from the name of the goddess of grain, Ceres? Scientists, too, make use of Greek myths. The space capsule flown by the first American in space was named, appropriately, *Mercury*. You will find this book a valuable reference as well as an interesting account of myths.

Cupid and Psyche retold by Edna Barth. Seabury Press. Psyche was a princess who was considered even more beautiful than the goddess Venus. Venus, becoming jealous, sent her son Cupid to place an evil spell on the princess. But, instead, Cupid fell in love with Psyche. This was the beginning of great trouble and misery for Psyche.

Children of Odin by Padraic Colum. Macmillan. There is a noticeable difference between Greek and Norse myths. Many of the Greek myths are lighthearted, but the Norse myths are somber. Here are some exciting Norse myths retold as good stories.

The Warrior Goddess: Athena by Doris Gates. Viking Press. Athena, daughter of Zeus, ruler of the gods, was the goddess of wisdom. Athena often came to the aid of people who had impossible tasks to perform, such as Jason in his quest for the golden fleece.

MUMBET
The Story of Elizabeth Freeman

Harold W. Felton

Introducing

MUMBET
The Story of
Elizabeth Freeman

Think about the kinds of things you do in an average day. You go to school to learn important skills and information. After school you may have to do homework or chores, but you also probably have free time for your friends, hobbies, or special interests. None of this may sound unusual or exciting to you, but the freedom to make these choices would not be available to you if you'd been born a slave.

A Slave's Life
Elizabeth Freeman, known as Bet or Mumbet, was born a slave in Massachusetts in 1744. Massachusetts was a colony then, and slavery was still permitted. Most slaves, including Bet, were not taught how to read or write. In fact, there were some places where teaching slaves to read or write was against the law. Bet would never have been able to choose the job she wanted to do. She had to do the work her master told her to do. Some masters treated their slaves kindly, while others were cruel. No matter how kind a master was, however, the slave was still considered as property.

In colonial days farmers would gather together to build homes or take the husks off corn so it could be stored. The women would sew quilts or cook big dinners for the workers during harvest times. Everyone worked hard and neighbors enjoyed gathering together. Slaves worked hard too, but they were not part of the community social life.

How Can We Really Know Mumbet?

You already know some facts about Mumbet. You know when she was born, where she lived, and that she was a slave. But there is much more to know about this remarkable woman. A good biographer will bring a historical personality to life, not just write facts. Reading just the facts would be boring. A good writer will use the facts, but put them together in such a way that a person like Mumbet becomes real to you. The facts about her life become a fascinating story. (For more about Fictionalized Biography, see your Handbook.)

As you're reading this excerpt on your own, find out how Mumbet battles for her freedom.

MUMBET
The Story of Elizabeth Freeman

In Which Colonel Ashley Has Important Visitors

Bet's wide apron sparkled like new snow. A white cap glistened above her black face and hair like a rising cloud catching the full rays of a morning sun. Her neat gray dress was ironed smooth and the tips of her worn shoes, freshly shined, twinkled from under her hem as she walked.

She had prepared for this day with the greatest care, for visitors were in the house. Important visitors. Mr. Tapping Reeve had come from Litchfield, in Connecticut. Mr. Theodore Sedgwick was there too. He was a pleasant young man, a lawyer from Sheffield, a few miles away, on the Housatonic River. And there were several others.

Bet didn't know why they had all come to the Ashley House, but she knew it was an important meeting. Perhaps she would find out why the men had come when she served them.

Bet was a slave. She was owned by Colonel John Ashley. He had bought her when she was a baby, with her sister Lizzie and several other slaves. When she had married, her name became Freeman—Elizabeth Freeman—but everyone called her Bet.

Colonel Ashley's house was the only home she had ever known. She had lived a good life, perhaps as good as a slave can live. The Colonel was distant and stern, yet not unkind. Mistress Ashley ruled her kitchen and her house with a firm hand, a sharp tongue, a shrill voice, and a quick temper. Nevertheless, it was not a bad life, as slaves' lives went.

Everyone worked hard. The slaves took pride in their work. Lizzie and Bet had discovered they were happiest when they were busy, but poor Lizzie was sickly and not always able to keep up with her sister and the other slaves. It was Lizzie who most often felt the sharpness of Mistress Ashley's tongue. It was Lizzie who, because she was not strong and quick, brought Mistress Ashley's shrillest voice into the kitchen, and it was Lizzie who sometimes felt the heavy weight of Mistress Ashley's hand.

John Ashley was one of the first settlers in western Massachusetts. With a few others he had made the long, hard trip over the Berkshire Mountains, cutting a narrow road through the forests. He had organized the Town of Sheffield in the southwest corner of the Commonwealth.

In 1735 he had built the Ashley House, a mansion on the banks of the river, near Ashley Falls. He had married Hannah Hogeboom of Claverack, New York. A rich man, with a big house and a beautiful wife, John Ashley bought slaves from the Hogeboom family. Bet and her sister had been brought to Ashley House on the straw-covered bed of a sleigh when Bet was six months old.

John Ashley had built a grist mill on the Housatonic River. He had interests in iron mines and quarries. He owned a great deal of land in the fertile valley and in the heavily wooded hills where his men operated lumber mills and prepared charcoal for use in the furnaces where iron was made.

Colonel Ashley joined with Theodore Sedgwick and the other men in Sheffield and wrote a Declaration of Rights in 1773 which declared that "Mankind in a State of Nature are equal, free and independent of each other." A town meeting on February 25, 1774, was called to discuss "the present inhuman practise of enslaving our fellow creatures, the natives of Africa." Colonel Ashley also took a leading part in the Revolutionary War in western Massachusetts.

Bet had come to occupy an important place in the household. She was respected and trusted. Under Mistress Ashley's supervision, the kitchen and the house were in her charge. The herb garden grew green and fragrant under her care.

Whenever the political and social leaders met at Ashley House, as they often did, Bet heard them talk of freedom and equality. She knew that the war against England was being fought for those goals. She wondered when freedom would come and what she would do when it came.

She felt that she would stay with Colonel Ashley. She had a good home. She liked everything about it, except Mistress Ashley. But then, a person couldn't have everything. It was too bad that Mistress Ashley lost her temper and raised her voice so often. Bet would like to be able to look Mistress Ashley in the eye and tell her, "If you don't stop pickin' on Lizzie, I'm goin' to quit." Perhaps then Mistress Ashley would not mistreat poor Lizzie, because Bet was an excellent cook and housekeeper and Mistress Ashley would not like to lose her.

And so there came this day in the year 1780, a day when Bet, dressed in her best clothes, carried a heavy wooden tray loaded with bottles and pewter tankards and meat and bread and pickles into the huge study on the second floor of the Ashley House.

The men in the room were leaders in the community and in the Commonwealth. They were men who spoke for and fought for freedom and independence. The men of the Massachusetts Colony had always been in the lead in the fight for freedom.

Bet's husband had been in the same fight. He had fought and died as a soldier in the War for Independence that was still going on. He had left her with a baby, Little Bet.

Bet knew about the Declaration of Independence that was adopted by the Continental Congress in Philadelphia on July 4, 1776. She had heard Colonel Ashley read the bold words it contained, and she had always felt her flesh tingle as he read. "We hold these Truths to be self-evident, that all Men are created equal, that they are endowed by their Creator with certain unalienable Rights, that among these are Life, Liberty and the Pursuit of Happiness."

The pastor had preached about these things—equality, freedom, and rights. Farmers at husking bees and house raisings spoke of them. So did their wives at quilting bees and harvest dinners.

Bet was sure it meant all women and children, as well as men. She didn't want Little Bet to grow up to be a slave. She wanted her baby to be free. Then she could learn to read and write and do sums. Then she could live and work in her own way and grow up to be a fine person, who could take part in community life.

The words held a promise to Bet during the days of war, when battles were fought north, south, east, and west of her home in Ashley Falls. They became filled with deeper meaning when the news came that her husband had died in the war. If he did not give his life for freedom, then he had given it for nothing at all.

Bet moved with quiet skill as she placed the shining tankards and bottles before the men, along with the platters of cold meat, bread, and the dishes of pickles. She felt excitement in the room.

"I am overjoyed that it is done," exclaimed Colonel Ashley. "Massachusetts has always led the way to independence and to freedom. This new constitution for Massachusetts is a noble document."

"True," said Mr. Tapping Reeve. "Massachusetts led the way at the Boston Tea Party. At Concord and at Lexington."

"And before that too," said Theodore Sedgwick. "The other Colonies have always followed Massachusetts. It is only fitting that Massachusetts have its new constitution contain a declaration of freedom and equality."

are Life, Liberty and the pursuit of Happiness.

Bet placed a tankard before him. He looked up, smiled and said, "Thank you." Not every man paused to thank a slave and smile. Bet's face brightened and she responded to his pleasant greeting.

"You are right, Theodore," said Colonel Ashley. He picked up the paper from the table before him. "Ah. Here it is." He read slowly, impressively. "All men are born free and equal."

"Good," said Mr. Sedgwick. "The supreme law of Massachusetts."

As it always did when she heard such words, a tingle came at the nape of Bet's neck and a shiver ran down her spine. She lifted the tray, but had to set it down on the table to keep it from trembling out of control in her hands.

Over and over the words raced through her mind. "All men are created free and equal . . . the supreme law . . ."

Freedom was coming nearer. When would it finally come? Why didn't some of these men who were so happy with the idea of freedom talk to her about it? She was a slave. No one could understand freedom better than she. She hurriedly left the room to give thanks for those wonderful words and for the freedom that she felt was coming closer to her.

■

In Which
Bet Makes Up
Her Mind

The months passed. Bet often wondered when someone would come and tell her she was free, that she was no longer a slave. If it was the law, someone ought to come and tell her about it.

She had discussed freedom with Lizzie and with Brom, the big Negro slave who cared for the yard and did the heavy work around the house. She talked about it with the other slaves too. Brom wanted his freedom almost as much as Bet did, but the others were not so sure. They wondered what they could do, how they could support themselves.

But there was not much time for wonder. There were meals to cook, laundry to be done, baking, ironing, scrubbing, polishing, sweeping, dusting, dishwashing, beds to be made, the herb garden to be tended. Yet if Bet's hands were always busy, so was her mind, and sometimes during the long, busy days, she did wonder.

Bet had spent an active day and now dinner was cooking in the great open fireplace in the kitchen. Lizzie had been sick all the night before and had felt weak since morning. Bet had not stopped all day, trying to do Lizzie's work, as well as her own.

From the pantry she heard Mistress Ashley screaming at Lizzie. Bet couldn't understand the words, so great was the anger in the voice, but the harsh sound went on and on, louder, more bitter, more uncontrolled. If only there was some way to stop that ill-humored voice. But what could Bet do?

She wanted to leave, to run away where she couldn't hear. But she couldn't do that. She couldn't leave Lizzie there alone with a woman in a tantrum.

Bet opened the pantry door. A terrible sight met her eyes. Lizzie was crouched near the kitchen table, on the floor. Mistress Ashley stood by the fireplace. She held the heavy iron shovel above her head. It glowed red with heat. Hot ashes were falling to the polished floor.

Bet rushed forward, and put out her arm to ward off the blow. The shovel fell and its hard metal edge struck her arm, cutting it to the bone. A red stain spread down her torn sleeve. Blood splashed to the kitchen floor like crimson drops of rain. A sharp cry of pain towered above the bitter words and the clatter of metal as the shovel fell on the hearthstone.

Colonel Ashley hurried down from his study. Brom came on the run to find out what happened.

Bet was filled with a great calm. Her mind was made up. She had decided what she was going to do as quickly as she had stepped in front of the falling shovel. She would find out about this new constitution. It said all men were born free and equal. But here she was, a slave. She was not free and she was not equal. Something was wrong, very wrong.

Bet had heard the lawyers and the other gentlemen talk. They all agreed it was right that the new Massachusetts constitution declared everyone was born free and equal. If no one else enforced the law, if no one else made the new constitution mean what it said, Bet would do it. She didn't know how. But she would do it. She would find a way.

She told Lizzie and Brom what she intended to do. Brom

asked that she speak for him too, but Lizzie was afraid. She didn't know what she could do unless she had the home Colonel Ashley gave her.

On a cold, wet day, Bet trudged through the heavy black mud. She carried Little Bet in her arms. It was four miles to the village of Sheffield. Mr. Sedgwick was a lawyer. He was the only lawyer she knew who might help her. Perhaps he could do something.

A refrain filled her mind as she moved her tired feet, weighted with mud. The words came to her again and again as the rain lashed at her. All men are born free and equal—free and equal—free and equal—

Theodore Sedgwick was seated in the small room that was his law office. He was still a young man and not many clients had made their way to his door.

"Come in," he said when he heard a firm, measured knock.

When the door opened and he saw Bet standing in the entrance, her clothes soaked with the cold spring rain, the book he was holding in his hands fell to the table with a thump.

"Why, Bet! Goodness! Come in, come in. Take your wet cloak off. Have a chair." He went to her. She put the baby on a bench and removed her dripping cloak.

His greeting warmed her almost as much as the fire, for she had not known how she would be received. She still did not know, for that matter, as she had not yet told him the purpose of her visit. She wondered how to tell him, how to start. She didn't have to wonder long. He asked the question.

"It is good to see you, Bet. How does it happen you are so far from the Ashley House? With Little Bet too? I hope nothing is wrong there?"

Bet straightened in her chair. "I am so far from the Ashley House, Mr. Sedgwick, because I want to be free," she said.

It was a simple statement and the words were clear, but she had said something that took them both into a strange and unknown world. Negro slaves were not made free because they wanted freedom. The law had recognized slavery in the American Colonies ever since they were founded. Slavery was an institution, a part of a way of life.

that all men are created equal;

Theodore Sedgwick perhaps had never thought of a slave trying to become free. "Well now, I don't know," was all he was able to say.

But if his mind was slow to grasp the point, Bet was quick to explain. "The Massachusetts constitution says that every-body is born free and equal," she declared.

"Yes, but—you are a slave and slaves are—" His words were slow in forming. He had been happy with the new constitution, but he had not thought of how a black slave might have freedom.

"I'm a person. I'm not a dumb beast. I was born, but I'm not free. The constitution ought to mean what it says, and I want you to go to law for me and get the law to say I'm free."

"Whatever gave you this idea, Bet?"

"I got it by keepin' still and mindin' things. I've heard you and other gentlemen talk at Colonel Ashley's house, and I've thought about it a lot," Bet answered.

"But it can't be simple, it can't—"

"I don't know 'can't.' The constitution says all men are free and equal, doesn't it?"

"Well, yes—"

"Then if everybody is free, there can't be any slaves, because slaves aren't free. Then when Mistress Ashley did what she did—"

The young lawyer listened as Bet told him what had happened in the Ashley House that day.

There had always been slavery in Massachusetts—indeed, in every colony in North America. Theodore Sedgwick had been active in the cause of freedom for slaves. He had wondered what effect the new constitution of Massachusetts would have on slavery. He was a sensitive, thoughtful man, but many such men found little objection to slavery as it was practiced in western Massachusetts and in most of the country areas of the northern states. There, black slaves and free white working people lived on the same level, wore the same kind of clothes, lived in the same kind of houses. Indeed, a slave of a wealthy master such as Colonel Ashley lived better than many white people.

But perhaps he had never realized the depth of the love of freedom in black people, even those as fortunate as Bet. He knew that blacks were fighting in General Washington's army, and everywhere were working with their masters to win the war. Possibly it had never occurred to him that their hearts led them to fight so well and do so much because they too dreamed of their own freedom as a goal.

It may be that he had not deeply considered that the black people of America, like the white people, also were suffering through a long, hard war and also sought their own rights of life, liberty, and the pursuit of happiness.

As he looked at Bet, the fact that she had lost her soldier husband in the war took on a new, fuller meaning.

How was it to be done? What legal proceedings? What arguments?

If he had never thought of these things before, he did now. His mind was caught by Bet's simple intensity and the logic of her words.

"I've talked to Brom. He wants to be free too." Bet added. "Can't you do something for us?"

There was a sound on the doorstep. The door opened and a gush of cold, wet wind broke into the room. It was John Ashley and his son. "Come with us, Bet," said Colonel Ashley. His voice was firm.

Bet rose and turned toward him. "I am free and equal," she said evenly.

"You are a slave," he said.

"The constitution says I'm free and equal," she replied, and her voice rose, burning with intensity.

"You are my servant for life," said John Ashley.

Bet turned to Theodore Sedgwick. Her face was alive with question.

"I'm afraid you will have to go with them," said Theodore Sedgwick.

■

In Which
The Verdict
Is Heard

John Ashley was not a cruel man. He owned slaves
because he was rich and could afford to buy them. With
their work, he became richer, and their toil made life easier
for him and his family. His slaves lived well. They lived in
comfort, compared to many other working people.

Of course Mistress Ashley should not have struck Bet. But
then many families, most families, have trouble now and
then and quarrels, even violent quarrels, were not
uncommon.

Slaves were property. That had always been true in
America and a man was entitled to his property. Ashley did
not believe that the law should take property from him. He
had cared for his slaves when they were children. He would
care for them when they were too old to work. Black people
could not support themselves alone, he thought. As farm
laborers, there would be no work for them in the winter,
and only a few people could afford to hire a woman for
housework.

He felt sympathy for Bet and tried to cheer her up. In the days that followed he did his best to explain that his wife was sorry she had lost her temper. Indeed, Hannah Ashley tearfully apologized.

Bet was forlorn. She wanted to forgive Mistress Ashley and she did forgive the poor woman who had so little control of herself. Yet Bet wanted her freedom. She didn't know what she would do as a free person. She would find it difficult, maybe impossible, to find work for wages. She would be lucky to find a place to live as comfortable as the Ashley household.

The long days passed. She was closely watched and had no way of again talking with Mr. Sedgwick, or anyone else who might help her. She began to think it was foolish to believe that anyone would come to her aid. Who would help a slave with no money and no property? Her heart was filled with emptiness as she went about her daily chores.

Still, Bet knew, little that is good or hoped for comes easily. The war had started in 1775. It was now spring of 1781, and still it went on. And before the years of the war there had been years of negotiations and the heartbreak that comes with failure. Yet the Colonists continued to fight.

Bet did not know how much her visit had turned Mr. Sedgwick's mind to thought and question. He spent long hours pouring over law books. He discussed the problem with Mr. Tapping Reeve.

One busy morning Bet answered a knock at the door. A man she recognized as the sheriff of the county stood on the stoop.

"You are Bet?" he asked.

"Yes sir," she replied.

"Is a man here by the name of Brom?"

"Yes sir. He's in the barn or in the garden, probably."

"I have a writ of replevin[1] for both of you from the Inferior Court of Common Pleas,"[2] he said as he drew a paper from his pocket.

Replevin. Common Pleas. Inferior Court. Most of these were words she had never heard. But—court. She knew that word. A flood of excitement trembled through her body.

"Is Colonel Ashley in?" the sheriff asked.

"Yes sir. I'll call him. Won't you step in?" Bet led the man to the sitting room and went upstairs to tell the Colonel of the visitor.

Colonel Ashley hurried down the stairs. Bet followed him.

"Good day, Colonel. I have a writ of replevin for Bet and Brom," the sheriff said.

"They are my servants for life," Colonel Ashley said.

"I must take them with me." The sheriff handed the paper to the Colonel.

The Colonel glanced at the paper. "I will not permit it," he said curtly.

"I am ordered by the court to take them," the man said firmly. Bet wondered how he dared to continue after the Colonel had spoken so sharply. Colonel Ashley was a lawyer, and although he did not practice law, his library was filled with important looking law books. How could anyone ever hope to overcome Colonel Ashley?

Her master replied again. "I will not permit them to leave with you. They are my chattels, my property."

There was a pause that almost suffocated Bet. Colonel Ashley turned to her. "Tell the sheriff you will not go with him, Bet," he said.

---

1. writ of replevin (ri plev′in): a formal written order issued by a court for the recovery of goods or chattels wrongfully taken or detained.
2. Inferior Court of Common Pleas: a court that deals with private law problems, such as business affairs and the transfer of property.

Bet felt she would sink through the floor. She had never disobeyed a direct order of her master. However, she drew herself up straight. Courteously and firmly she forced herself to say, "Colonel Ashley, sir, I want my freedom, like the constitution says."

She was surprised at herself, surprised she could speak out, speak her mind to the Colonel.

Colonel Ashley was just as direct, just as firm. "I will not permit you to leave," he said.

"I will have to report this to the court," the sheriff said.

"Do that. Say to the court that if they are to go, I must have security. I must have a bond.[3] They are my property. I do not have to surrender my property without a proper bond."

The sheriff moved to the door. Bet opened it for him. He turned to Colonel Ashley. "Thank you, Colonel," he said. "Good day."

Colonel Ashley nodded. Bet was left alone with him. She was not sure what had happened. She did not know about courts and sheriffs, but she felt that Mr. Sedgwick must not have forgotten her after all. In the silence, despair came over her.

"I don't want you to leave the house, Bet," Colonel Ashley said. "Do you understand?"

What could be done now? Colonel Ashley owned a thousand acres of land, the grist mill, saw mills, so many other things. He had dozens of servants and tenants and there were scores of other men he could call upon. Certainly, no one could rescue her. Mr. Sedgwick had sought the help of the law and the law had failed. It could never succeed against a man as powerful as Colonel Ashley.

---

3. bond: a written promise against loss.

that they are endowed by their Creator

Men desiring ...

with certain unalienable Rights,

very ... ent

The small glow of hope that had flickered within her was gone.

But Bet did not know the ways of the law. In a few days the sheriff once more rode into the backyard. Several men were with him.

"May I see Colonel Ashley?" he said as he stood at the door.

"Yes sir," Bet replied, and went for the Colonel.

When the Colonel appeared on the stoop, he greeted the officer who handed him some papers. One bore a red seal of wax and two small red ribbons fluttered from it. It was a writ of replevin, an order of the Inferior Court of Common Pleas at Great Barrington. There was also a bond for security.

The Colonel spoke to Bet. "The court has ordered me to let you and Brom go with the sheriff. I ask you to remain with us."

Bet said simply, "Colonel Ashley, I want to be free."

Brom had drawn close. He had heard the conversation. "Me too," he said. "I want to be free too."

"Yes, Brom. The writ includes you too," his master said.

"I'll come back and work for you when I am free," Brom said.

"You'll be glad to have steady employment if you do get your freedom. But I doubt that you will," said Colonel Ashley.

He turned to Bet. "Haven't we given you a good home?" he asked.

"Yes," Bet replied.

"Good food?"

"Yes sir."

"Good clothing?"

"Yes sir."

Mistress Ashley had come out on the porch. "I am sorry,

Bet. I apologize humbly for what I did," she said. "We want you to be happy."

"I forgive you, Mistress Ashley. I do. But I want my freedom."

"Where will you find another home as good?"

"I don't know," said Bet. "Maybe I won't find one. Maybe I'll live in rags and starve. But I want to be free and equal, like the constitution says."

The sheriff took Bet, with Little Bet, and Brom to the court where Mr. Sedgwick soon appeared. The legal details were cared for. It was May. The trial would be in August. Brom got a job with a farmer until the trial. But Bet was in a different position. She was a woman with a baby.

Colonel Ashley was right. There seemed to be no place for Bet to stay, nothing for her to do, no job.

"Come home with me," said Mr. Sedgwick. "You may stay with us until we can find something for you to do. It is now late May. Your case will not come up before court until August."

Three small children were in the house. Eliza was six, Frances was three, and little Theodore was almost six months old. Mr. Sedgwick's wife was a frail woman. The servants were careless and worked without instruction. The household was untidy.

It seemed that magic entered Theodore Sedgwick's home. It was the magic of Bet's enthusiasm, her skill in management, her wholesome approach to life and the people about her.

Now the children were always clean and happy. Meals were served on time. Furniture took on a new shine, pewter bore a deeper, richer glow, silver sparkled. Floors glistened, hearthstones were swept, the linen was spotless. Beds were made and changed at the proper time. The whole household gleamed. Stain, strain, argument, and unhappiness sped away. Bet's influence was everywhere. She was a happy and contented person once more, and cared for Eliza, Frances, and Theodore as though they were her own.

Mr. Sedgwick was deep in political and business matters. He was often away from home. When he returned he always found that his household and family had received devoted and loving care in his absence.

On an August day in 1781, Bet and Brom, with Theodore Sedgwick and Tapping Reeve from Litchfield, went to the court in Great Barrington. There, before the judge, they met Colonel John Ashley and his lawyers.

Bet seemed calm as the lawyers went about their affairs in the conduct of the trial, but a great turmoil was within her as the jury was selected and Jonathan Holcomb was named foreman.

Bet had lived on the western frontier all her life. She knew people often disagreed with each other. Sometimes disagreement led to fights and warfare. The Indian wars and the Revolutionary War were fought because people could not agree. As the August sun, shining through the windows, spread neat patterns of light on the floor of the courtroom, she was moved with the simplicity and the beauty of this peaceful way of settling disputes. She wondered why all men at all times could not find the answer to their problems in law instead of conflict.

"I am troubled, Bet," Mr. Sedgwick whispered.

"About my trial?" Bet asked.

"Yes."

"There's no reason for that," Bet replied.

Mr. Sedgwick looked at her curiously. "Why do you say that?" he asked.

If Mr. Sedgwick was troubled about legal points, Bet was

not. "The constitution says all people are free and equal. If that is so, how can I, how can anybody, be a slave?" she said.

Mr. Sedgwick smiled and nodded. Here was a remarkable woman. She would have made a good lawyer, he thought.

"There is no law that makes me a slave. You told me that."

"That's right. But there are laws about slaves. And there is custom, and custom is something stronger than law," he said.

"There's nothin' about custom in the constitution. Jes' you tell those things to the judge and jury in lawyer words. Then everything will be all right."

She heard the evidence and the arguments of the lawyers and no outward sign betrayed the tension that filled her. Her future was at stake. She lived in Massachusetts and she was testing the law of the land she lived in. As the trial went on a great feeling of serenity replaced all the disturbing emotions of the past months.

The judge listened. The jury leaned forward in their seats so that no word would escape them.

Bet sighed with soft contentment when she heard the verdict. She was not the servant of John Ashley for her lifetime. She was awarded thirty shillings lawful silver money as damages, and for costs, five pounds, fourteen shillings, and four pence.

Soon she was alone with Mr. Sedgwick in the silent courtroom. "You have been given damages for your services since you were twenty-one years old, and costs. What shall I do with the money?" Mr. Sedgwick asked with a smile.

"Pay Mr. Reeve and pay yourself for your lawyers' fees. Pay well because now I have the dearest thing on earth— my freedom. Then, I'd be obliged to you if you will keep what may be left for me. Keep it so I can use it if I need it."

No one was waiting to cheer her for her great victory. There was only Brom to grasp her hand in friendship. But Massachusetts and the County of Berkshire had done their part. They had fulfilled the promise of the constitution. Bet was a free person!

There was no doubt what she would do now. She was so much needed, so completely capable. She, with Little Bet, remained in the Sedgwick household. To the satisfaction of everyone, she became the gentle, intelligent force behind its daily operation.

Lizzie did not want to leave Ashley House. When Bet had asked her about it, she said, "Oh, no. I wouldn't want to leave. Mistress Ashley has been nice to me lately. She doesn't scold so much any more. I'd be afraid to leave Colonel Ashley's house."

The months became years and the Sedgwick family moved to Stockbridge. Theodore Sedgwick's law practice grew rapidly after his success in handling Bet's case. More and more clients sought his services as a lawyer. The size of the family increased.

To the children who depended on the black woman so much, the one who cared for them so tenderly, she became Mumbet or Mamma Bet. Soon she was Mumbet not only to the children, but to the parents, friends, and neighbors. It was a name that fixed Bet's position in the family, a name created of honor, of respect, of love.

■

After gaining her freedom, Mumbet continued to live as a respected member of the Sedgwick household. Theodore Sedgwick, her lawyer, became a member of the Continental Congress and a United States Senator. Mumbet later moved into a home of her own. Working as a nurse, Mumbet helped educate her grandchildren and great-grandchildren. She lived to the age of eighty-five. When she died, she was buried in the family circle of the Sedgwick cemetery in Stockbridge, Massachusetts.

Meet the Author:
Harold Felton

Harold W. Felton is a lawyer who has long been interested in American folklore. His first widely acclaimed book was a collection of legends about Paul Bunyan. Since that time he has pursued folk heroes and tall tales with enthusiasm, and his stories for young people about Pecos Bill, John Henry, Fire-Fightin' Mose, Bowleg Bill, and Sergeant O'Keefe rank him as a master yarn-spinner. Felton has also written biographies about people whose real lives rivaled those of tall-tale heroes.

Felton's father was the source of Felton's interest in folklore. As a boy in Iowa, Felton used to help his father on their farm. On their way to their home in town, Felton's father would spin yarns about folktale people. Felton says those trips home at night stood out in his memory.

Felton also has fond recollections of his mother reading to him. He says there was plenty of time for reading. There was also plenty of time for swimming, fishing, and camping.

Responding to Literature

1. In researching information for his biographies, Harold Felton discovered that "biographies are more astonishing than fiction." After reading *Mumbet*, do you agree with Felton that biography can be more amazing than fiction? Explain your answer.

2. The colonies are fighting for independence from England as Mumbet begins her own battle for freedom. Retell one of the major events of the biography.

3. In Colonel Ashley's house, Mumbet lived perhaps as good a life as a slave could live. Name one good thing and one bad thing about Mumbet's position.

4. Mumbet keeps repeating the phrase she hears from the Massachusetts constitution that "all men are born free and equal." Name one person in Mumbet's story who would agree with that statement and tell why you think so.

5. If Mumbet were living today, what might she be doing? What might she enjoy about modern life?

Hold Fast Your Dreams

Within your heart
Keep one still, secret spot
Where dreams may go,
And sheltered so,
May thrive and grow—
Where doubt and fear are not.
Oh, keep a place apart
Within your heart,
For little dreams to go.

Louise Driscoll

Appreciating Author's Craft

Thinking About Style in Biography

When Harold Felton began working on his biography of Mumbet, he examined court records, read accounts written by the children of Judge Sedgwick, looked at Mumbet's will, and read the inscription on her tombstone. Most people, reading these original sources, would find them lifeless and uninspiring. To a good author like Felton these sources were the beginning of a good story because he had the talent to choose vivid details to give a picture of Mumbet's life and character. Then, to give some order to those details, he organized them around the theme of freedom.

In writing Mumbet's biography, Felton could have stated that freedom was important to Mumbet. Instead, he provided us with details of what she said and how she felt in order to convey this idea. For example, her strong feelings about freedom become evident when Felton describes Mumbet's reaction to hearing "All men are created free and equal . . ."

"As it always did when she heard such words, a tingle came at the nape of Bet's neck and a shiver ran down her spine. She lifted the tray, but had to set it down on the table to keep it from trembling out of control in her hands."

By writing in this detailed and personal way, the author helps us understand and care about Mumbet, which makes the biography a good true story.

Writing Biography with Style

Suppose you are a newspaper reporter who has been assigned to write a feature about Mumbet's battle for freedom. You would follow her and gather facts.

Prewriting You can keep a notebook with the events listed in order. Your notebook would look like this:

NOTES
Order of Events

Event 1. *M. learns about declaration of freedom in Mass. const.*

Event 2.
Event 3.
Event 4.

Copy the notebook, and with a partner list three other events showing how Mumbet attained her goal of freedom.

Writing Write a news account about "How Mumbet Won Her Freedom," putting the events in order. The news story should not be just a list of facts but interesting and vivid. Add details to make the scenes personal. (For more ideas about writing, look at The Writer's Handbook.)

Revising Go over your draft. Then read your draft to your partner to make sure the events are in order and that the story has vivid details that make Mumbet come alive. Revise your draft and write your final copy.

Presenting Present your story to your history class. Dim the lights to set the mood for the "I was there" feeling. Then hold a press conference and invite the audience to ask you questions about Mumbet.

Extending Your Reading

Expressing Yourself
Choose one or more of these activities:

Act Out a Scene Find the section in the story on page 134 where the sheriff comes for Bet. Have several pupils take the parts of Bet, the sheriff, Colonel Ashley, Mistress Ashley, and Brom. Come up with a plan of where each person would be standing. Develop your lines and act out the scene for the class.

Make a Historical Poster The opening lines of the Declaration of Independence thrilled Mumbet and are very famous. Using your best printing or cursive writing, write those words to be displayed in your classroom.

Draw a Time Line Draw a time line that begins with Mumbet's birth in 1744 and ends with her death in 1829. Reread the story to find other important dates such as leaving the Ashley home, and her trial. You may also want to include the dates of the Boston Tea Party, the battles of Lexington and Concord, and the Declaration of Independence.

Hold Fast Your Dreams Read the poem on page 141. How might it help you to pursue your dreams?

More Books About Justice

Hazel Rye by Vera and Bill Cleaver. Lippincott. Young Hazel Rye owns a few acres of land and a house which her father gave to her. She has no special plans for it until a poor family appears to rent it. Hazel is a sassy, bossy girl, but she tries to keep a fair and open mind. Hazel is surprised at how she ends up.

Can't Catch Me, I'm the Gingerbread Man by Jamie Gilson. Archway. A lot of things in Mitch McDandel's life don't seem fair. His parents' health food store burns down, and the baking contest he is sure he'll win doesn't net him any prizes. But Mitch and his family have lots of spunk. Some surprisingly funny moments keep them all going.

No Promises in the Wind by Irene Hunt. Ace Books. America's Depression years were times of great suffering for millions of people. This is the story of two young brothers who, in an effort to survive, make their way on foot across much of the land. The times are harsh, but many people help the boys along their way.

Justice by Joan Johnson. Franklin Watts. Have you ever wondered what happens to people who are arrested? This book takes readers step-by-step through two fictional cases and shows how the justice system in America works to protect the innocent and to treat everyone fairly.

Lizzie Lies a Lot by Elizabeth Levy. Dell. Lizzie doesn't know why she lies; in fact, she sometimes doesn't even realize she's doing it. A complicated set of stories Lizzie tells makes her more and more uncomfortable with her family and friends. Finally Lizzie must do something and do it fast!

Anastasia
On Her Own

Lois Lowry

Introducing

Anastasia
On Her Own

Have you ever made a schedule for yourself?
Maybe you've written a list of the homework you
have, thought about how long each item would take,
and decided when you would do each task. Your
family probably operates on some understanding of
who will do what when. No matter what kind of
schedules you're familiar with—for homework,
housekeeping, errands—you've probably learned
one thing: schedules often don't work out exactly as
planned.

Do You Think Housekeeping Is Simple?

Housekeeping should be simple. But is it? Think
about it. In many homes, everyone has several
responsibilities: school or work, plus taking care of
the youngest children, doing laundry, fixing meals,
running errands, cleaning the house. It can be a
tough situation, especially when one person gets
sick, takes a trip, or somehow throws off the delicate
balance. It can also be a funny situation when a
writer like Lois Lowry describes it.

What Makes a Situation Funny?

How does Lowry make this situation funny? She shows that we need to expect the unexpected. She tells us that it's hard to fit little children into predictable time slots. Lowry also shows that situations and the things people say can be humorous even—or especially—when things don't run smoothly.

In *Anastasia on Her Own,* Lowry turns the little disasters of everyday life into a realistic story. (For information about realistic fiction, see your Handbook.) Although Lowry puts Anastasia in realistic situations, the situations take unexpected turns. Anastasia no sooner gets one problem solved when another takes its place. Like many of us, Anastasia takes herself very seriously, but the author helps us laugh at Anastasia and at ourselves.

As you're reading this excerpt on your own, discover what Anastasia learns about running a household with the help of a housekeeping schedule.

Krupnik Family Nonsexist Housekeeping Schedule

7:00 A.M.   Everyone gets up.
Anastasia makes bed.
Myron makes bed.
Katherine makes Sam's bed.
Katherine helps Sam dress.
Katherine makes breakfast.
Everyone eats.

8:00 A.M.   Katherine takes food out of freezer.
Myron and Anastasia leave for school.
Nursery school carpool picks up Sam.
Katherine goes to work in the studio.

10:00 A.M.   Katherine's coffee break.

NOON   Carpool brings Sam home.
Katherine and Sam have lunch.

1:00 P.M.   Clothes into washing machine.
Sam and Katherine do shopping.

2:00 P.M.   Clothes into dryer.
Sam takes nap.
Katherine works in studio.

3:00 P.M.   Sam and Katherine fold clean laundry.
They play.

4:00 P.M.   Katherine starts dinner.
Anastasia comes home from school.

5:00 P.M.   Myron gets home.

6:00 P.M.   Anastasia sets table.
Everyone eats.

7:00 P.M.   Katherine, Myron, or Anastasia does
dishes, depending on whose turn.

8:00 P.M.   Someone bathes Sam and puts him to bed.

*** vacuuming, window-washing, etc., on Saturdays.

Anastasia
On Her Own

nastasia has schoolwork to do. Her father, Professor Myron, has classes to teach. Mrs. Krupnik has books to illustrate, and Anastasia and her father organize a schedule for easy housekeeping. It is designed to help organize everyone's responsibilities so that three-year-old Sam is taken care of and all the other household chores get done smoothly. (See the Krupnik Family Nonsexist Housekeeping Schedule on the opposite page.)

On the very first day of the schedule Mrs. Krupnik informs the family that the schedule doesn't work.

"The problem is," announces Anastasia's father, "that there were a lot of unexpected events, things we didn't anticipate when we made the schedule."

"There always are," says Mrs. Krupnik. "Every day there are unexpected events."

So Dr. Krupnik revises the list. (See the Krupnik Family Nonsexist Housekeeping Schedule, Version 2, on pages 152 and 153.)

When Mrs. Krupnik learns that she has to go to Los Angeles on business, she places Anastasia in charge of the house while she is gone for ten days.

"Ten days!" cries Anastasia. "I can't—how do you expect me—how on earth can a thirteen-year-old person—"

"Easy," her mother says, "you have this wonderful schedule."

Krupnik Family Nonsexist Housekeeping Schedule

Version 2

7:00 A.M.   Everyone gets up.
Anastasia makes bed.
Myron makes bed.
Katherine makes Sam's bed.
Katherine helps Sam dress.
Katherine makes breakfast.
Everyone eats.

8:00 A.M.   Katherine takes food out of freezer.
Myron and Anastasia leave for work and school.
Nursery school carpool picks up Sam.
Katherine goes to work in the studio.

INSERT: Unexpected event. For example, furnace makes odd sound like small explosion. Katherine calls gas company. Repairman comes and tracks muddy snow onto kitchen floor. K. has to clean kitchen floor. Unexpected event #2. Anastasia calls from school to say that she has forgotten to feed Frank, her goldfish, and would like Katherine to do it. Katherine argues that Frank will survive a few more hours without food but Anastasia expresses grave concern over Frank's welfare and her future affection for her mother should Frank die of starvation. Katherine goes to third floor to feed Frank.

10:00 A.M.   Katherine's coffee break. (Has to be eliminated if there are unexpected events. See above.)

NOON   Carpool brings Sam home.

INSERT: Unexpected event. Sam's carpool driver has flat tire and arrives forty-five minutes late. In meantime Katherine has called nursery school in panic. Nursery school calls police, police finally locate car and assist carpool driver. Katherine sits frantically by phone wondering if Sam has been kidnapped.

Katherine and Sam have lunch. (This is postponed until later in case of unexpected events. See above.)

1:00 P.M.   Clothes into washing machine.
                  Sam and Katherine do shopping.

INSERT: Unexpected event. Katherine discovers, walking home from grocery store, that Sam has shoplifted package of gum. Return to store so that store owner can have serious moralistic talk with Sam.

2:00 P.M.   Clothes into dryer (Postponed if unexpected events. See above.)
                  Sam takes nap. (Preceded by long talk about shoplifting. See above.)
                  Katherine works in studio. (Canceled in case of unexpected events. See above.)

3:00 P.M.   Sam and Katherine fold clean laundry.

INSERT: Unexpected event. Discovery, upon removing wash, that Myron's black socks have been included with white things, requiring white things to be rewashed with bleach to remove dye.

                  They play. (Postponed in case of unexpected events. See above.)

4:00 P.M.   Katherine starts dinner.
                  Anastasia comes home from school.

5:00 P.M.   Myron gets home.

6:00 P.M.   Anastasia sets table.
                  Everyone eats.

(All of the above is adjusted according to unexpected events.)

7:00 P.M.   Katherine, Myron, or Anastasia does dishes, depending on whose turn.

8:00 P.M.   Someone bathes Sam and puts him to bed.

*** vacuuming, window-washing, etc., on Saturdays

nastasia sat on her parents' bed Sunday evening, watching her mother pack. From the nearby bathroom came the sounds of her father bathing Sam.

"I'm worried about several things, Mom," Anastasia said.

Her mother looked up from folding a silk blouse. "Really?" she asked. "Like what?"

Anastasia arranged her legs underneath herself so that she was sitting like Buddha. "Well," she said, "don't be insulted or anything, but I'm afraid you're not going to go over real well on this trip."

Mrs. Krupnik placed the blouse in the suitcase and began taking some dresses out of her closet. "I'm not? Why not? I did terrific illustrations for that book. It was that really sophisticated children's book, remember—the one about the wedding of two gazelles? It won some awards."

"No, it's not your work, Mom," Anastasia explained. "You're one of the best illustrators around. It's a couple of other things. One is your clothes."

"My *clothes?*" Mrs. Krupnik held up the blue silk dress she was about to pack. "What's wrong with my clothes? I should have had this cleaned, I suppose, but there wasn't time. And it's not *grossly* dirty, just sort of vaguely smelling of perfume from the last time I wore it." She sniffed the dress. "It really is perfume, Anastasia, not perspiration or anything."

"Mom, it's not the condition of your clothes. It's the *style*."

"What's wrong with the style?" Her mother looked at the simple blue dress again, puzzled.

"Mom, when you're on the Coast—and incidentally, you're supposed to call it the Coast, not California or Los Angeles—"

"I am? How do you know that?"

"From magazines."

"Oh. Well, I'll practice on the plane. I'll practice saying, 'Hello. It's so nice to be here on the Coast.'"

"Make sure it sounds casual. It has to sound casual."

"I'll try. What's wrong with this dress?"

"Mom, on the Coast, you're supposed to *glitter*."

"I'm supposed to *what*?"

"Glitter. You're supposed to be, well, *glitzy*."

Her mother frowned at her. "Anastasia, I don't know what you're talking about. All of a sudden you're speaking a foreign language. Can you give me an example of glitzy?"

Anastasia chewed on a strand of hair. "Well, do you by any chance have any leather pants?"

"Good grief. Of course I don't have any leather pants. You know that. You're always prowling around in my closet, trying to find something to borrow."

"Well, it's an example. You asked for an example. If you had leather pants, you could wear those, and then you could put that dress *over* the leather pants, like a giant blouse, and around the waist you could put a big cowboy belt. And huge earrings, of course."

Her mother was making a terrible face. "Then I'd glitter?" she asked.

"Yeah, I think so."

Mrs. Krupnik sighed and put the blue dress into the suitcase. "I've decided I don't want to glitter. Huge earrings make my ears hurt. It wouldn't be any fun to glitter if I had an earache. I guess I'll just be the only unglittery person in Los Angeles—excuse me, I mean on the Coast. Maybe that will make me seem interesting."

Anastasia was dubious. She thought it would make her mother seem boring. "There's another thing, too," she said. "The way you talk."

Her mother took a pair of shoes out of the closet, licked her finger, and rubbed a smudged spot off one. "Do they talk differently out there?" she asked.

Anastasia nodded. "I know you can't learn it all in one evening," she said. "But I could just teach you a few expressions, and then you could fake it."

"Okay. Teach me one."

"Well, if something happens that you don't like—say, for example, they tell you that they want you to redo the gazelles—"

"They won't. Those gazelles are perfect."

"It's just an example, Mom. If they tell you that, you should say, 'Make my day.'"

"'Make my day?'" Her mother made the same sort of face she had made about the glittering. "I don't understand what that means, even."

Anastasia stood up. "Here, I'll show you. It's all in the inflection. It has to be casual, and bored, and sarcastic. You play the part of the film producer, okay? And I'll be you. Tell me I have to redo the gazelles."

Her mother grinned and put down the shoes. She glanced around, picked up a ballpoint pen from the dresser, and clamped it between her teeth like a cigar. "Here's the thing, Ms. Krupnik," she said in a deep, harsh voice. "We're going to need a whole new set of gazelles here, something a little cuter, you get the idea?" She flicked some ashes from the imaginary cigar.

Anastasia leaned in a casual, languid pose against the bedpost. She looked at her mother, the film producer, with a bored stare, her eyes half closed. In a low, sarcastic voice, she said, "Like, maaake my *daaay.*"

Her mother dropped the ballpoint cigar and roared with laughter. "I love it," she said. "I *love* it, Anastasia." She picked the shoes back up and put them into the suitcase. "But I can't do it. It just isn't me."

Anastasia flopped back down on the bed. She handed her mother some pantyhose that were waiting to be packed. She sighed, "Well," she said "I just sincerely hope that you're not too humiliated out there."

Sam dashed into the room, naked and giggling. He glanced over his shoulder and called, "You can't catch me!" He dropped to the floor and disappeared under his parents' bed.

Dr. Krupnik appeared at the door with Sam's pajamas in his hand. "Where did he go?" he asked.

Anastasia and her mother pointed under the bed. "He's going to need another whole bath, Myron," Mrs. Krupnik said. "There are a thousand dust balls under there. I forgot to vacuum yesterday, even though it was on the schedule."

Sam's carpool driver honked in the driveway in the morning. Sam kissed his mother good-bye, pulled on his mittens, and trudged out through the snow to the car. Before he got in, he turned and waved cheerfully toward the kitchen window.

"I've never been away from Sam before," said Mrs. Krupnik after she had waved back and the car had driven away. "What a strange feeling."

"We'll take good care of him, Mom," Anastasia said.

She sighed. "I know you will. It's all set with the nursery school. They'll keep him for lunch and for the afternoon session. He'll be home by three-thirty every day. Now you be sure to be here, Anastasia. They won't leave him at an empty house."

"I will, Mom, I promise. It's going to ruin my social life for ten days. But I'll be home by three-thirty."

A backfire sounded from the garage. Then another. Anastasia and her mother looked out the window and saw clouds of black smoke coming from the tail pipe of the car.

"He'll have the car warmed up in a minute," Anastasia said. "Did he take your suitcase?"

"It's in the trunk of the car." Mrs. Krupnik put on her coat. "Now, let's see. Am I forgetting anything?"

"Tickets?"

"I'm picking them up at the airport."

Anastasia looked around the kitchen. "We all forgot the breakfast dishes," she pointed out. "But I'll do them when I get home from school."

"Right." Her mother pulled on her gloves, picked up her briefcase, and headed for the door. "You're in charge, Anastasia. I'll call you tomorrow night, just to make sure everything's okay."

"It will be, Mom. I'm a very organized person, you know."

"All right, then. I'm off." Her mother gave her a hug. Anastasia watched through the window as she got into the car, which jerked and bounced down the driveway toward the street. She kept waving until it was out of sight.

Then Anastasia got into her ski jacket and hat. She collected her schoolbooks and was halfway down the back steps before she remembered something and turned back.

"I almost blew it the first day," she said to herself. Quickly she went to the freezer, pulled out a package of rock-hard hamburger, and deposited it on the drainboard of the kitchen sink.

"Okay," she said, glancing at the schedule tacked to the bulletin board. "None of the beds is made, but I'll do that when I get home. Meat's out of the freezer. Breakfast dishes can wait. And if I don't leave this instant, I'm going to be late for school."

She headed for the door again. The telephone rang.

She hesitated.

It rang again. She went back and answered it.

"Ms. Krupnik?" asked a bubbly voice.

"Yeah."

"E-Z Telephone Shopping!" the voice said. "Anybody in your family in need of new underwear? We're having a special!"

Anastasia blinked. "That's a very personal question," she said.

"How about blankets?" the voice asked.

Anastasia looked at her watch. She was definitely going to be late for school. Talk about Unexpected Events. "The blanket on my brother's bed is kind of ratty," she said. "It was his security blanket when he was younger, so he used to suck on it and chew on it all the time, and now he doesn't do that, but the blanket is all messed up."

"How many new ones would you like?" the voice asked. "And what color?"

"Blue, I guess. Just one."

"Twin, full, queen, or king?"

Anastasia thought. "Twin," she said.

"Standard, or electric?"

"Stand—no, wait. Electric. Sam would like electric. He likes to fool with switches."

"Sheets or towels?"

Anastasia groaned. She didn't have time to think about sheets or towels. "No," she said. "Thank you," she added.

"Credit card number?"

Oh, *no.* "Just a minute," Anastasia said. "I have to get it."

She dashed to her father's study and opened the second drawer of his desk. There, in a typed list, were all of their credit card numbers. She ran back to the phone and read a credit card number to the voice.

"I really have to go," she said. "I'm late."

"Bye, now," said the voice.

Anastasia picked up her books again and headed off for school. Already it wasn't quite as easy as she had anticipated, being in charge.

She arrived home just a few minutes before Sam. Anastasia was mad. All of her friends had stayed after school for a basketball game. The streets were absolutely deserted as she walked home, and she imagined that she could hear the cheering junior high crowd back there at the gym. She imagined that Steve Harvey was making basket after basket and was wondering why she hadn't stayed to cheer for him.

Back home, there were three unmade beds—she had pulled the covers up hastily—and a sink full of dishes with congealed egg on them.

And Sam was bratty. He was tired after an unaccustomed day at school, and he whined. He wanted Anastasia to play trucks with him.

"I can't play trucks," Anastasia said. "I have to do these dishes."

"Mom always plays trucks," Sam whimpered.

Anastasia looked at him in exasperation. "Tell you what," she suggested finally. "Bring your trucks down here and you can transport the clean dishes to the cupboard."

He trotted off and returned with a large red dump truck. On his hands and knees he *rrrrrrr*ed each clean dish to the pantry and put it away. Anastasia waited impatiently, holding cups and glasses after they were dry, for the trucking company to return for a pickup.

When the last one was done, she hung up the dish towel and wiped the sink with a sponge. She sat down wearily in a kitchen chair, and Sam climbed into her lap.

"Scratch my back," he said. "My back itches."

Automatically Anastasia scratched his little back through his shirt.

"More," Sam said when she stopped.

Anastasia sighed and scratched again. She was still scratching when the back door opened and her father appeared.

"Greetings," he said. "Your mom's in sunny California by now!"

"You're home early," Anastasia began, but then she looked at her watch. "How did it get to be five o'clock?" she asked.

Sam flopped himself around in her lap. "Scratch my front," he said. "My front itches, too."

Anastasia lifted him down to the floor. "I can't," she told him. "I have to start dinner. What vegetable do you guys want? Corn okay?"

"Sure," said her father. "Good thing I remembered to take some meat out of the freezer."

"Yeah," said Anastasia. "I was halfway down the back steps before I remembered to—what do you mean, *you* remembered?"

Her father went to the pantry and came back with a plate full of something, which he set on the table.

"Chicken breasts," he announced. "I remembered just before I went out to warm up the car this morning."

Anastasia looked at the chicken breasts in dismay. She took her own package of meat from the side of the sink. "But I thawed out hamburger!" she wailed.

Sam looked at both of them. Then he trotted off to the small counter beside the refrigerator, the one where the toaster stood. He reached up, pushed aside the toaster, and took down a package.

"Hot dogs," he announced. "I did hot dogs."

Anastasia stared at the hamburger. Then she stared at the chicken breasts. Then she stared at the hot dogs.

"Well," she said flatly, "make my day."

"Actually," her father replied, "I think what we have to make is a new schedule."

Sam sat down on the kitchen floor and began to cry. "Make me stop itching!" he howled. "I itch *all over!*"

Krupnik Family Nonsexist Housekeeping Schedule
Version 3

7:00 A.M.   Everyone gets up.
Nobody bothers making beds. They only get slept in again anyway.
Anastasia feeds Frank Goldfish.
Myron helps Sam get dressed.

7:30 A.M.   Everybody eats cold cereal.
Anastasia rinses dishes. Detergent is not required for cold cereal dishes.
ANASTASIA takes something out of the freezer for dinner.

8:00 A.M.   Everybody leaves.
Do not go back to answer phone. Only go back if house is on fire, or something.

3:30 P.M.   Anastasia and Sam come home.
They do laundry.

5:00 P.M.   Myron comes home.
Anastasia and Myron cook dinner.
Everybody eats, from paper plates.
Throw away paper plates.

EVENING: Someone puts Sam to bed. Sam does not need a bath every night, only if he is unusually grubby.
Anastasia does homework.
If Katherine calls, NOBODY TELLS KATHERINE ABOUT CHANGE IN HOUSEKEEPING RULES.

Saturday: vacuuming, window-washing, etc.

163

nastasia opened her eyes sleepily when her father called "Seven o'clock!" up the stairs to her third-floor bedroom. She groaned. Why was it so hard to get up in the morning?

Frank, her goldfish, was swimming in circles, chasing his own tail around his bowl. Frank was always wide-awake and cheerful in the mornings. He was the kind of guy who would go jogging at dawn, if he had legs.

Groggily, she reached over to the fish-food box and tapped some into Frank's bowl. If only she could do *all* the household chores without getting out of bed.

"You and I have very little in common, Frank," Anastasia said, yawning, "except that we both like to eat."

Frank stared out at her with his bulging eyes through the side of the bowl. He flipped his tail.

Down on the second floor, she could hear sounds: the shower running, her father's feet squeaking in the bathtub, and Sam—Anastasia groaned and got out of bed. Sam was crying again. Ordinarily Sam *never* cried; once she had seen him fall right over the railing of the back porch, head over heels, into a prickly bush. Then he had climbed out of the bush, covered with scratches, brushed himself off, remarked, "Ouch," and gone scampering off to find his tricycle.

But last night he had cried and cried. He hadn't eaten any dinner—even though there were several choices—and he had complained about a hundred different things. His head hurt. His toes itched. His nose ached. His belly button felt too tight.

Finally he had fallen asleep on the hard linoleum floor of the kitchen while Anastasia and her father ate.

"What a hypochondriac," Anastasia had said, whispering, so that he wouldn't wake up and start wailing again.

"He just misses his mom," Dr. Krupnik had pointed out.

They had both looked at Sam curled into a sleeping ball on the floor. "Should we wake him up for his bath?" Dr. Krupnik had asked.

Anastasia had shaken her head. "He's not that dirty. And if we wake him up he'll just start missing Mom again, and crying. Let's just put him to bed with his clothes on."

Dr. Krupnik had frowned. "He'll wet the bed if we don't take him to the bathroom."

It was true. They had both thought about that. "Well, said Anastasia finally, "I think I'd rather change his sheets tomorrow than listen to him howl anymore tonight."

Her father had nodded. "Me too," he agreed. Carefully, he had scooped Sam up and carried him upstairs to his bed. "By morning, after a good night's sleep," he had said when he came back down, "he'll be fine. It's just a difficult adjustment."

But now it was morning, and Sam was howling again. Anastasia sighed and pulled on her clothes, noticing as she did that this was the last of her clean underwear. The jeans didn't matter—she had worn these for three days anyway—but she would have to wash underwear after school today. And socks.

She found Sam standing in the hall, his hair damp and matted, his face bright pink, his yesterday's clothes wrinkled and wet.

"I want my pajamas!" Sam yowled.

Anastasia took his hand and led him to his bedroom. "It's morning, Sam. Time to put on clean clothes for school. You can't wear pajamas to school, silly."

"I don't want to go to school," Sam whined as she began taking off his clothes. "I hate school."

Never get sucked into an argument with a three-year-old, Anastasia remembered her mother saying. Because you can't win one. An adult will lose against a three-year-old every time.

"I know," she said soothingly. "Sometimes I hate school, too. But we have to go anyway. There's a *law* that says you have to go to school." She pulled his shirt off over his head. "Now stop crying, because it makes you all sweaty."

Then she stared at him "Sam," she said, "what are all these spots?"

Sam looked down at his own bare chest dotted with pink. It was so interesting that he stopped crying. "I've turned into a polka-dot person." he said. "Look at me, poking the dots." He began to poke each one with his finger.

Anastasia turned him around. His back, too, was covered with spots.

"Dad?" she called through the closed bathroom door. "Something's wrong with Sam. Something *bit* him! Could we have bedbugs?"

Sam grinned. "Bedbugs," he said. "Millions of bedbugs."

Dr. Krupnik came out of the bathroom, tying his tie. "Of course we don't have bedbugs," he said. Then he looked at Sam. "Holy—"

"Holy moley." Anastasia completed it for him. She finished undressing Sam. "*Look*. Every inch of him."

Now that he was the center of attention, Sam was completely happy. "Every single inch," he announced proudly. Naked, he began to dance around his bedroom. "Puff, the magic bedbug," he sang, "lived by the sea—"

"What's his doctor's name?" Anastasia's father asked. "Didn't your mom leave a list with all the important phone numbers on it? Where is it? I'd better call the doctor."

"He's my doctor, too, Dad," Anastasia said. "Dr. Nazarosian. I'll call him. He's in his office early. The list's right by the phone in your bedroom."

Sam was still prancing around.

"Do you feel okay, Sam?" Anastasia asked. "I need to tell the doctor all your symptoms."

"Tell him I'm like a leopard," Sam suggested. "A spotted leopard." He began to crawl across the rug, growling. "Lookit me, being a leopard," he said. He grabbed the corner of the rug between his teeth and shook it back and forth with a ferocious growl.

"Dr. Nazarosian," Anastasia said on the phone, "this is Anastasia Krupnik. I'm calling because—"

"Anastasia!" he said heartily, interrupting her. "How *are* you? I haven't seen you in ages. You're one of my favorite patients because you're never sick. Don't tell me you're sick!"

"No, I'm not. But my mother is in California, so—"

167

"California! Getting a little sunshine, is she? Can't say I blame her. I'm getting pretty sick of this snow. Of course if I had time to take a vacation and do a little skiing, I might feel differently. Do you ski?"

"No," said Anastasia, looking at her watch. She was going to be late for school *again*. "I'm calling because I'm in charge, and it's about Sam. Sam's—"

He interrupted her again. "Good old Sam—my very favorite patient, in all due respect, Anastasia. Remember the time Sam fell out of the window and—"

This time Anastasia interrupted *him*. "Dr. Nazarosian," she said, "Sam's entire body is covered with pink spots."

He chuckled. "Not surprising," he said. "Not at all surprising."

Anastasia was taken aback. Not surprising to be covered with pink spots? *She* found it surprising. What on earth would surprise Dr. Nazarosian? Blue spots, maybe? Green?

"They're even on his ears," she went on.

"How old is Sam now—three?" the doctor asked. "Let me get his chart out. Here it is. Three years old, like I thought. Does he go to nursery school?"

"Yes," said Anastasia. She told him the name of Sam's school.

"I should have guessed. Half the kids in that nursery school have it. The other half will by next week. Except for a few. There are always a few who for some reason seem to be immune. We've never been able to figure that out. And then sometimes the ones who don't get it when they're three suddenly come down with it as *adults,* for some reason, even though they were undoubtedly exposed to it when they were young—"

"Exposed to *what?*"

"Chicken pox," the doctor said. "Sam has chicken pox."

Anastasia's father came into the room and looked at her quizzically. He pointed to his watch at the same time.

"I don't need to see him, unless he has special problems," the doctor was going on. "Give him a little baby aspirin for the fever. And if he itches—well, that was a foolish thing to say; of *course* he itches—add some baking soda to a bath and let him soak in that. He'll feel fine in a day or two. But of course he'll have to stay out of school until the lesions heal. Well, that was a foolish thing to say, too; they're probably going to close that school down for a couple of weeks. Can't run a school when everybody has chicken pox, now, can you?" He chuckled.

Anastasia looked up at her father and mouthed the words "chicken pox."

"*Chicken pox?*" her father mouthed back.

"Now, let me just get out *your* chart and see if you've had chicken pox, Anastasia," the doctor was saying.

"I had it when I was—"

"Here we are. Krupnik, Anastasia. You were right in the filing cabinet next to your brother. Let's see, you're thirteen now. Pretty soon you won't even need a pediatrician. For heaven's sake, look at this—"

"I had chicken pox when I was—"

"I'd forgotten all about that time we had to pump your stomach when you were two. You ate ant poison. Well, that's nothing compared to what *some* toddlers eat. I had one who drank a whole bottle of window cleaner once. Wouldn't you think it would taste terrible? Now, let's see, you had an ear infection that same year, and—"

"I had chicken pox when I was four years old."

"Here we are. You had chicken pox when you were four years old, Anastasia."

Anastasia sighed.

"Well, kiddo," Dr. Nazarosian went on, "I'd love to chat with you a bit longer, but you know how it is. Duty calls. Half the mothers in this town are trying to get me on the phone right at this very minute, and you know why?"

"Because their kids have—"

"Because their kids have chicken pox, that's why. Now you call again if Sam has any complications. But he should be just fine, maybe a little irritable until the fever goes down, that's all."

Anastasia heard a sound and glanced over. Sam had wandered into the room, still naked, holding a pen. He was carefully drawing green lines from one pink spot to the next across his chest. He looked up and grinned. "Follow the dots," he said.

Anastasia said good-bye politely to the doctor and hung up.

Sam handed her his underpants and socks. "Help me get dressed for school," he said.

Anastasia sighed. "We can't go to school," she told him. "You can't go to school because you have chicken pox, and I can't go to school, unless—" She looked hopefully at her father.

But he shook his head. "I'm sorry Anastasia," he said, "but I have a lecture scheduled at nine o'clock, and a department meeting after that, and I'm giving an exam at one, and—well, I'll try to get home early. I'm sorry."

Sam's face puckered and he began to cry again.

"There's a *law* that you have to go to school!" he wailed. "I *want* to go to school! I want to show *everybody* my dots!"

"Well, you *can't*," Anastasia said irritably. She wandered into his room and picked up his clothes from the floor. She began to pull the wet sheets off his bed.

"I guess I'll do laundry this morning," she muttered. "And good grief, we haven't even had breakfast yet."

The telephone rang.

"Good morning," said a spirited voice. "This is the National Telephone Survey Association. Do you have a few minutes to spare to participate in an important poll?"

Anastasia sat down with the laundry in her lap and balanced the phone on her shoulder. "I guess so," she answered grudgingly. At least it would be more interesting than laundry.

Then she gave her opinion on various political issues for fifteen minutes while Sam sat at her feet and connected the dots on his legs with green ink.

By four in the afternoon Anastasia was rewriting the entire housekeeping schedule. She was exhausted. And she was mad.

She had done all the laundry, and after she had done the laundry, she had decided to vacuum, even though it wasn't Saturday. And when she ran the vacuum cleaner under her parents' bed, it had made a strangling noise and died.

"It ate something it wasn't supposed to," Sam said solemnly. She had been trying to keep Sam in bed—she had even dressed him in his pajamas—but he kept getting out.

171

So she took the vacuum cleaner apart, unwound a wire coat hanger and poked it through the vacuum cleaner hose, and out came three of Dr. Krupnik's socks. She peered under the bed, and there were at least six others that the vacuum cleaner hadn't eaten.

Then she found her father's pajamas behind a chair, on the floor.

So she had a whole new stack of laundry and made another trip to the washing machine. No wonder she was exhausted. And no wonder she was mad. She was mad at her father for leaving his dirty clothes all over the place; but mostly she was mad at the telephone. It had been ringing all day. Total strangers had been calling her all day.

Now, at four o'clock, just when she was about to relax with a cup of hot chocolate with a marshmallow in it, the phone rang again.

Angrily she picked it up and began talking before the other person had a chance.

"No," Anastasia said assertively. "I do not want to be part of an important political poll.

"I do not want to have my family's photographs taken even if it is a special offer and includes a gold-painted plastic frame.

"I have absolutely zero interest in a full set of encyclopedias.

"I do not want to test a new gelatin dessert, even if it *is* free of charge.

"I have all the magazine subscriptions that I need, and furthermore"—she took a deep breath—"I am not going to donate money to *anything* even if it *is* a good cause, because I *don't* have any money."

She was about to slam the receiver down when she

recognized the voice at the other end.

"Well," said Steve Harvey sarcastically, "I suppose that means you don't want to go to the movies Friday night, either, even though I was willing to pay."

Anastasia gulped. "Hi, Steve," she said in a meek voice.

"Why weren't you in school?"

"My brother is sick, and my mother's away, so I'm in charge, and—" Anastasia talked on, explaining to Steve, but her mind was on what he had said. Had he asked her to go to the movies Friday night? And he would pay? Didn't that make it a *date?*"

Anastasia had never had a date in her life. She had *daydreamed* about having a date, and she had even daydreamed about having a date with Steve Harvey. Sure, she had played tennis with Steve in the summer; and sure, she and he had gone to the movies with groups of kids; and once or twice they had even gone, just the two of them—but she had always paid her own way, so it didn't count as a date.

Sam was watching her with interest. He had finished his own hot chocolate and was starting on hers. Good thing she'd already had chicken pox, Anastasia thought, because Sam was slurping chicken pox germs right into her cup. Well, that wasn't important. What was important was that Steve Harvey was actually calling and asking her for a date—the first one of her life—and she was worried about what she would wear, how she would act, what they would talk about, whether he would put his arm around her in the movie theater, and . . .

"Anastasia? Are you still there?" Steve asked.

"Yeah."

"Will you be in school tomorrow?"

She sighed. "I won't be there all week. I have to stay with Sam and take care of him and the house. Next week my father's going to do it until my mom gets home next Wednesday, and . . ."

Good grief. She was babbling, and being boring. If she was that boring when they had a date, he would never ask her for another date; he would probably ask someone like Marlene Braverman, and her whole life would be . . .

"Well, can you go to the movies Friday night?" Steve was asking.

"Sure."

"My dad'll drive us and pick us up afterward."

"Okay. Fine." Anastasia tried to sound casual, as if this happened all the time.

"Sam!" she squealed, after she had hung up. "Guess what! I have a date Friday night with Steve Harvey!"

Sam glanced up from the cup of hot chocolate. "Watch this," he said. "It's like the vacuum cleaner, with Daddy's socks." He consumed the melted marshmallow with a loud sucking noise.

Well, thought Anastasia, Sam's too young to understand the significance. Wait till Dad gets home and I tell *him.*

But when her father came through the door at five, he was not his usual cheerful self. His shoulders sagged, and his face had a terrible look. He put his briefcase down, hung up his coat slowly, and sat down on a kitchen chair.

Krupnik Family Extremely Sexist
Housekeeping Schedule

Version 4

7:00 A.M.   Everyone gets up.
              Everyone eats breakfast.

8:00 A.M.   Myron leaves.
              Anastasia stays home and does nothing
but grimy household tasks all day long, and answers
the phone continually, and never even has a chance to
read a book or anything. Sam just watches stupid TV
shows which have no educational value at all or else he
follows Anastasia around, whining, and doesn't help
with anything, and whatever she offers him for lunch,
he just says "Blecch" and does barfing imitations.

NIGHT: Everybody goes to bed, wearing clean pajamas
because Anastasia has been standing over a hot
washing machine all day long, but probably no one will
even notice that, much less say "Thank you."

NOTE: When Mom calls, do not mention new
housekeeping schedule, or CHICKEN POX or SCHOOL.

*** Vacuuming and window-washing—Forget it.

"How's Sam?" he asked, finally, in a disheartened voice.

"Fine," said Anastasia. "Just look at him."

Sam was running a truck around the kitchen floor. His chicken pox spots were all connected by green ink lines, even on his face, which he had done in front of the mirror, and he was making truck noises very happily.

Dr. Krupnik stared gloomily at the floor after glancing at Sam. Wait'll I tell him my news, thought Anastasia with glee. Wait till we tell Mom on the phone tonight. They'll both be so excited. It's the first time one of their children has ever had a real date.

"Did you have a bad day, Dad?" Anastasia asked sympathetically. She was feeling so happy that she decided not even to tell him about *her* bad day, with the endless phone calls from strangers wanting to sell her things. She wasn't even going to bug him about his dirty socks under the bed, or show him the new housekeeping schedule that she made in a fit of anger.

"I don't want to talk about it," he muttered.

■

The Krupnik Family Nonsexist Housekeeping Schedule crumbles further as Anastasia is faced with another emergency. An unexpected guest arrives and Anastasia prepares a gourmet dinner complete with candlelight and passionate purple tablecloth. To help her organize her time efficiently, Anastasia writes her sixth version of the Krupnik Housekeeping Schedule.

Sam eventually gets over the chicken pox, and the Krupnik's housekeeping problems are solved in an unexpected way. You can read the rest of the book to find out. Can you imagine what it will be?

Meet the Author: **Lois Lowry**

Where does Lois Lowry get the ideas for her writing? Partly she's gotten them from her own four children. Anastasia is based on Lowry's two daughters when they were young. But most of her ideas come from her imagination.

Anastasia started out as a short story. Lois Lowry was working on a serious book at the time and just for comic relief she wrote a short story about Anastasia. She had intended to sell it to a children's magazine, but she grew so fond of the little character that she continued writing the story until it became book length. Even though Lois Lowry is fond of Anastasia, she says she wouldn't want to live with her.

When Lowry is at home she works five hours a day writing, reading the work of students she teaches, and answering mail. She says she doesn't wait to be inspired with her writing because she would never get anything written.

Lowry writes a new book about Anastasia each year. In the first book about her, *Anastasia Krupnik*, Anastasia is nine years old. In the last three books, she is thirteen. During that time, she gets a baby brother and moves from Boston to the suburbs with her family, and has many hilarious adventures.

In addition to reading the rest of *Anastasia on Her Own*, you may want to read other books in the series: *Anastasia Again!; Anastasia at Your Service; Anastasia, Ask Your Analyst; Anastasia Has the Answer,* and *Anastasia's Chosen Career.*

1. Lois Lowry has written seven books about Anastasia. Would you be interested in reading the rest of the books in the series after reading this excerpt from *Anastasia on Her Own?* Why or why not?

2. On Housekeeping Schedule Version 4, Anastasia made a note that when Mom called no one should mention what was *really* going on at home. Suppose that Anastasia decided to tell her mother the important things that had happened. What would Anastasia tell her?

3. What does Anastasia learn about running a household with the help of a housekeeping schedule?

4. The author doesn't tell us what Sam thinks in the story—just what he does and says. Do you think Sam feels that Anastasia took good care of him? Give two examples to explain your answer.

5. Do you think Anastasia meets challenges well? Tell why or why not.

I Am Running in a Circle

I am running in a circle
and my feet are getting sore,
and my head is
spinning
spinning
as it's never spun before,
I am
dizzy
dizzy
dizzy.
Oh! I cannot bear much more,
I am trapped in a
revolving
. . . volving
. . . volving
. . . volving door!

Jack Prelutsky

179

Thinking About What Makes Characters Funny

How do you run a household smoothly? You follow a schedule, or so Anastasia thinks. And then the author puts Anastasia in charge. Lowry has several unexpected events pop up to test Anastasia, and Anastasia doesn't find it easier to cope than her mother does.

Lowry excels at this kind of humor—humor in situations that are unexpected or exaggerated and that makes the characters act in unexpected ways.

Lowry not only puts Anastasia in situations that make us laugh, she also puts funny words in Anastasia's mouth. We don't expect her to say "That's a very personal question," when the voice from the shopping service asks her if anyone in her family needs new underwear.

Writing About Humorous Characters

You will be writing a funny business letter to entertain your class. (For ideas about writing, look at The Writer's Handbook.)

Prewriting The chart below shows a funny situation or a funny comment from the story and what we might naturally expect. Copy the chart and add two more examples.

Funny Situation or Comment	What We Expected
Anastasia talks to the shopping service. She tries to act like a grown-up.	Anastasia would act her age and say, "Sorry, my mother isn't home."

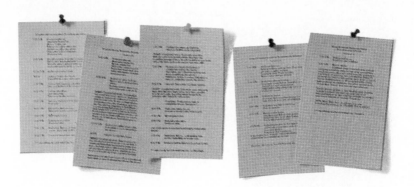

To begin your funny business letter, look at the situations or comments on your chart. Think about what makes them funny. Is a situation or comment unexpected? Now, with a partner, brainstorm three possible funny incidents that could lead to writing a business letter, such as receiving an electric blanket that stops working every time the sleeper rolls over. In writing the business letter, you will take Anastasia's point of view.

Writing Select one of the incidents and write a business letter to someone to try to correct what happened. Remember that a good business letter is short, polite, and includes an inside address where the letter will be sent and a colon after the greeting.

Revising With your partner, go over your draft. Between the two of you, see if the letter clearly communicates your message. Then revise your draft. Have your partner check to see if the letter has proper form. Then write your final copy.

Presenting Practice reading your letter aloud with your partner. Then read your letter to your classmates. Ask how they would react to your letter.

Extending Your Reading

Expressing Yourself
Choose one or more of these activities:

Create a scene for TV With some of your classmates, invent a situation Anastasia would find herself in and act it out. Make it up as you go along or actually write out the dialogue.

Sam's Schedule Pretend that Sam has his own ideas for a schedule. Tell what Sam would put in his schedule.

Create a Poster Assume that the story of Anastasia has been made into a movie. The movie will be shown in your school next week. Draw a poster that makes your classmates want to see the movie. Your poster may feature Anastasia in one of her memorable situations. Decide on a time and a place in school when the movie will be shown.

Anastasia and Poetry Let's assume that Anastasia herself ran across the poem "I Am Running in a Circle" on page 179. In Anastasia's own words, tell what she thinks of that poem. Does it, for instance, tell her feelings or doesn't it?

More Books About Meeting Challenges

The Magic of the Glits by C. S. Adler. Macmillan. Jeremy's summer at Cape Cod looks as if it will go from bad to worse. He arrives with a cast on his leg and is then informed that he must care for a seven-year-old girl. What surprises Jeremy, though, is that the girl, Lynette, turns out to have an intriguing past.

The Illyrian Adventure by Lloyd Alexander. Dutton. If you like adventure stories filled with action and suspense, this is the book for you. A fearless orphan sets off with her guardian to search for a legendary treasure in a remote European kingdom in 1872. This heroine of yesteryear soon finds herself involved in a rebellion, and her life is at stake. This story moves at a fast pace to an exciting ending.

Raising a Mother Isn't Easy by Elisabeth McHugh. Greenwillow. Eleven-year-old Karen is an adopted Korean orphan. She has made up her mind that her mother, a veterinarian and a single parent, needs a husband. In her search Karen learns that you can't plan another person's life.

What do you do when your mouth won't open? by Susan Beth Pfeffer. Delacorte. The twelve-year-old heroine of this story is a good student. She is so good, in fact, that she is chosen to read her essay aloud in an important competition. How she conquers her extreme fear of public speaking makes for humorous reading.

DRAGON OF THE LOST SEA

by Laurence Yep

DRAGON OF THE LOST SEA

Dragon of the Lost Sea

In ancient China, books were very rare and precious. Only a few highly educated people could read these treasures, so for most people, news, stories, and entertainment came from word of mouth. Sometimes storytellers roamed from village to village, bringing with them the legends and tales that had been passed on from one generation to the other. Their skill as storytellers and their wonderful tales always made them welcome guests.

The Dragon in China

Among the most popular tales in China were stories about dragons. Unlike the frightening, fire-breathing dragons of some myths, Chinese dragons were basically decent creatures. The dragon wandered about the earth and heavens passing out blessings. Dragons also gathered clouds and moisture and sent life-giving rain. But sometimes, like the rain, dragons could be destructive. The dragon often had fins and wings and could make itself invisible or transform itself into something else. Because of this important status, the dragon became the symbol for the imperial, or ruling, family of China.

The blue pebble is the most important thing in the world to the dragon princess. Shimmer, outlawed before Civet's theft, has been forced to wander alone, in one outlandish disguise after another. If Shimmer can capture Civet, if she can make the enchantress restore the sea, Shimmer will be able to restore her clan's home and regain her rightful place as a princess among dragons. If only she could be rid of this human boy . . .

But Shimmer doesn't count on Thorn's almost dragonish courage, or his fierce loyalty, or his kindness.

On one of Shimmer and Thorn's adventures, they had met Monkey. Monkey had once ambushed Civet, who managed to escape. Shimmer decided she would follow Civet to her mountain home. Monkey said he would sooner jump into a pit of vipers than do this, but Thorn said he would go.

As the story opens, Shimmer, who has converted to dragon form, and Thorn are flying to the home of the enchantress near the Lost Sea. Thorn is on Shimmer's back. Shimmer is the narrator of this adventure.

THE MOON WAS AS BRIGHT and shiny as a new silver coin when we flew over the mountains. During that time, I had been able to do some thinking. It was easy to say that I was going to use tooth and claw to fight my way to Civet, but quite another thing to do it. I didn't want to be a warrior like Monkey, who fought more with his tongue than with his mind.

I had taken a northeastern course, so that we passed over a different stretch of mountains. Ahead of us, beyond the dark huddled shapes of the mountains, the Lost Sea began to glow as a long white line on the horizon.

Suddenly I caught a glimpse of something shiny underneath me. I banked slowly to circle back and saw something glittering beneath like a glass chip.

"What is it?" Thorn asked.

"It's a pool, if I'm not mistaken. Let's have a drink before we go on."

The pool lay in a rocky hollow and hardly seemed more than four meters long and a meter at its deepest. Hundreds of tall, slender reeds, almost black in color, surrounded the northern edge of the stagnant water.

After taking a long, thirsty drink, I felt the grassy stems of some of the reeds that grew at one end of the pool. "These would make torches, I suppose. They would be good against Civet's magical cutouts."[1] I tried to yank out some of the reeds but their stems slipped through my claws. "Bring your knife over."

Under my direction, Thorn gathered all of the reeds, splitting some of them into long slender fibers so that we could begin to tie the other reeds into bundles of twelve. Then, with a sack improvised from the boy's shirt, we flew on.

The sun was just beginning to rise as we reached the edge of the Lost Sea; but since we were flying, we had no trouble at all during the crossing. Shortly before noontime we reached the northern edge of the sea, where the land rose in a series of ledges until it ended in a wide spacious plateau. In the very center of the plateau rose a perfect black cone of a mountain a kilometer or so high.

"That's Civet's home," I said.

I began to work my way downward until we were in the

---

1. Civet's magical cutouts were made of paper and created an illusion of real people or animals.

lesser currents. I banked slowly, descending in a slow spiral through the air. The mountain seemed to loom higher and higher.

Odd white lumps dotted the plateau everywhere. It wasn't until we had swept lower that we saw that they were bleached bones—spines and ribs strewn all about like broken necklaces. Here and there were large skulls as slender and pointed as arrowheads.

"What happened?" Thorn called in awe.

"Those are bones of some of the dragons who have tried to capture Civet." I landed gently. "I can't say that I like her sense of decor very much."

When the boy had slid off my neck, we stalked warily toward the gate. It had been carved from some translucent stone like jade into the likeness of a massive, gluttonous beast with a mouth big enough to swallow whole oxen. Its eyes were huge and faceted, but its cheeks seemed to be covered in feathers swelling from either side of the hungry, fanged mouth.

As we drew closer, we could see that the feathers and the lips and even the fangs had each, in turn, been carved into pouncing birds and coiled snakes, each trying to devour the other. And the facets of the eyes were really some hungry little demonic faces, each one distinct from the other. The green stone itself was shot with little red veins that made the monstrous gate seem almost like real flesh.

"It almost looks alive," Thorn murmured.

"It may very well have been once." I took out one of the torches from the bag over Thorn's shoulder. "When I was little, we used to come here for picnics. But this is one of her 'improvements.'"

Thorn lit the torch before we entered the gate. It seemed to leer as we stepped through, and a breeze suddenly slipped out

as if the mountain itself were heaving a great moan—like some sleeper finally coming awake.

We followed a narrow tunnel that wound downward for about thirty meters and then suddenly spiraled sharply upward again, then twisted to the left and then corkscrewed downward once. Tunnels led away on either side, and I began to lose track of all the twists and turns. It seemed that Civet had made a good many changes within the mountain as well.

We had almost burned through the third torch when we reached the first of the caverns. Nearly fifty meters in diameter and fifteen meters high, it was filled with stalactites hanging from the ceiling and stalagmites rising from the floor. I kicked the nearest one. "They were formed by mineral deposits as the water slowly seeped through the mountain," I explained. "There's a tale that my grandfather imprisoned his own brother somewhere inside this mountain."

"When did that happen?" Thorn poked the nearest stalagmite.

"Back when the world was young and an alliance of greedy creatures tried to claim it as their own; but they were opposed by the Five Masters—the Serpent Lady, the Archer, the Lord of the Flowers, the Unicorn, and my great-grandfather." I looked around, feeling the weight of history.

"It was a desperate war, and for a time we were driven from our kingdoms into the mountain wildernesses beneath the sea. My granduncle allowed an enemy war band into the fortress itself. My great-grandfather died allowing the other Masters to escape." I touched a drop of moisture on one of the stone columns. "Later, when my grandfather led the dragons to victory, he captured his brother. One day they disappeared and my grandfather returned by himself. No one knows what happened, but he's said to have placed his brother somewhere inside this mountain. The water is supposed to be his tears."

Thorn shuddered. "I don't know about that. But the stones look like rows of teeth."

I should have made Thorn light a new torch, but I got caught up in my own memories instead. "We used to call this place the throne room," I whispered, and the words circled eerily around the walls.

Thorn held his torch near the closest wall. The stone was shaped in wide, curving surfaces like curtains, complete with folds. And as we walked toward the center of the cavern, Thorn would point to smaller sections of stone that, in his own mind, suggested banners or even tapestries blowing in the wind.

At the other end we paused by a squat, pyramid-shaped stalagmite some two meters high. Part of one side had collapsed so that it almost resembled a throne. I nodded to the strange stone formation. "My brother and I and all our cousins used to take turns sitting there." I made a face. "Of course, my brother hogged it most of the time. He said he was already king anyway."

"But did he—" Thorn's words were drowned out by a growl from the distant shadows. The torch dropped from his startled fingers. A newer torch would have continued to burn; but this one, almost completely used up already, simply sputtered and died. The cavern was plunged immediately into darkness. The growl echoed and reechoed until it sounded as if there were a hundred beasts around us.

"I'm sorry—" he began, but my groping paw found his shoulder.

It was a catastrophe, but this was no time to scold him. "Never mind. Light a new torch." While he fumbled in his sash for his flint and knife, I found the bag of torches and took out a new one. As the growling drew closer, he began frantically striking sparks with mad scratching sounds. I held the torch

close to where I thought I had seen a momentary spark. He kept on stroking the flint feverishly until the torch caught fire in a sudden flash of bright, fierce light. At that very instant, we saw the huge, low-slung body of a tiger not more than five meters away.

With a gasp, Thorn dropped the flint and knife.

"Steady," I snapped at him and thrust the torch into his hands. "This is our best weapon anyway." The tiger crouched, snarling as if it hated the light. It was answered by a growl behind us. I turned to see a second tiger pad between the stone columns, and then a third.

"Watch the first one," I told the boy and took another torch from his bag.

The tiger by the throne began to lash its tail, its body tensing, as I held my torch against his. It lit almost immdiately.

"But why—" the boy started to ask. His eyes were on me rather than on the tiger.

It chose that very second to spring. "Watch out," I cried. The tiger's body arched through the air with its muscular front legs extended, its roar deafening our ears.

One moment the tiger loomed over us, murderous fangs bared, its claws reached for a deadly slash. And then I had used my own torch to strike one of its legs. The next moment the tiger had disappeared. All that remained was a large piece of black paper burning in the air as it slowly fluttered to the rocky floor. There was just enough of the paper left to show the outline of a catlike tail and hindlegs.

"That's what you have to do." I faced behind us toward the two other tigers. They had just been in the act of springing when they saw me turn. They caught themselves, settling back for a moment.

"Was it real?" the boy asked.

"You would have found out quickly enough if those claws had ever struck." I watched, satisfied, as the tiger's ashes drifted overhead. "It has substance until the fire destroys its powers."

One of the tigers swung away suddenly, so that it was lost behind a row of stalagmites. Its paws struck the stones like velvet hammers.

I glanced at Thorn to make sure he was watching the front. He was turning his head slowly while he scooped up his flint and knife to tuck away in his sash. "Did you kill it?" he wondered.

"It wasn't truly alive." I swung carefully around to face the third tiger. "Or rather it had only been given a little bit of Civet's soul. She's even weaker now for its loss." I looked all around the cavern but I couldn't see the second tiger. About ten meters away I saw the oval mouth of a tunnel. It was perhaps a meter wide but two meters high—enough to take myself and a rider. Even better, the tigers could only attack from one direction.

"I want you to climb on my back," I explained to the boy, "so that you can face behind us. I'm going to make a dash for the tunnel. And be ready to duck when I tell you."

"All right," Thorn said tensely.

I squatted down on the stones, twisting my head this way and that to watch for tigers. Even so, I couldn't look in every direction while the boy got onto my back.

"Look out," I heard the boy call and turned my head just in time to see the tiger leaping over the throne. The boy thrust his torch up stiffly, but I had the reach on him. The next moment my torch had found the creature; and it had disappeared in a quick puff of flame.

Claws suddenly raked my back. The last tiger had taken the opportunity to strike from behind. Craning my head around me,

I saw it clinging to my hindquarters, one paw stretching out to slash the boy. The boy swung his torch wildly at the tiger and just caught its paw. The tiger just had time to snarl before it changed into a bit of fiery paper.

"Well done." I blew out my own torch and triumphantly handed it back to him to stow away. "You're becoming a regular little warrior."

"That's more than I ever expected to hear from you." He sounded rather pleased, but it was quickly replaced by worry. "You're bleeding."

"The scratches look like shallow ones," I said and gave them a quick lick after he had hopped down.

"Shouldn't you do something else for those cuts?" he sounded worried.

"The longer we delay, the more time Civet has to prepare new surprises for us." I began to limp forward grimly.

THE TUNNEL EVENTUALLY LED to a flight of forty steps that opened into a cavern so large that we could not even see the ceiling or the far walls, only the tall rocky cones that in some places had fused into columns.

A wide canyon divided the cavern in half—with only a high stone arch linking the two sides. The arch was so thin and narrow that it seemed more like milky, orange-colored glass than stone.

Thorn tested it uncertainly with his foot. "It seems solid enough."

"It was when we used to play on it." I nudged the boy from behind. "Let's go."

Taking one cautious step at a time, he was nearly to the

center of the arch when a crossbow string twanged maliciously.
"Down." With one foot I flattened him against the stone, and
then I felt the sharp point of a crossbow bolt hit my left
shoulder and stay there. I fell from the bridge, blinking at the
pain. In knocking the boy down I had also made him lose his
torch, so that it fell with me into the canyon, and a large
number of unlit torches as well—I suppose they had fallen from
his bag.

Painfully I spread my wings and banked, almost scraping my
snout against one side of the canyon. Scrabbling, my claws
found holds among the rocks and I held on for a moment,
trying to get my breath back. The torch was a small bright
circle of light as it tumbled lazily down into the canyon.

I was still clinging to the rocks when the boy called from
above the canyon. "Shimmer, are you all right?"

I almost told the boy that I was fine; but I suddenly realized
it was better for the moment if everyone thought I was dead.
That way we might be able to draw the enemy out into the
open, because the sniper would probably go directly after
Thorn. I knew it was cruel not to answer the boy and even
crueler to use him as bait; but I didn't intend to let him come
to any harm. I resolutely shoved myself from the rock and
began to climb upward with slow, quiet beats of my wings.

The boy called to me several times, each time his voice
sounding higher and more worried. Even so, I held my tongue.
The last time the boy tried to speak to me, his words broke off
in a sob as if he were mourning my death. I was startled for a
moment, since I don't think there was anyone else in this world
who cared whether I was alive or dead. I nearly answered him
right then, but I held my tongue when I heard the slow scraping
noises—as if someone, most likely the boy, was crawling on
his or her belly.

I decided it was probably the boy retreating back along the stone arch. Turning my face to the canyon side where we had been, I tried to hover as I probed blindly for footholds among the rocks. Then, moving as carefully as a fly, I made my way out of the canyon. I had just managed to slip in among the stalagmites when I saw the light appear on the far side of the canyon.

I wondered what a light was doing over there. Suddenly a small hand appeared, holding a lit torch. "Come and get me if you can," Thorn shouted in a voice that would have sounded more defiant if it hadn't cracked with nervousness. And he thrust the torch firmly into a crack in the side of one stalagmite.

A crossbow string twanged and a heavy bolt knocked chips from a stalagmite just to the left.

"Try again," Thorn taunted, his voice sounding firmer.

I simply closed my eyes and sighed. Instead of returning to my side of the canyon, as I had expected, Thorn had gone to the other side—I suppose with some fool notion of avenging me. I might have appreciated his show of bravery and grief if he had displayed them on the same side as myself. As it was, I would now have to reveal myself and fly across the canyon to protect him—and that meant risking another crossbow bolt.

"Come on," the boy jeered at our invisible enemy. "What are you waiting for?"

There was only the slow cranking sound of a crossbow string being drawn back. The enemy could afford to wait. Unfortunately, I couldn't—not if I wanted to save the boy.

Trying as much as possible to keep my weight off my wounded shoulder, I slipped among the stalagmites until I had the stone arch between myself and our enemy. Then, bracing my hindlegs against the base of a column, I picked out a wide space between two stalagmites on the far side. It seemed to me

I could hear the sounds of boots scraping over the rocks—as if the sniper were finally closing in on Thorn.

I had definitely made better takeoffs than that particular one; but then I usually had four legs to use, not three. Recovering from my clumsy leap, I began to beat my wings rapidly, trying to keep my flight path paralleling the natural curve of the archway. Even so, I was anxiously aware of how much of me was still exposed to the sniper.

The crossbow string twanged. I resisted the urge to cringe because it would only slow me down—perhaps fatally. Instead, I dove for the far edge. The bolt ricocheted from the top of the archway, barely missing me.

I landed on my wounded shoulder and couldn't help gasping at the jagged pain that raced from my shoulder through the rest of my body. Even so, I managed to scramble to my legs and drag myself into the safety of the stone columns.

I lay there, breathing a deep sigh of relief. The crossbow string was drawn back with the slow, steady clicks of the crossbow gears. There was something deadly and ominous about the sound, as if it were some timepiece slowly counting down our last few minutes of life.

"I'm here now, boy," I whispered. "So don't worry anymore."

But there was only a grim, deadly silence.

"Thorn?" I called softly, but there was still no response.

"Speak to me, Thorn." Worried now, I didn't even bother trying to keep my voice down. My words echoed around the cavern and I waited tensely. When the boy did not answer, I began to think the worst. Had the enemy already managed to kill him? Was I too late? I desperately began to wriggle through the maze of stalagmites toward the light that marked Thorn's spot.

"Are you all right, boy?" I thrust my head urgently between

two narrow stalagmites. To my surprise and confusion, I found Thorn's bag with a dozen torches—and no Thorn.

I squirmed into a small oval space surrounded by tall stone columns. I still found it hard to believe that the boy was gone. Amazed, I picked up the bag as if the boy could be hidden beneath it. Apparently Thorn had gone out hunting the sniper by himself. With a shake of my head, I laid the bag back down. I was definitely going to have to stop underestimating that boy. I found it impossible simply to sit there while the boy was doing all the fighting. Deciding to help, I stuck my head out from around the stalagmite that held the torch.

A crossbow twanged from only a few meters away. I barely ducked in time as the wicked-looking bolt embedded itself in the stone just about where my head had been. And then the next moment, I heard Thorn giving out the war cry of the Lost Sea clan—I suppose in imitation of me. It was followed by a yell of pain. Was it the sniper or Thorn?

"Thorn?" I called out in alarm. Suddenly I had this strange, helpless feeling—as if someone had ripped off my wings and pitched me back into the canyon.

"Thorn?" I said, and when there still wasn't any answer, I shouted, "THORN?" But there was only silence.

It was odd; but after my mother died, I thought I had armored myself against ever again feeling that wild sense of grief. But it was back now—a terrible aching kind of emptiness that gnawed at my insides and made everything in the world seem petty and ridiculous compared to my loss.

Of course, I hadn't let anyone get close to me since I had begun my years of wandering. But I had liked the boy's cheerfulness and his courage, which would have done credit to someone triple his size and age. Despite that affection—or because of it—I should have followed my first instincts and left

him with Monkey. My own moment of weakness had now cost Thorn his life.

Something scraped on the rocks nearby. I might be too late to save the boy, but at least I could avenge him. Shouting my war cry, I sprang out from behind the stalagmites.

It was a combination of shock and my bad shoulder that made me fall flat on my face. There, lounging against a stone column as if he owned the cavern, was Thorn. "I thought you were dead." He sounded angry and confused all at the same time.

"It was to fool the sniper." Embarrassed, I got to my feet. "Bring something for bandages, will you?"

Thorn fetched the bag of torches and emptied them on the floor. "You set me up as a target." He showed me a hurt expression.

I sat down on my haunches and yanked the torch from the stalagmite. "Before you call me any nasty names, let me point out that you turned the tables on me rather neatly." I set the torch against the bolt in my shoulder. Instantly, the bolt disappeared in a quick spurt of smoke. "After all, I became the bait instead." When the wound began to bleed, I started to lick it.

"You almost spoiled it with your talking." He began to tear the bag into strips—and looked as if he wished he was ripping up my hide instead.

I stuck the torch back into the crack. "It takes a while to perfect teamwork."

"Teamwork?" He began to knot the strips together with short, hard jerks. "I thought you said only equals could make up a team."

I chose my compliment carefully. There was no sense swelling his head "Yes, well, associating with me seems to

have brought out some rather dragonish qualities in you." I sat back as he started to wind the bandage around the wound in my shoulder.

"I don't know if I like that idea." He tied the ends of the bandage into a knot. "In the past few days, I've heard an awful lot about a dragon's sense of honor and precious little about a dragon's sense of gratitude."

He could be as exasperating as he could be brave; and I forgot just how much I had missed him a moment ago. "There's no pleasing you, is there? Isn't it enough that a princess of—"

He gave a laugh and waved his hand airily. "I know all about your pedigree." Leaving me still sputtering in indignation, he gathered the torches in one arm. "Are we going to have enough torches?"

I got to my feet. "We'll find out soon enough, won't we?"

WE HAD TO FIGHT OUR WAY through more tunnels and caverns, but I must say that the boy proved steady enough—making up in courage what he lacked in skill. Unfortunately, we ran all too quickly through our precious store of torches. We only had two left as we entered the largest and loveliest and most dangerous cavern of all. But if we captured Civet, we wouldn't have to worry about traps. Anything less than her capture would mean our own deaths. It simplified matters considerably.

The cavern was circular in shape and about three hundred and fifty meters in diameter. The walls themselves seemed covered with giant tapestries of lace that glowed a soft rosy red in the torchlight.

"What made those?" Thorn stared up at the stone lacework.

I knew the cavern well from my childhood and had asked the very same question then, so I could now give Thorn the very same explanation my own father had given me. "Long ago, some plants must have managed to grow here, or moss, or lichen." I glanced only momentarily at the lovely stone tapestries. My attention was all for the center of the cavern, where I was sure we would meet Civet. "Water seeped in and the minerals settled out to take the form of the plants until the plants were dead. Now only the shapes remain."

Thorn's eyes seem to trace the shapes and patterns in the stony lace. "It's beautiful."

I plucked at the strap of his bag. "Come along. We're not on a pleasure tour, you know."

In the very center of the cavern, the lacy stalagmites and stalactites had fused together to form what looked like a groove of trees with intricate webs of roots and branches. Hanging from the ceiling all around the grove were stone formations that looked like chandeliers and lamps of delicate scrollwork.

We had just neared the edge of the grove when five swordswomen dropped from out of the tops of the trees. For a moment their hair flared like black flame as they fell. In each of their left hands was a huge cutlass and in each of their right hands was a whip.

Thorn thrust his torch at the women, but they only smiled. One of them flung back her right hand and then brought it forward with a sudden jerk, wrapping the thongs around the torch itself. Thorn gave a cry as the torch was torn from his grasp. Almost immediately the flames spread up the thongs to the first woman; and she vanished even as the torch itself went flying past. Her sisters, however, were now between us and the torch.

Sounding my clan's war cry, I charged them, but my shoulder slowed me down. Three of them threw back their whips and, with sharp cracks, wrapped the thongs of their whips around my left leg, below my injured shoulder. I tried to resist them when they pulled, but the pain was too great. My leg went out from underneath me and I fell face forward. The last swordswoman had dropped her own whip so she could swing her cutlass up over her head in both hands.

As she stepped in, I thought it was all over for me. I was lying helpless with my chest against the rock floor and my neck stretched out conveniently for a beheading. I didn't reckon with Thorn and neither did she.

His knife went flying through the air, turning end over end. Of course, a kitchen knife isn't meant to be used quite that way, so the woman had time to duck; but it brought me the precious seconds that I needed.

I twisted my long neck around, got hold of her leg and, with a sudden jerk, flung her into the others so that the four of them fell backward in a heap onto the torch. Immediately they flared into fiery paper cutouts.

I got to my feet sullenly. "I guess I truly owe you my life this time."

He trotted over to fetch the torch. "You make it sound like a crime."

"It would be to some creatures." When the paper warriors had burned up, the thongs about my leg had disappeared. I got up rather shakily. "I've never been too keen on the social graces—"

"Then you haven't changed any." The boy shrugged.

I swung my head around to glower at him. "Please allow me to thank you in my own way."

The boy mocked me lightly with his eyes. "Oh, is that what you're doing? I'm glad you told me, or I wouldn't have recognized it."

I wagged a claw at him. "If I had known you were going to be so obnoxious, I would never have let you save my life."

He gave me an insolent bow. "My apologies. Next time I'll let the sword cut your neck."

The whole notion was so ridiculous that I couldn't stay annoyed with him. He had a knack for poking holes through my sense of dignity.

"Well"—I wrinkled my snout—"you needn't go that far."

We lit the second-to-last torch as we entered the grove of stone trees. It was slow progress trying to climb over the tree roots and ducking underneath the branches. But suddenly we found ourselves in a kind of clearing in which sat seven pools.

An outer ring was formed by six pools, each about five meters wide and two meters deep. Drops of water struck their surfaces in soft, liquid music. When Thorn held his torch near the surface of one pool, we could just make out the white and yellow crystals growing on the bottom. They grew in such tight clusters that they looked like flowers. Some had long, slender spikes and looked a little like chrysanthemums.

Thorn looked longingly at the pool. "I wish I could throw myself in there."

I felt rather hot and dusty myself. "So do I—but in a place like this, it's best to be cautious."

A larger pool sat in the center of the ring. Ten meters wide and four meters deep, the pool itself seemed completely empty of water now, but the stalagmites rising from its center were encrusted with golden flowers that glowed with a soft light of their own.

I crept warily over to a bare column of orange stone that

grew on the left side of the pool. A small metal hammer hung
by thongs from a projection. "Keep a sharp lookout," I warned
Thorn and, getting up on my hindlegs, stretched myself over the
pool's edge so I could strike the column with my good foot.

The column gave off a low ringing sound—like a bell buried
far beneath the earth, but so low and deep that it was almost
like a moan.

The air began to stir leisurely over the center of the pool, and
a small dot of green light appeared, widening as it rippled
outward to touch the very edge of the pool. I drew back
quickly, waiting for Civet's next trick.

Another circle appeared and a third, and the pool was filled
with a subdued, dark green light that reminded me of the
shadows beneath the ancient forest giants. Far, far away I heard
a soft hissing that grew steadily louder as the green light began
to bubble and spin in little whirlpools and send strange
shadows whirling around the stone trees.

Slowly, a small, dainty girl of about sixteen rose from out of
the pool until she seemed to be standing on the surface of the
green light. I blinked my eyes, a little surprised. She was
wearing clothes that humans had not worn for thousands of
years—though instead of plain cotton her costume had been
cut of expensive silk. Over her shoulders was a short, pleated
jacket with brown batik designs that reminded me of the
markings on a civet cat. Her long, trailing dress matched her
jacket, and I suppose that the soft hissing sound I had heard
had been made by the dress hem sliding over stone. On her
head, though, was a turban of costly gold cloth.

She also seemed to have emptied out a small treasure chest
of gold, jade and precious stones to wear. Besides her earrings,
she wore a ring on each finger and bracelets, brooches and a
massive necklace. Despite all that I managed to pick out the

mist stone,[2] which hung from a slender golden chain around her neck. So I knew that this must be Civet.

I suppose she had meant to impress us, but her entire outfit only struck me as being a bit flashy and overdressed—like that of a child who has borrowed her mother's best clothes so she can play at being a hostess.

She only added to that impression when she actually spoke, because her voice was childishly high—no matter how haughty she tried to sound. "Who dares to summon me?" she demanded.

I crouched, ready to fight my way through hordes of monsters and warriors. "You've much to answer for."

"And so have you." One hand gripped the side of her dress as she whisked the hem elegantly over the surface of the pool. "By the power of the water and earth, take them."

Immediately the water in the three farther pools pushed upward like living worms that arched over Civet's head to cascade down upon both of us. I was knocked over by the sudden force of the flood and washed backward until I came up hard against the grove of stone trees. Stunned, I lay gasping among their roots.

Lithe as a cat, Civet strode to the very edge of the pool and leaped down. At her word of command, the roots of the nearby trees suddenly slipped out of the rocky floor and rose like gritty tentacles to wrap themselves around my legs and body. One even caught me across the mouth like a gag. I shut my eyes, straining every muscle as I pulled and wiggled, but even my immense strength could not break their stony grip. To my right I could hear Thorn grunting as if he, too, were trying to break free.

---

2. The mist stone is a magic stone which has the power to transform people and things.

Then I thought of shrinking myself or changing into some more slippery shape, like that of a snake. Desperately I sketched a magical symbol in the air with my claw; but without a spoken spell to power the sign, my claws were simply scratching the air.

Civet's dress hissed with silken softness over the stone floor as she strode right up to me. "It's no use struggling, you know, I've got you." She spoke with all the smugness of a child who had just bested another in some wrestling match.

I slumped bitterly. I had failed, like all the other dragons. Eventually, I supposed, my bones would be tossed outside to be added to the remains of all the other failures.

"I'm sorry that I had to do this, but only one of us can survive." She tested my bonds. "I do hope you're going to be a good sport about the whole thing."

My only answer was to squirm against the stone roots, but I merely succeeded in rubbing my hide raw in several places.

"You see, it's useless." She patted the root that bound my chest. "So why don't you give me your word of honor not to use your magic. Then I could remove your gag and give you a last meal and have a little chat before I . . . ah . . . well, do away with you." She smiled at me awkwardly.

Unfortunately, she hadn't gagged Thorn. "And who's going to cook your meals?" he asked.

Civet started to motion behind her. "Why, my servants . . ." She rubbed her forehead in annoyance.

"Oh, bother, you've disposed of all of my servants." For once she didn't seem to know what to do—like an actress who finds she's using the wrong script. Her puzzlement and frustration were plain in her voice when she spoke again. "And it's going to be quite a while before I'll have the energy to make more. Making the water and stalagmites move has tired me out."

"How would you like a real flesh-and-blood servant?" Thorn sounded anxious and excited. "One who didn't have to be afraid of a cooking fire?"

I twisted, but the gag held my head rigid so I couldn't see the boy. Well, I thought to myself bitterly, so much for the promise he had made when he had first asked to go with me. At that time, he had said that he would never let me down; and during our long journey I had actually begun to have faith in him. But now I knew he was just as treacherous and deceitful as the rest of his kind.

Civet cupped her chin in one hand. "Hmm, I do have a rather high casualty rate with my cooks. One step too close to the fire, and poof"—she flung out her hand to accent the word—"they go up in smoke."

"And paper servants can't be much company for a clever person like you," Thorn coaxed.

"No, they aren't very good conversationalists," she said with a sad little laugh. "No matter what spells I use, I can't make them think."

Thorn's voice was warm and friendly. "How can you celebrate your victory when you have to cook your own meal?"

Civet seemed amused as she pushed a strand of hair underneath her turban. "And I suppose you want to help me, is that it?"

Thorn's voice took on an almost professional assurance—as if he were mimicking Knobby, his old employer. "People were giving parties all the time at the inn where I worked. I know what to do."

I struggled to tell her that the boy was probably lying, but the only sounds I could make around the gag were angry snarls. Civet nodded to me. "Your former employer doesn't seem to like the idea."

"I wasn't about to use her as a reference anyway," Thorn said.

Civet bit her lip thoughtfully. "Well, it really *has* been a long time since I've had any real company." She smiled almost shyly. "Perhaps I'll give you a try." She swept her hand through the air as she murmured something. A moment later I heard a harsh, grating sound—as if the tree roots were sliding back.

Thorn appeared almost immediately in my line of sight. He moved slowly as he tried to rub the circulation back into his arms. "Now, which way is it to the kitchen?" he asked eagerly.

"It's back there." She pointed beyond the pools toward the shadows at the rear of the cavern and then swung her arm around so she could wag her index finger at him—almost like a stern, older sister. "But just remember one thing. I'm only going to give you this one chance. Give me any reason to doubt you and you'll be sorry."

The boy swallowed. "I've seen what you've done to your enemies." He turned and started for the kitchen. As he shuffled past, I tried to trip him with the tip of my tail, but I could not even move that.

"Traitor," I shouted, but, much to my frustration, the sound only came out as a growl because of the stone root gagging my mouth.

Thorn gave a little jump. He stared at me as if hurt, and then he shrugged his shoulders in a great show of carelessness. "I want to live."

I squirmed against the dense tangle of roots. "I trusted you," I said, but again the sound was muffled by the gag.

He spread out his hands. "I can give a good guess as to what you're saying. Try to look at things from my point of view. What's honor and good faith to a skeleton?" But while his back was to Civet, he managed to wink at me. Then he slipped quickly out of sight.

Had I underestimated the boy once again? And yet what could he hope to do against anyone so powerful as Civet? I could only lie there helplessly, waiting to find out.

I STILL HADN'T FIGURED OUT what he was up to when he returned with a large green bowl. Civet was sitting on a stumplike rock beside me. For the tenth time or so, she asked me to give her my oath not to use magic. "We could have a very nice chat while we eat," she suggested wistfully. "I really would like to talk to someone who remembers the old days."

I simply glared at her as I had the other times.

"Well, perhaps you'll change your mind," she sighed, and held out her hands for the bowl. Long streamers of steam rose from its mouth.

"It's hot," Thorn warned her as he handed her the bowl.

Civet balanced it carefully between her fingertips.

"Noodles?" she asked unhappily. "Is that all?"

"I thought you wanted a quick meal." Thorn smiled ingratiatingly.

Exasperated, Civet set the bowl down on her lap. "I thought you knew a lot of elegant party dishes."

Thorn slapped a hand to his forehead. "Did I make you think that?" He spread out his hands apologetically. "We did have a lot of parties at the inn, but they were always for simple farmers."

Civet pressed her lips together tightly as if she were trying to decide if Thorn was making fun of her. I think she was really much less confident and secure than she pretended to be. "I've a good mind to turn you into a cockroach and stamp on you."

Thorn dropped his head like a good servant. "And who'd wash the dishes?"

"Who indeed?" Civet wondered in a dry voice. She picked up the ivory chopsticks that had been laid across the mouth of the bowl. "In any case, the joke is on you, because I had intended to give you the first taste."

Even in the dim light, I could see how Thorn paled. Had he put some kind of poison in it? I began to regret some of the harsh things I had thought about him.

"I . . . unh . . . nibbled in the kitchen," he mumbled.

Civet smiled as if he had just confirmed her suspicions. "Really?" She stirred her chopsticks around inside the bowl. "They say that poison discolors ivory." She held the chopsticks up to study the tips and seemed mildly surprised that they were the same color as before. "Still, there are so many sophisticated poisons nowadays."

"But I wouldn't use a poison," Thorn insisted—rather guiltily I thought. "You can trust me."

Civet raised her eyebrows in a superior fashion. "I haven't trusted anyone since my own dear, loving father sent me to my death."

"He what?" Thorn's eyes widened in horror.

"The King Within the River had seen me on the riverbank and wanted me for his bride." With an abrupt swoop of her hand, Civet dipped her chopsticks back into the bowl. "And my father was too scared to refuse."

"And who was the King?" Thorn asked.

"He was a magical creature who once ruled all of the Arrow River." She regarded Thorn with frosty contempt. "The waters didn't rise or fall a millimeter without his permission, and all the boats and river villages had to pay tribute to him—including my village, which became River Glen."

Such things used to happen thousands of years ago when the humans still lived in weak, isolated tribes. Disorganized, they

had been easy victims for certain powerful magical creatures who might call themselves kings and queens but who were little more than bandits at heart. At least her story matched her ancient costume.

"I think I would have run away," Thorn said. He seem fascinated by the long, trailing noodles lifted from the bowl.

"So would most people." Civet dumped the noodles back into the bowl. "And I was tempted to hide. Who would want to go live in that muddy old river when they could live in my valley?" Her face grew suddenly peaceful. "There was never a valley quite as lovely as mine."

Seized by some strange impulse, she turned to me. "Do you remember how the pine trees filled almost the whole valley?" she asked eagerly. "I spent as much time as I could in the cool, fragrant shadows." She lifted her arms in a slowly rising angle, as if she could trace the sweep of the forest top. "And do you remember how the trees used to go right up the sides of the mountains?"

At that moment she seemed more like some homesick child than a wicked sorceress. I had gotten so used to thinking of her as a hateful creature that it was hard to believe she was capable of loving anything. But in her own way, I suppose, she had loved the forest as much as I had loved my sea, or she wouldn't have gone to the King Within the River.

Perhaps she had been telling the truth when she had said that she wanted to reminisce with me about the old days. Unfortunately for her, I wasn't quite that old. We had been trading with the humans for some hundred and fifty years by the time I had been taken to the city as a fifty-year-old infant. Even so, some of the forest had been left and I remembered how the green shadows beneath the trees had reminded me very much of my own home. However, because of my bonds,

all I could manage to do right then was nod my head ever
so slightly.

Civet's hand dropped abruptly to her lap, as if she was
disappointed by my inability to respond. She turned again to
Thorn, finding him to be a better audience. "At any rate," she
said with great dignity, "I couldn't let the King destroy my valley."

"That was a brave thing to do." Thorn shook his head as if in
admiration.

"So everyone said." She smoothed her dress over her knee.
"They tried to make it up to me by fussing over the 'wedding,'
as they called it. I was given the best cloth for my wedding
robe and the most precious stones, and they held a big feast on
the riverbank. And my father and all the elders made speeches
about what a noble sacrifice I was making and how generations
to come would remember what I had done for my people. And
they all wept and promised."

Her face had grown very still and her eyes took on a distant
look, as if she were seeing the scene once again. "And then
almost everyone crowded into the boats and escorted me out to
the middle of the river.

"The people had to paddle hard just to keep the boats steady
in the currents." Her lips moved mechanically as if controlled
by someone else. "One by one the items of my dowry were
pitched overboard." Her own head moved from side to side
slowly as if she were watching. "And then there was only me."

"Father held out his hand." She raised her own hand to
illustrate. "And he said, 'It's time to go.'

"And I looked beyond him for one last look at my beloved
valley. The green tops of the trees looked so soft and
comfortable in the warm, misty air.

"'The King must be waiting,' Father reminded me. I turned. His
eyes pleaded with me silently not to make a scene but to go

willingly. Even now, he was afraid of angering the King.

"I looked at my father contemptuously. I was willing to give up my life and he would still begrudge me these few moments. I stood up carefully then so that I didn't rock the boat. Over the side I saw my face reflected on the surface of the water—a distorted reflection upset by all the ripples from the paddles. And then I jumped and I was breaking through the surface.

"I struggled to swim as I had once swum so easily before, but my wedding robe became soaked with water quickly and felt as heavy as if it had been cut from stone. And all of my jewelry weighed like boulders." Her arms paddled furiously for a moment in the air. "I tried everything. I even wiggled like an eel, but it was no use. I felt myself falling down, down into the depths.

"It was so muddy that it was hard to see, but I was looking for the King. If anyone had ever seen him, that person had never lived to tell about it. To me he was just this big voice booming from the water when he wanted something.

"And then I thought I could just make out a shape. At first I thought it was a mask because it was so ugly. But then I realized it was a real face with a long, waving beard like pondweed. His shoulders were covered with scaled armor and his legs were squat and bent like a frog's. Slowly he raised his arms in welcome."

She looked downward, her eyes widening slowly, her mouth opening in horror and revulsion. Her reactions were so real that I almost felt as if I, too, could see the shadowy King Within the River. She seemed to be not simply remembering the scene but actually going through her death all over again. I couldn't help shivering.

Civet tilted back her head desperately, but her words came out only as a whisper, as if she were simply voicing her

thoughts. "Help me, Father. Mother. Someone. Please help me." Her body twitched and one leg angled out. "He's got hold of my ankle." She wriggled and squirmed as if panicked. "He's pulling me down." Her face grew a little harsher, as if anger were replacing her fear. "He's so ugly. So terrible. How could you send me to him without asking what he looks like? It's not right. It's not right at all.

"I need air. I need light." Suddenly she gave a gasp. "The water's cold. So cold inside my lungs. I can't breathe." She made a choking sound and stiffened.

Thorn tiptoed close to her.

Her eyes blinked once. They blinked again. She relaxed a bit, staring at Thorn with sudden recognition "Step back," she warned him.

Thorn obeyed hastily. "I was just trying to see if you were all right. You looked like you were dying."

Civet's breath came in short, sharp hisses, as if she were still fighting to regain her breath. "The King preserved my body exactly as it was at the moment of drowning." Her shoulders rose and fell more slowly as her lungs recovered. "This is my true shape."

"And everything else has stayed fresh in your mind—like dying?"

"Yes." She touched a hand to the mist stone to reassure herself that Thorn hadn't stolen it. "That's the unfortunate drawback to that particular spell." She gestured toward her heart. "Even now I can feel the hatred welling up inside me, hot and scalding."

"I don't blame you." He made a sympathetic face. "The King sounds terrible."

"It's not just the King." She closed her eyes as her breathing grew even. "It's also the fault of my father and my tribe. They didn't even try to argue with the King or do anything." Her

eyelids slid back up. "But our noodles are getting cold." Her chopsticks raised a portion of noodles again. "You really must eat your share now."

There is no poison in the noodles, but there is a magical hair, which Monkey had given to Thorn. When Civet swallows the hair, her body is rendered helpless.

The dragon princess, now free of her bonds, says she will spare Civet's life if she will restore the sea. Civet, however, says, "Can't. The spell only works once." (Shimmer would have spared Civet anyway, after hearing Civet's sad story of her life with her husband, the King Within the River.)

Shimmer realizes she will have to find another magician to restore the sea. Thorn insists that Shimmer take him with her, saying "We've gone this far together. Why not go a little farther?"

Shimmer and Thorn, taking the enchantress Civet with them, set out on another adventure to restore the Lost Sea.

Meet the Author: **Laurence Yep**

Laurence Yep grew up in San Francisco. He attended grammar school in San Francisco's Chinatown, but he felt like an outsider because he spoke no Chinese.

Yep has written a number of books. One of his best known is *Dragonwings*, which was a Newbery Honor book of 1976, as well as the winner of other prestigious awards.

The source of his inspiration for *Dragon of the Lost Sea*, Yep writes, was this: "When I ran across the story of a river spirit who destroyed a city, I tried to tell it as a picture book. Unfortunately, it took me two hundred pages to do what another writer could do in five. I kept wondering why the river spirit was doing such an awful thing.

"Worse, two minor characters—a dragon and her pet boy—kept stealing the spotlight whenever they were on stage. As a result, I wound up junking most everything that I had written and started writing about them. *Dragon of the Lost Sea* and *Dragon Steel* were the results."

RESPONDING TO LITERATURE

1. In his book *Dragon Steel,* Yep has continued the adventures of Shimmer and Thorn in their struggles to force Civet to restore the Lost Sea. Based on the selection you have just read, would you like to read *Dragon Steel?* Give reasons for your answer.

2. The selection begins with Shimmer and Thorn flying to find Civet, and ends with Thorn serving Civet dinner. Imagine that Shimmer has time to think back on all the important events of that amazing day. What would she tell?

3. After perilous adventures, Shimmer and Thorn finally encounter Civet. What did they find out about Civet that was unexpected?

4. A dragon is a creature from myth and legend. Shimmer often behaves and feels emotions as if she were an ordinary human being. Give at least two examples of Shimmer's human actions and feelings.

5. Shimmer and Thorn become a good team, helping each other and working together. Do you think either one of them could have survived without the other? Explain.

6. You have been reading about an adventurous journey to another land. What other fantasy world would you like to read about?

THE PAINT BOX

"Cobalt and umber and ultramarine,
 Ivory black and emerald green—
 What shall I paint to give pleasure to you?"
"Paint for me somebody utterly new."

"I have painted you tigers in crimson and white."
"The colours were good and you painted aright."
"I have painted the cook and a camel in blue
 And a panther in purple." "You painted them true."

"Now mix me a colour that nobody knows,
 And paint me a country where nobody goes.
 And put in it people a little like you,
 Watching a unicorn drinking the dew."

E. V. Rieu

APPRECIATING AUTHOR'S CRAFT

Thinking About Character and Setting in Fantasy

One of the wonderful things about fantasy is the way an author can stretch your imagination. Yep creates the character of Shimmer, a dragon, and has made it quite reasonable for us to believe that dragons do exist. The time period of the story is sometime in the distant and unreal past when dragons roamed the countryside, and yet we become convinced of the reality of the setting.

Perhaps most imaginative are the details describing Civet's mountain and caverns. Think of what this fantastic place must look like: "In the very center of the cavern, the lacy stalagmites and stalactites had fused together to form what looked like a grove of trees with intricate webs of roots and branches. Hanging from the ceiling all around the grove were stone formations that looked like chandeliers and lamps of intricate scrollwork." Because Yep writes about his imaginary world so clearly, it becomes almost real.

Writing About Character and Setting in Fantasy

Now it's time to stretch your own imagination. Think of something else that could happen to Shimmer, Civet, or Thorn. Might there be other creatures lurking? Could more magic be in store? You can describe this new incident, using the character and setting details you already know. (For ideas about writing, look at the Writer's Handbook.)

Prewriting The chart below shows two important parts of this fantasy, character and setting. Several details about the characters and setting are listed. Copy the chart, and with a partner add more details about character and setting from the story.

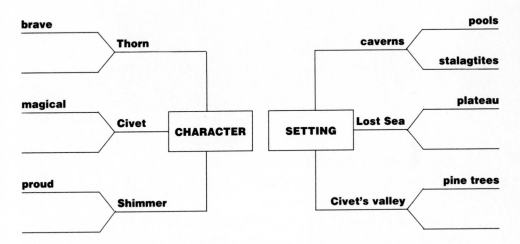

Writing Imagine that you are Shimmer, Thorn, or Civet. Use what you know about the characters and setting from your chart to help you write about a new event that takes place. For example, Shimmer and Thorn's attempt to find their way back again to the entrance of the mountain.

Revising Go over your draft. Ask your partner to underline details which tell about the character or setting. If you need to add more, ask your partner to help you find places that could use vivid details. Revise your draft and write your final copy.

Presenting As you read your adventure aloud, ask your classmates to close their eyes and use their imaginations. Play appropriate background music to add to the suspense.

EXTENDING YOUR READING

Expressing Yourself

Choose one or more of these activities:

Chinese Paper Cutouts The tigers and swordswomen turned out to be paper cutouts, made alive by Civet's magic. Draw these figures, cut them out along the outer edges, and display them.

Draw a Movie Poster *Dragon of the Lost Sea* could be made into a great movie. Draw a poster advertising the movie. You may want to include who the stars and director of the movie will be.

Papier-mâché People in huge dragon costumes lead Chinese New Year parades. Create a papier-mâché dragon head that would be large enough to fit you.

Tell a Tale The author of the poem on page 227 writes about an imaginary world just as Yep has done. Find a picture of a painting in a book or an encyclopedia and make up a fanciful tale about it. Tell it to a friend or to your class.

More Books About Other Lands

The First Two Lives of Lukas-Kasha by Lloyd Alexander. E.P. Dutton. Lukas, the town loafer, pays a penny to see a theatrical trick. Suddenly, he finds himself transported to a strange land, where *he* is the king. It's no dream, and Lukas, now King Kasha, is thrown into the middle of a web of treasure, runaway captives, rogue-poets, and power-hungry advisers. Will Lukas-Kasha escape alive?

The Riddle of the Ring by Karin Anckarsvard. Harcourt Brace Jovanovich, Inc. Fourteen-year-old Tommi and her new friend Henrik try to unravel a tangle of evidence surrounding a precious ring which Tommi believes she has lost. What adds interesting elements to this already exciting story of mystery and thievery is that Tommi and Henrik live in a small town in Sweden.

Sun Horse, Moon Horse by Rosemary Sutcliff. E. P. Dutton. The country is England, the time is the Iron Age, over 2,000 years ago. Lubrin, the youngest son of a chieftain, is captured by invaders. In exchange for his people's freedom, he agrees to carve the giant figure of a horse into the chalk hills. It is a piece of art which is to last for centuries.

The Nargun and the Stars by Patricia Wrightson. Macmillan. Simon Brent, an orphan, comes to live with his aunt and uncle on their 5,000-acre Australian sheep farm. Creatures, some friendly and some not, populate the land. Simon and his aunt and uncle, afraid for their lives and their farm, decide to challenge one of the unfriendly creatures.

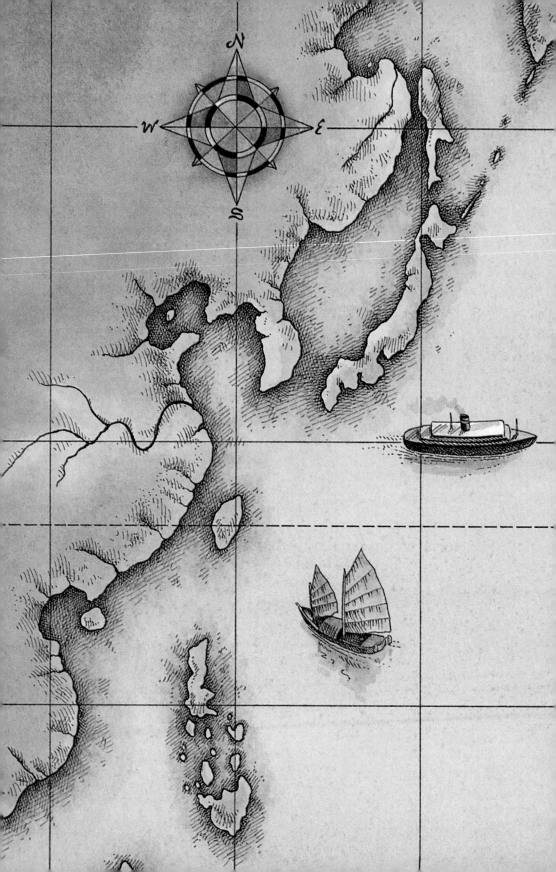

HOMESICK
MY OWN STORY

Jean Fritz

Introducing

HOMESICK
MY OWN STORY

Jean Fritz was homesick for the United States. She had been born and reared in China and at the age of thirteen, she was going to the United States with her mother and father. Jean was happy with her life in China, but she always felt that she was growing up on the opposite side of the world. She felt she should have been growing up in America and doing the things that thirteen-year-olds did there, such as roller skating and singing "The Star-Spangled Banner" instead of "God Save the King," which she had to do in her British school.

What Was the United States Like in the 1920s?

The United States that Jean Fritz is homesick for would seem like a foreign land to you. It is the 1920s in America. On the streets, you see one of the most popular cars, Henry Ford's Model T, a square-shaped car manufactured only in black. Clothes are different too. Boys wear knickers, short pants that come just below the knee. Men wear bow ties and straw hats. For women, the latest fashion is short hair and straight dresses that seem very daring because the hems reach just below the knee.

You can talk on the telephone, but if you want to make a call across the ocean you have to send a cablegram. Instead of turning on the television, you turn on the radio for news and entertainment. Families gather around and listen for hours to their favorite shows and music and often dance the

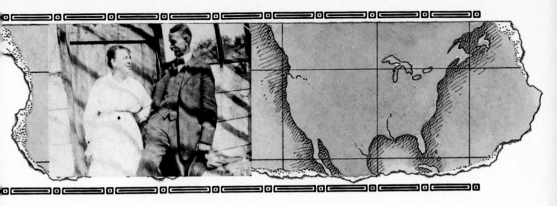

Charleston in their living room. One of the most exciting new things to do is go to the movies and see such famous stars as John Gilbert, Mary Pickford, or John Barrymore. But early movies have no sound. You just watch the people on the screen and read the subtitles. Piano players often play music that suits the action on the screen. It is not until 1927 that the first "talkie," or sound motion picture, appears. In the same year, Charles Lindbergh amazes the world by being the first person to fly across the Atlantic Ocean. At this time, ships are the only way to cross the oceans, and trains and cars are the only way to cross the United States. The flag of the United States has only forty-eight stars because Hawaii and Alaska are still territories.

Thinking About Point of View and Imagery

One of the wonderful things about reading is that you can look at the world through someone else's eyes. An author must decide through whose eyes and mind, or point of view, a story is told. The "I" in this excerpt is the author Jean Fritz herself narrating, or telling, what she sees, hears, and feels throughout her great adventure. By her choice of words, she stirs our imaginations.

As you're reading this excerpt on your own, find out how Jean knew that she had finally arrived home.

HOMESICK
MY OWN STORY

The 1920s were a period of turmoil in China, when foreigners were becoming more and more unpopular. The time had come for Jean and her mother and father to leave China.

Sailing on the same ship with Jean and her family was Jean's best friend, Andrea Hull, Andrea's mother, her brother Ed, and twelve-year-old David, who was the oldest child. David was adopted and felt different. He was always wondering who his real father and mother were, even though the Hulls said they didn't know, couldn't find out, and it didn't matter. Mr. Hull was staying in China to finish some business and would be leaving as soon as possible.

O n the twenty-sixth, just before we went on the ship, my father sent my grandmother a cablegram: SAILING TODAY. I wanted him to add "Hooray," but every word cost money, he said, and besides she'd recognize the hooray even if it wasn't there. Certainly on board the *President Taft* the hooray feeling was all over the place. On deck the ship's band was playing "California, Here I Come," and people were dancing and singing and laughing. A steward was handing out rolls of paper streamers for passengers to throw over the railing as the ship sailed.

Although my mother, father, and I had spoken to Mr. Hull

when he'd first come on board with the boys, we'd left him to visit alone with his children. I tried not to look in their direction so I wouldn't spoil my hooray feeling, but when the whistle blew for visitors to leave, I went to Andrea and stood beside her. Together we threw our streamers as the ship began to pull away from the dock. Everyone threw. Roll after roll until the distance from the ship to the dock was aflutter with paper ribbons—red, yellow, blue, green. Flimsy things, they looked as if they didn't want to let Shanghai go, but of course as the ship moved farther away, they broke, fell into the water, or simply hung bedraggled over the ship's side. Andrea leaned over the railing, waving to her father as long as she could see him. Then suddenly she turned and ran—to her cabin, I supposed.

My mother, father, and Mrs. Hull went into the lounge for tea. Edward went exploring, and I walked to the back of the ship with David trailing behind me. It seemed to me that once we were completely out of sight of land, I would really feel homeward bound. But as I looked at the Shanghai skyline and at the busy waterfront, I had the strange feeling that I wasn't moving away at all. Instead the land was slowly moving away and leaving me. Not just Shanghai but China itself. It was as if I could see the whole country at once: all the jogging rickshas, the pagodas, the squeaking wells, the chestnut vendors, the water buffaloes, the bluebells, the gray-coated soldiers, the bare-bottomed little boys. And of course the muddy Yangtse with my own junk looking at me with its wide eyes. I could even smell China, and it was the smell of food cooking, of steam rising from so many rice bowls it hung in a mist over the land. But it was slipping away. No matter how hard I squinted, it was fading from sight. I glanced at David, woebegone as always, but I knew he wasn't sad at leaving Mr. Hull or at leaving China. He was just feeling sorry for himself in the same old way.

Suddenly I was mad. "You make me sick, David Hull," I said. "Cry-babying over something in the past that you can't know a thing about. Don't you know your real past is right there? Yours and mine both." I pointed at China. "It's been under our noses the whole time and we've hardly noticed."

I didn't want to talk to David Hull, so I went down to the cabin to open Lin Nai-Nai's[1] present. That would make me feel better, I thought. I took the red package out of my suitcase and tore off the tissue paper. Inside was a folded square of cloth that was obviously a piece of Lin Nai-Nai's embroidery. As I unfolded it, I drew in my breath. This was no iron-on pattern. This was Lin Nai-Nai's own design: a picture of a mountain, a thin black line climbing up to a scallop of clouds. In the center of the picture was a pool with bluebells and tiger lilies growing all around it. I started to cry—not just a flurry of sniffles but such huge sobs I had to throw myself on my bunk and bury my head in my pillow.

I heard my mother and father come into the cabin but I kept on crying. My mother leaned over me. "Whatever is the matter?" she asked.

I couldn't talk. I held up Lin Nai-Nai's embroidery for her to see.

"Of course," my mother said. "You miss Lin Nai-Nai."

That was true, but I was crying for more than that. For more than the memory of Kuling.[2] For more than I could ever explain.

My mother put her arms around me. "You're just tired," she said. "You'll feel better after a good night's sleep."

"That's right," my father agreed. "You'll be fine in the morning."

I wasn't tired. I knew I had good reasons for crying even if they were too mixed up to put into words.

Still, I did feel better the next morning. At eleven o'clock I was stretched out on a deck chair, my steamer rug over my legs. I was looking at the ocean and waiting for the steward to bring me a cup of beef tea.

---

1. Lin Nai-Nai (lin nī′nī′), Jean's amah (ä′mə), a nurse in China.

2. One summer the family went to the beautiful mountains in Kuling (Kü′ling).

It took twenty-eight days to go from Shanghai to San Francisco, and on that first morning I thought I'd be content to lie on my deck chair and stare at the ocean and drink beef tea the whole time. Not Andrea. She thought the ocean was one big waste. We should be watching the people, she said, and sizing them up as they went by. So we did. We found that mostly they fit into definite types. There were the Counters, for instance: fast-walking men, red-cheeked women, keeping score of how many times they walked around the deck, reveling in how fit they were. Then there were the Stylish Strollers, the Huffers and Puffers, the Lovebirds, leaning on each other, the Queasy Stomachs who clutched the railing and hoped for the best.

"You notice there's no one our age," Andrea said.

That was true. We had seen young people who were probably in their twenties, children who were Edward's age, and of course the majority who were our parents' age or older. But not one who might be in seventh or eighth grade or even high school.

Andrea jumped from her chair. "I'm going to explore."

Normally I would have gone with her but I hadn't had a chance yet to get my fill of the ocean. It was the same ocean as I'd had in Peitaiho[3] and I looked and looked. I walked up to the top deck where I could see the whole circle of water around me. I was smack in the middle of no place, I thought. Not in China, not in America, not in the past, not in the future. In between everything. It was nice.

By the time I went back to my chair, Andrea had returned from her explorations.

"There really is no one our age on board," she reported.

"Well, we can play shuffleboard and deck tennis. There are lots of things we can do."

Andrea sighed. "I was hoping for some boys."

---

3. The family spent three months every summer in Peitaiho (bā′tī′hō′) on the ocean north of Peking.

I knew that Andrea had begun to like boys. She said everyone at the Shanghai American School had a crush on someone else and when your love was requited—well, that was the cat's. What I couldn't understand was how someone could be in love with John Gilbert and a kid in knickers at the same time.

I suppose Andrea could see that I was trying to figure out the boy business. She gave me a curious look. "Just how do you picture your school in Washington, P.A.?"[4] she asked.

Well, I knew exactly what it would be like, so I told her: I'd be an American in a class with nothing but Americans in it. When we fought the American Revolution, we'd all fight on the same side. When we sang "My country 'tis of thee," we'd yell our heads off. We'd all be the same. I would *belong*.

"There'll be boys in your class," Andrea pointed out.

"Naturally. I've seen boys before. So what?"

"Well, I think you're going to be surprised."

I didn't want to be surprised. For years I'd planned my first day at school in America.

"So how do you picture your school in Los Angeles, California?" I asked.

Andrea looked out at the ocean as if she expected to see her school sitting out there on the water. Then suddenly she shut her eyes and dropped her head in her hands. "Oh, Jean," she whispered, "I can't picture anything anymore. All I keep thinking about is my father. Alone in Shanghai."

This was as close as I'd ever seen Andrea come to crying. I put my hand on her shoulder. "I'm sorry," I said. Sorry! Such a puny word. You'd think the English language could give you something better. "I'm so sorry," I repeated.

Andrea dropped her hands and took a deep breath. "Well, let's play shuffleboard," she said.

From then on we played a lot of shuffleboard. Sometimes

---

4. Her parents always called their hometown in Pennsylvania, Washington, P.A.

David joined us, but mostly he stayed in the ship's library, reading books about boys with real families. Edward kept busy in programs planned for children his age and the grown-ups made friends and talked their usual boring grown-up talk.

On the whole, Andrea and I had a good time on the *President Taft*. In the evenings we often watched movies. In the afternoons we made pigs of ourselves at tea where we had our pick of all kinds of dainty sandwiches, scones, macaroons, chocolate bonbons, and gooey tarts. Actually, I even liked going to bed on shipboard. I'd lie in my bunk and feel the ship's engines throbbing and know that even when I fell asleep I wouldn't be wasting time. I'd still be on the go, moving closer to America every minute.

Still, my "in-between" feeling stayed with me. One evening after supper I took Andrea to the top deck and told her about the feeling. Of course the "in-betweenness" was stronger than ever in the dark with the circle of water rippling below and the night sky above spilling over with stars. I had never seen so many stars. When I looked for a spot where I might stick an extra star if I had one, I couldn't find any space at all. No matter how small, an extra star would be out of place, I decided. The universe was one-hundred-percent perfect just as it was.

And then Andrea began to dance. She had slipped off her shoes and stockings and she was dancing what was obviously an "in-between" dance, leaping up toward the stars, sinking down toward the water, bending back toward China, reaching forward toward America, bending back again and again as if she could not tear herself away, yet each time dancing farther forward, swaying to and fro. Finally, her arms raised, she began twirling around, faster and faster, as if she were trying to outspin time itself. Scarcely breathing, I sat beside a smokestack and watched. She was making a poem and I was inside the poem with her. Under the stars, in the middle of the Pacific Ocean. I would never forget this night, I thought. Not if I lived to be one hundred.

Only when we came to the International Date Line did my "in-between" feeling disappear. This is the place, a kind of imaginary line in the ocean, where all ships going east add an extra day to that week and all ships going west drop a day. This is so you can keep up with the world turning and make time come out right. We had two Tuesdays in a row when we crossed the line and after that when it was "today" for me, I knew that Lin Nai-Nai was already in "tomorrow." I didn't like to think of Lin Nai-Nai so far ahead of me. It was as if we'd suddenly been tossed on different planets.

On the other hand, this was the first time in my life that I was sharing the same day with my grandmother.

Oh, Grandma, I thought, ready or not, here I come!

It was only a short time later that Edward saw a couple of rocks poking out of the water and yelled for us to come. The rocks could hardly be called land, but we knew they were the beginning of the Hawaiian Islands and we knew that the Hawaiian Islands were a territory belonging to the United States. Of course it wasn't the same as one of the forty-eight states; still, when we stepped off the *President Taft* in Honolulu (where we were to stay a couple of days before going on to San Francisco), we wondered if we could truthfully say we were stepping on American soil. I said no. Since the Hawaiian Islands didn't have a star in the flag, they couldn't be one-hundred-percent American, and I wasn't going to consider myself on American soil until I had put my feet flat down on the state of California.

We had a week to wait. The morning we were due to arrive in San Francisco, all the passengers came on deck early, but I was the first. I skipped breakfast and went to the very front of the ship where the railing comes to a point. That morning I would be the "eyes" of the *President Taft*, searching the horizon for the first speck of land. My private ceremony of greeting, however, would not come until we were closer, until we were sailing through the Golden Gate. For years I had heard about the Golden Gate, a narrow stretch of water connecting the Pacific Ocean to San Francisco Bay. And for years I had planned my entrance.

Dressed in my navy skirt, white blouse, and silk stockings, I felt every bit as neat as Columbus or Balboa and every bit as heroic when I finally spotted America in the distance. The decks had filled with passengers by now, and as I watched the land come closer, I had to tell myself over and over that I was HERE. At last.

Then the ship entered the narrow stretch of the Golden Gate and I could see American hills on my left and American houses on my right, and I took a deep breath of American air.
" 'Breathes there the man, with soul so dead,' " I cried,
" 'Who never to himself hath said,
   This is my own, my native land!' " [5]

I forgot that there were people behind and around me until I heard a few snickers and a scattering of claps, but I didn't care. I wasn't reciting for anyone's benefit but my own.

Next for my first steps on American soil, but when the time came, I forgot all about them. As soon as we were on the dock, we were jostled from line to line. Believe it or not, after crossing thousands of miles of ocean to get here, we had to prove that it was O.K. for us to come into the U.S.A. We had to show that we were honest-to-goodness citizens and not spies. We had to open our baggage and let inspectors see that we weren't smuggling in opium or anything else illegal. We even had to prove that we were germ-free, that we didn't have smallpox or any dire disease that would infect the country. After we had finally passed the tests, I expected to feel one-hundred-percent American. Instead, stepping from the dock into the city of San Francisco, I felt dizzy and unreal, as if I were a made-up character in a book I had read too many times to believe it wasn't still a book. As we walked the Hulls to the car that their Aunt Kay had driven up from Los Angeles, I told Andrea about my crazy feeling.

---

5. From a poem by Sir Walter Scott. Also quoted in "The Man Without a Country," a famous short story by Edward Everett Hale, which Jean knew well.

"I'm kind of funny in the head," I said. "As if I'm not really me. As if this isn't really happening."

"Me too," Andrea agreed. "I guess our brains haven't caught up to us yet. But my brains better get going. Guess what?"

"What?"

"Aunt Kay says our house in Los Angeles is not far from Hollywood."

Then suddenly the scene speeded up and the Hulls were in the car, ready to leave for Los Angeles, while I was still stuck in a book without having said any of the things I wanted to. I ran after the car as it started.

"Give my love to John Gilbert," I yelled to Andrea.

She stuck her head out the window. "And how!" she yelled back.

My mother, father, and I were going to stay in a hotel overnight and start across the continent the next morning, May 24, in our new car. The first thing we did now was to go to a drugstore where my father ordered three ice-cream sodas. "As tall as you can make them," he said. "We have to make up for lost time."

My first American soda was chocolate and it was a whopper. While we sucked away on our straws, my father read to us from the latest newspaper. The big story was about America's new hero, an aviator named Charles Lindbergh who had just made the first solo flight across the Atlantic Ocean. Of course I admired him for having done such a brave and scary thing, but I bet he wasn't any more surprised to have made it across one ocean than I was to have finally made it across another. I looked at his picture. His goggles were pushed back on his helmet and he was grinning. He had it all over John Gilbert, I decided. I might even consider having a crush on him—that is, if and when I ever felt the urge. Right now I was coming to the bottom of my soda and I was trying to slurp up the last drops when my mother told me to quit; I was making too much noise.

The rest of the afternoon we spent sight-seeing, riding up and down seesaw hills in cable cars, walking in and out of American stores. Every once in a while I found myself smiling at total strangers because I knew that if I were to speak to them in English, they'd answer in English. We were all Americans. Yet I still felt as if I were telling myself a story. America didn't become completely real for me until the next day after we'd left San Francisco and were out in the country.

My father had told my mother and me that since he wasn't used to our new car or to American highways, we should be quiet and let him concentrate. My mother concentrated too. Sitting in the front seat, she flinched every time she saw another car, a crossroad, a stray dog, but she never said a word. I paid no attention to the road. I just kept looking out the window until all at once there on my right was a white picket fence and a meadow, fresh and green as if it had just this minute been created. Two black-and-white cows were grazing slowly over the grass as if they had all the time in the world, as if they knew that no matter how much they ate, there'd always be more, as if in their quiet munching way they understood that they had nothing, nothing whatsoever to worry about. I poked my mother, pointed, and whispered, "Cows." I had never seen cows in China but it was not the cows themselves that impressed me. It was the whole scene. The perfect greenness. The washed-clean look. The peacefulness. Oh, *now!* I thought, Now I was in America. Every last inch of me.

By the second day my father acted as if he'd been driving the car all his life. He not only talked, he sang, and if he felt like hitching up his trousers, he just took his hands off the wheel and hitched. But as my father relaxed, my mother became more tense. "Arthur," she finally said, "You are going forty-five."

My father laughed. "Well, we're headed for the stable, Myrtle. You never heard of a horse that dawdled on its way home, did you?"

My mother's lips went tight and thin. "The whole point of driving across the continent," she said, "was so we could see the country."

"Well, it's all there." My father swept his hand from one side of the car to the other. "All you have to do is to take your eyes off the road and look." He honked his horn at the car in front of him and swung around it.

At the end of the day, after we were settled in an overnight cabin, my father took a new notebook from his pocket. I watched as he wrote: "May 24. 260 miles." Just as I'd suspected, my father was out to break records. I bet that before long we'd be making 300 miles or more a day. I bet we'd be in Washington, P.A., long before July.

The trouble with record breaking is that it can lead to Narrow Squeaks, and while we were still in California we had our first one. Driving along a back road that my father had figured out was a shortcut, we came to a bridge with a barrier across it and a sign in front: THIS BRIDGE CONDEMNED, DO NOT PASS. There was no other road marked DETOUR, so obviously the only thing to do was to turn around and go back about five miles to the last town and take the regular highway. My father stopped the car. "You'd think they'd warn you in advance," he muttered. He slammed the door, jumped over the barrier, and walked onto the bridge. Then he climbed down the riverbank and looked up at the bridge from below. When he came back up the bank, he pushed the barrier aside, got in the car, and started it up. "We can make it," he said.

It hadn't occurred to me that he'd try to drive across. My mother put her hand on his arm. "Please, Arthur," she begged, but I didn't bother with any "pleases." If he wanted to kill himself, he didn't have to kill Mother and me too. "Let Mother and me walk across," I shouted. "Let us out. Let us OUT."

My father had already revved up the motor. "A car can have only one driver," he snapped. "I'm it." He backed up so he could get a flying start and then we whooped across the bridge, our wheels clattering across the loose boards, space gaping below. Well, we did reach the other side and when I looked back, I saw that the bridge was still there.

"You see?" my father crowed. "You see how much time we saved?"

All I could see was that we'd risked our lives because he was so pigheaded. Right then I hated my father. I felt rotten hating someone I really loved but I couldn't help it. I knew the loving would come back but I had to wait several hours.

There were days, however, particularly across the long, flat stretches of Texas, when nothing out-of-the-way happened. We just drove on and on, and although my father reported at the end of the day that we'd gone 350 miles, the scenery was the same at the end as at the beginning, so it didn't feel as if we'd moved at all. Other times we ran into storms or into road construction and we were lucky if we made 200 miles. But the best day of the whole trip, at least as far as my mother and I were concerned, was the day that we had a flat tire in the Ozark Mountains. The spare tire and jack were buried in the trunk under all our luggage, so everything had to be taken out before my father could even begin work on the tire. There was no point in offering to help because my father had a system for loading and unloading which only he understood, so my mother and I set off up the mountainside, looking for wild flowers.

"Watch out for snakes," my mother said, but her voice was so happy, I knew she wasn't thinking about snakes.

As soon as I stepped out of the car, I fell in love with the day. With the sky—fresh, blotting-paper blue. With the mountains, warm and piney and polka-dotted with flowers we would never have seen from the window of a car. We decided to pick one of each kind and press them in my gray geography book which I had in the car. My mother held out her skirt, making a hollow out of it, while I dropped in the flowers and she named them: forget-me-not, wintergreen, pink, wild rose. When we didn't know the name, I'd make one up: pagoda plant, wild confetti, French knot. My mother's skirt was atumble with color when we suddenly realized how far we'd walked.

Holding her skirt high, my mother led the way back, running and laughing. We arrived at the car, out of breath, just as my father was loading the last of the luggage into the trunk. He glared at us, his face streaming with perspiration. "I don't have a dry stitch on me," he said, as if it were our fault that he sweat so much. Then he looked at the flowers in Mother's skirt and his face softened. He took out his handkerchief and wiped his face and neck and finally he smiled. "I guess I picked a good place to have a flat tire, didn't I?" he said.

The farther we went, the better mileage we made, so that by the middle of June we were almost to the West Virginia state line. My father said we'd get to Washington, P.A., the day after the next, sometime in the afternoon. He called my grandmother on the phone, grinning because he knew how surprised she'd be. I stood close so I could hear her voice.

"Mother?" he said when she answered. "How about stirring up a batch of flannel cakes?"

"Arthur!" (She sounded just the way I knew she would.) "Well, land's sakes, Arthur, where are you?"

"About ready to cross into West Virginia."

My grandmother was so excited that her words fell over each other as she tried to relay the news to my grandfather and Aunt Margaret and talk over the phone at the same time.

The next day it poured rain and although that didn't slow us down, my mother started worrying. Shirls Avenue, my grandparents' street, apparently turned into a dirt road just before plunging down a steep hill to their house and farm. In wet weather the road became one big sea of mud which, according to my mother, would be "worth your life to drive through."

"If it looks bad," my mother suggested, "we can park at the top of the hill and walk down in our galoshes."

My father sighed. "Myrtle," he said, "we've driven across the Mohave Desert. We've been through thick and thin for over three thousand miles and here you are worrying about Shirls Avenue."

The next day the sun was out, but when we came to Shirls Avenue, I could see that the sun hadn't done a thing to dry up the hill. My father put the car into low, my mother closed her eyes, and down we went, sloshing up to our hubcaps, careening from one rut to another, while my father kept one hand down hard on the horn to announce our arrival.

By the time we were at the bottom of the hill and had parked beside the house, my grandmother, my grandfather, and Aunt Margaret were all outside, looking exactly the way they had in the calendar picture.[6] I ran right into my grandmother's arms as if I'd been doing this every day.

"Welcome home! Oh, welcome home!" my grandmother cried.

I hadn't known it but this was exactly what I'd wanted her to say. I needed to hear it said out loud. I was home.

Jean spent the summer doing the things she had dreamed about in China. Her first day at school in Washington, P.A., however, did not turn out exactly as she had hoped. When a classmate asked Jean, "Are you glad you came back?" what do you think Jean replied? You can read the novel to find out.

---

6. Jean's grandmother had sent her a calendar for Christmas. Pasted over the whole month of July was a picture of her grandmother and grandfather and her Aunt Margaret. July was the month Jean was to come home.

Meet the Author: **Jean Fritz**

From the time Jean Fritz was a little girl growing up in China, she knew that she wanted to be a writer. Her first story was called "Sue and Margery." It was about twins who did all the American things Jean wished she could do. They set off fireworks on the Fourth of July, went to grandmother's for Thanksgiving dinner, and drank water without having to boil it first.

Jean Fritz's interest in American life continued, and her first historical book was called *The Cabin Faced West*. The story was based on the life of her great-great-grandmother, who was a pioneer in Pennsylvania. While writing this book, Jean Fritz discovered the joys of research. As she delved into American history, she felt that she was putting down her roots.

American history continues to fascinate Jean Fritz. She is the author of many popular books, such as *I, Adam*, which is about life in New England during the 1850's, and *Early Thunder*, which is about life in Salem during the Revolutionary War. She has also written many entertaining biographies about American heroes such as *And Then What Happened, Paul Revere? Why Don't You Get a Horse, Sam Adams?* and *Where Was Patrick Henry on the 29th of May?*

RESPONDING TO LITERATURE

1. When a person writes the story of his or her own life, it is known as an autobiography. But Jean Fritz writes of her book, "Since my childhood feels like a story, I decided to write it that way." Did Jean seem like a real person to you? Explain.

2. Imagine that Jean writes postcards to her grandmother to describe the important events of the journey. Writing as Jean might have written, tell what would be on the postcards, beginning with when she left Shanghai, China, and arrived in Washington, Pennsylvania.

3. Jean and her parents traveled thousands of miles from China to her grandparents' home in Washington, P.A. How did Jean know that she had finally arrived home?

4. Jean sees many wonderful things on her journey. If you could be with her for just one day, what would you like to see with her and why?

5. One of the first things Jean and her parents do in San Francisco is order ice-cream sodas. If you and your family were in a foreign land for many years, what do you think you would miss most? Explain.

This Land Is Your Land

As I was walking that ribbon of highway,
I saw above me that endless skyway.
I saw below me that golden valley.
This land was made for you and me.

This land is your land,
This land is my land
   from California to the New York island,
From the redwood forest to the Gulf Stream waters;
This land was made for you and me.

I've roamed and rambled
   and I followed my footsteps
To the sparkling sands of her diamond deserts.
And all around me a voice was sounding:
This land was made for you and me.

This land is your land,
This land is my land
   from California to the New York island,
From the redwood forest to the Gulf Stream waters;
This land was made for you and me.

When the sun came shining and I was strolling,
And the wheatfields waving,
   and the dust clouds rolling.
As the fog was lifting, a voice was chanting
This land was made for you and me.

Woody Guthrie

APPRECIATING AUTHOR'S CRAFT

Thinking About Imagery

When writing a story, an author chooses words as an artist chooses color to convey feelings. An author chooses words that help you see, hear, smell, taste, and feel something in your imagination. These words help form pictures in your mind. This is called imagery. For example, Jean tells you, "I fell in love with the day. With the sky—fresh, blotting-paper blue. With the mountains, warm and piney and polka-dotted with flowers we would never have seen from the window of a car." It is easy to know how Jean feels, and if you use your imagination, you can see the blue sky, feel the warm day, and maybe even smell the pine trees and wildflowers.

This selection is also made more vivid because it is told in the first person point of view. You can really understand what "I" is thinking and feeling.

Writing About Imagery

Think of the way Jean Fritz has created memorable word pictures. This will help you write a descriptive paragraph in such a way that when you share it with your classmates, they will also see beautiful pictures. (For ideas about writing, look at The Writer's Handbook.)

Prewriting This chart has an example of imagery. Copy the chart and complete the second example by looking on page 242.

Ordinary Language	Literary Examples
They threw streamers.	. . . the dock was aflutter with paper ribbons—red, yellow, blue, green. Flimsy things . . .
Andrea danced an "In-between" dance.	

Review the completed chart and then think of something special you have seen. It could be a place, person, or event. You may want to use the chart to help you make some notes.

Writing Imagine that you are Jean and that she sees your special place, person, or event for the first time. Write a descriptive paragraph from the first person, "I," point of view. Make sure to include sensory words that tell how things look, sound, smell, feel, and taste.

Revising Have a partner read your paper. Ask your partner to underline the words that describe how things look, sound, smell, feel, or taste. Make changes in your paper so that the description is clear. Then proofread and make your final copy.

Presenting Ask your classmates to close their eyes as you read your paper. Afterwards, it may be fun to ask them to draw pictures of your scene, based on your description.

EXTENDING YOUR READING

Expressing Yourself

Choose one or more of these activities:

Trace Jean's Journey Find a world map and trace Jean's journey. You might put a pin on each of the places mentioned in the excerpt, such as Shanghai, China, the International Date Line, the Hawaiian Islands, San Francisco, the Mohave Desert, Texas, Ozark Mountains, West Virginia, and Pennsylvania.

Prepare a Speech Pretend that Jean is going to make a speech about the things that surprised her most when she came to the U.S. List the surprises and prepare four pictures that she might show during the speech—for instance, flowers, cars, and so on.

Research Antique Cars Find a book in the library that has photographs or illustrations of old cars. Show the class pictures of cars that were driven about the same year as the 1927 car that Jean and her parents drove cross-country.

A Song Writer's Feelings Read Woody Guthrie's lyrics for his song, "This Land Is Your Land," on page 255. Then pretend you are Jean Fritz and write a poem about her impressions of the United States.

More Books About Coming to America

The Knee-High Man and Other Tales by Julius Lester.
Dial. Black people who came to America as slaves brought
many of their legends and tales with them. The six stories in
this collection have their origins in Africa, but are sure to
bring a knowing nod or chuckle to any American reader.
Some stories show us wise ways of getting through life;
others involve clever tricksters.

First Farm in the Valley: Anna's Story by Anne Pellowski.
Putnam. It is 1876. Our country is one hundred years old,
and young Anna's Polish-American family is firmly settled in
their farm in Wisconsin. Although Anna dreams of seeing
Poland one day, she finds her days are filled. New families
arrive in the valley. There is an epidemic of diphtheria,
everyone celebrates Independence Day, and Anna learns the
tasks of farming.

An Album of the Jews in America by Yuri Suhl. Watts. The
story of immigration to America begins many centuries ago,
and Jews were among the first settlers. This book tells about
famous as well as unknown people who helped make our
country what it is today. Many photographs show us some
familiar faces and not-so-familiar sights and scenes of
history.

A Boat to Nowhere by Maureen Crane Wartski.
Westminster. Many Asians have recently arrived in our
country after hazardous voyages by sea. This novel tells the
story of three children and an elderly man who escape from
Vietnam. Setting sail in their village's small fishing boat, they
have many frightening encounters.

船長 サ
四十五間
幅 十六間
車 八間
乗人 倶シ
水主共
三百人
煙出シ廻
九尺

COMMODORE PERRY
In the Land of the Shogun

ク シ 船
ミ 主 号
ト ス
云 ナ

Rhoda Blumberg

COMMODORE PERRY
In the Land of the Shogun

Commodore Perry in the Land of the Shogun

Wouldn't it be great to own a time machine? Suddenly you could be surrounded by the people, sounds, and way of life of another time.

Commodore Matthew Perry had such an adventure without the benefit of a time machine. In 1853 Perry was sent by the President of the United States to deliver a letter to the Emperor of Japan. Perry was an uninvited visitor to a land that had been shut off from the rest of the world for centuries. What would the Japanese think of this stranger and his letter?

The United States and Japan in 1850

In 1853 the United States was only seventy-seven years old. Through purchase, war, and treaty, the boundaries of the United States grew and stretched from the Atlantic Ocean in the east to the Pacific Ocean in the west. With this rapid growth and many new inventions, life changed forever. Ships with steam-powered engines began to replace sailing ships. Ocean travel became faster, and Americans began to look with greater interest at the world beyond the vast oceans.

One of the most interesting countries across the Pacific was Japan, a mystery to most of the outside world. In 1637 the Japanese had forced most foreigners to leave the country. Their law said, "For the future, let none, so long as the sun illuminates the world, presume to sail to Japan . . .

and this declaration is never to be revoked on pain of death." From then on, no one was allowed to enter or leave Japan. And with few exceptions, that law was obeyed.

Shut off from the outside world, powerful shoguns (shō′gunz, shō′günz) ruled over a prosperous and peaceful country, but desire for change began to stir in Japan. It was at this time that Commodore Perry came steaming into the harbor. As the two groups gazed across the water at each other, the word "barbarian" quickly came to mind, a word used throughout history by people to describe anyone they don't know. It would be difficult to imagine two groups of people who had more to learn about each other than the Americans and Japanese at that moment.

Thinking About Point of View in Nonfiction

You will be reading about a very important historical event and you will have the benefit of being able to see that event from two different points of view. What did the uninvited guests, the Americans, think and do? What was the reaction of the unwilling Japanese hosts? What can the author tell you, writing about this event over a hundred years later?

As you're reading this excerpt on your own, think about how Commodore Perry got his message to the Japanese when so many people before him had failed.

COMMODORE PERRY
In the Land of the Shogun

Aliens Arrive

If monsters had descended upon Japan the effect could not have been more terrifying.

People in the fishing village of Shimoda were the first to spot four huge hulks, two streaming smoke, on the ocean's surface approaching the shore. "Giant dragons puffing smoke," cried some. "Alien ships of fire," cried others. According to a folk tale, smoke above water was made by the breath of clams. Only a child would believe that. Perhaps enemies knew how to push erupting volcanoes toward the Japanese homeland. Surely something horrible was happening on this day, Friday, July 8, 1853.

Fishermen pulled in their nets, grabbed their oars, and rowed to shore frantically. They had been close up and knew that these floating mysteries were foreign ships. Black ships that belched black clouds! They had never seen anything like it. They didn't even know that steamboats existed, and they were appalled by the number and size of the guns.

Barbarians from out of the blue! Will they invade, kidnap, kill, then destroy everything? What will become of the sacred Land of the Rising Sun?

Steamships were new to the Japanese.

General alarms were sounded. Temple bells rang, and messengers raced throughout Japan to warn everyone that enemy aliens were approaching by ship.

Rumors spread that "one hundred thousand devils with white faces" were about to overrun the country. People panicked. They carried their valuables and furniture in all directions in order to hide them from invading barbarians. Women and children were locked up in their homes or sent to friends and relatives who lived inland, far from the endangered shore.

Messengers rushed to the capital of Edo (now Tokyo) to alert government officials. Edo, the world's largest city with more than one million occupants, went into a state of chaos the very day the ships were sighted. Women raced about in the streets with children in their arms. Men carried their mothers on their backs, not knowing which way to turn.

Who could control the turmoil? The Emperor Komei was isolated in his royal palace at Kyoto. Although he was worshiped as a divine descendant of the sun goddess, Amaterasu, he was a powerless puppet, responsible primarily for conducting religious ceremonies. During his leisure hours he was expected to study the classics and compose poetry. The Japanese referred to their emperor as "he who lives above the clouds." By law, he was not permitted to leave his heavenly palace unless he received special permission from the government. An emperor's sphere of influence was otherworldly. All down-to-earth decisions were made by shoguns who had been wielding power for more than 700 years.

The word *shogun* means "barbarian-expelling generalissimo." How appropriate at this time! Surely the Shogun would take command!

But Shogun Ieyoshi who occupied the palace at Edo in 1853 was a weakling. No one even bothered to tell him the frightening news. Three days after the ships arrived he overheard chatter about them while enjoying a Noh play that was being performed for him in his palace. The news affected him so badly that he went to bed, sick at heart.

Because the Shogun was inept, his councillors, called the *Bakufu*, ruled the country. But according to a Japanese reporter, "They were too alarmed to open their mouths." The Bakufu should not have been so surprised. Before reaching Japan the American fleet had stopped at Loo Choo (now Okinawa). Japanese spies stationed there had sent word that American ships were on their way to Japan. Dutch traders had also alerted the Bakufu. But for mystifying reasons, the government did not take these reports seriously until the Black Ships arrived on July 8. After recovering from shock they ordered the great clans to prepare to battle barbarians.

Locked away from the rest of the world, using the Pacific Ocean as its moat, Japan had maintained a feudal society similar to that of Europe during the Middle Ages. There were lords (*daimyos*), knights (*samurai*), and vassals who labored in their lord's domain and paid tithes to their masters.

A samurai readies for battle.

The country had not been at war since it invaded Korea in 1597. That was 256 years earlier. Nevertheless, feudal lords were able to mobilize troops. Men who had never dressed for warfare worked to get rust off spears. They placed new feathers in their families' antique arrows. Tailors were pressed into service so they could fix the silk cords on ancient armor, make warriors' cloaks, and sew cotton skullcaps that would cushion the weight of heavy helmets. Seventeen thousand soldiers were readied for battle.

When the ships moved toward land that first day, Japanese guard boats set out to surround the enemy. But they could not catch up with aliens whose ships were so magical that they steamed ahead against the wind without using sails or oars.

At five o'clock in the afternoon the foreign ships anchored a mile and a half from shore, at Edo Bay. They were less than thirty-five miles from the capital city. Beautiful cliffs, rolling green hills, and, above all, snow-capped Mount Fuji made a breathtaking scene. After dusk, beacon fires dotted the land, and there was an incessant toll of temple gongs.

That night a meteor with a fiery tail streaked through the sky like a rocket. An omen from the gods! Shrines and temples were jammed. Priests told worshipers that barbarians were about to punish them for their sins.

The Black Ships
of The Evil Men

Four ships and 560 men of the U.S. Navy had created this furor. The *Mississippi* and the *Susquehanna* were steam powered. The *Plymouth* and the *Saratoga* were three-masted sailing ships in tow behind the steamers. The Japanese referred to these four vessels as "The Black Ships of the Evil Men."

Commodore Matthew Calbraith Perry was in command of the squadron. He had not come to invade. He hoped to be a peacemaker who would make the isolated Empire of Japan a member of "the family of civilized nations" of the world. His mission was to unlock Japan's door. It had been slammed shut against all but a few Dutch and Chinese traders, the only ones officially allowed in for over 200 years.

Perry expected to deliver a letter from President Millard Fillmore to the Emperor of Japan, proposing "that the United States and Japan should live in friendship and have commercial intercourse with each other." The letter requested that ports be opened so that American ships could obtain coal and provisions.

America had invested seventeen million dollars in the Pacific whaling industry, and it needed Japanese ports to replenish coal and provisions for the whalers. Whale oil was essential for lighting and for lubricating machinery.

President Fillmore's letter also asked that men who had been shipwrecked on Japanese shores be treated with kindness. This point was emphasized because many

American whaling ships had been wrecked off Japan's coast by violent storms, and their castaways had been jailed and abused.

Perry intended to deliver the letter and sail away peacefully. He would winter in Hong Kong. With only four ships and supplies that could last no more than one month, he would not attempt to wait for the Emperor's reply, but he planned to return in the spring—when he would have more supplies and a larger fleet.

The Commodore was determined not to use force unless attacked. But he felt that he could not trust the actions of unknown Orientals. He dared not take chances, for he remembered the *Morrison,* an American ship that had sailed into Edo Bay on a peaceful mission in 1837. Its intent was to return seven Japanese castaways to their homeland. The Japanese had opened fire and forced the ship to leave.

As a precaution, Perry's squadron anchored in battle formation facing the shore. Cannons and guns were loaded. All hands took up their battle stations.

Japanese guard boats approached the moored American ships. Each vessel, propelled by six to eight standing oarsmen, was filled with about thirty soldiers. Fastening ropes to the ships, they tried to climb on board. Commodore Perry ordered his sailors to cut the guard boats' ropes and use pikes and cutlasses to keep the Japanese away. A few tried to climb the *Mississippi*'s anchor chain. A rap on the knuckles sent one soldier into the water. All of the Japanese soldiers howled and shouted angrily.

Commodore Matthew C. Perry

Perry's stubborn refusal to allow them on board was based on the terrible experience of another American commodore. Seven years before, in 1846, Commodore James Biddle had anchored at Edo Bay, hoping to deliver a letter to the Emperor from the United States government. The letter requested trade relations between the two countries. As a friendly gesture, Biddle allowed swarms of Japanese soldiers to come aboard. A rude soldier gave Biddle a shove that knocked him off his feet. Anxious to keep peace, Biddle graciously accepted an apology, which was interpreted as weakness and cowardice. Japanese officials mocked him, refused to deliver documents, and ordered him to leave at once. Because his orders were not to create an incident, Biddle immediately sailed away.

Perry resolved that until negotiations were successful, he would not allow more than three officials on board at a time.

A Japanese guard boat rowed close to the Commodore's flagship, the *Susquehanna*. Its men held up a scroll, written in large letters, in French, that said, "Go away! Do not dare to anchor!" Then one of the Japanese shouted in English, "I can speak Dutch." He asked to come aboard. Antón Portman, Perry's Dutch-Japanese interpreter, came on deck. He explained that the Commodore would only allow the highest officials on his ship. When told that there was an important person in the guard boat, he lowered a gangway ladder.

Nakajima, introduced as vice-governor of the small nearby village of Uraga, climbed up. In fact, Nakajima was *not* a vice-governor but merely a minor official. He was accompanied by a Dutch-speaking interpreter.

Commodore Perry secluded himself in his cabin. He refused to be seen by a vice-governor or, indeed, by any but the most important emissaries of the Emperor.

Lieutenant John Contee was told to speak with Nakajima. Contee explained that the Commodore's intentions were friendly. Perry merely wished to present a letter from the President of the United States to the Emperor of Japan. Nakajima replied that the American ships must go to the port of Nagasaki, where there was a Dutch trading post so that the Dutch could act as go-betweens.

Through his lieutenant, Perry let it be known that he would never go to Nagasaki and if all guard boats didn't disperse immediately there would be trouble. Nakajima went to the gangway, shouted an order, waved his fan, and all guard boats except his own departed at once. When Nakajima took his leave he promised that a higher official would see Perry the next day, Saturday, July 9.

That night, when the meteor streaked across the sky, Perry noted in his journal that this was a favorable omen: ". . . we pray God that our present attempt to bring a singular and isolated people into the family of civilized nations may succeed without resort to bloodshed."

His High and Mighty Mysteriousness

At dawn the Americans were amazed to see a boatload of artists near the *Susquehanna*. Using fine brushes, ink stones, and rolls of rice paper, they were making sketches of the ships and any of the crew they could see. Their curiosity was obviously stronger than their fear. Within a week, pictures of the Black Ships and "hairy barbarians" were hawked in the streets and sold in shops. They were also reproduced on souvenir banners, scrolls, fans, and towels.

While these artist-reporters were acting like war correspondents, the coastline was bustling with activity. Women and children carrying baskets of dirt helped men build new fortifications. Thousands of soldiers marched to and fro while their leaders decided upon strategic battle positions. They displayed colorful banners emblazoned with their lords' arms. Some trained muskets on Perry's squadron. Strips of canvas had been set up along the coast to hide these activities, but the Americans could see over them. The sailors were amused and dubbed the canvases "dungaree forts."

At seven o'clock in the morning, Kayama, so-called "governor" of Uraga, was welcomed aboard the *Susquehanna*. Actually he was *not* a governor but a police chief. Uraga's real governor, who did not wish to meet barbarians, gave Kayama permission to take his place. Dressed for the occasion in an embroidered silk robe, a lacquered hat with padded chin straps, and clunky clogs, this little man looked comical and ill at ease, even when his

Dutch interpreter introduced him as a person of great importance.

Commodore Perry would not see him. He secluded himself in his cabin again, for he rightly guessed that Kayama was not an eminent envoy of the Emperor. Because he remained hidden like a holy man, the Japanese soon spoke of Perry as "The American Mikado," and called his quarters "The Abode of His High and Mighty Mysteriousness."

Commanders Franklin Buchanan and Henry Adams spoke with Kayama. The conversation was awkward because it had to be translated from English into Dutch and then into Japanese, and back again. Perry's son Oliver acted as go-between. On board as his father's secretary, he rushed to and fro with orders for Buchanan and Adams, and reports for his father.

Kayama insisted that the Americans had to go to Nagasaki. He explained that Japanese law made it impossible for a letter to be received at any other port. Perry refused to budge and threatened to deliver the letter in person at the royal palace in Edo. Frightened at the thought, Kayama promised to contact the Emperor, then timidly asked why four ships were needed in order to carry one little letter to the Emperor. "Out of respect for him," Perry retorted. (The Commodore had no way of knowing that the Shogun occupied the Edo palace, and that the Emperor was a powerless figurehead who lived in Kyoto surrounded by the Shogun's spies.)

Kayama became even more alarmed when he noticed that small boats launched from the ships were cruising close to the mainland. He exclaimed that the Americans were violating Japanese law. The officers countered by saying that they were obeying American law. They had to survey coastal waters—a preparation in case Perry decided to land.

Surveying parties met Japanese guard boats on Monday,
July 11, 1853. (At left, a Japanese coastal junk)

During the surveys one of the Americans looked at some
Japanese soldiers through a telescope. The soldiers ducked,
probably believing that the spyglass was a new type of gun.

Strange music came from the ships on Sunday, July 10.
The crew sang hymns, accompanied by a band whose
instruments were unheard of in Japan. A boatload of
Japanese asked to visit, but they were refused admission
because Sunday was the Christian day of rest.

On Monday morning surveying boats were sent farther
than ever up Edo Bay. Kayama came aboard in a panic.
The activities of the Americans had caused great distress in
Edo, because the city's principal food supply depended
upon boat traffic. Fear of the foreigners prevented supply
boats from sailing.

Despite Kayama's pleas, the Americans continued to chart the coastal waters. Their survey boats came near enough to fortifications to observe that they were made of dirt and wood. There were a few cannons, but they were small and old. Most of them were 8-pounders, 200 or 300 years old, and they had not been used for a long time. The Japanese probably did not even know how to fire them. One of Perry's crew quipped that he could load all the Japanese cannons into the American 64-pound cannons and shoot them back.

Soldiers loyal to two daimyos requested permission to shoot at the Americans. Fortunately, their lords decided to hold fire, thus preventing an incident that might have started a war.

Although officials were terribly alarmed, many ordinary citizens calmed down after the first day of shock. A few hailed the men in the surveying boats and offered them water and peaches. A Japanese guard boat welcomed some of the surveyors aboard. The Americans amused and fascinated their hosts by shooting revolvers in the air.

The Americans were enchanted by the kindness and friendliness of the Japanese. At one time they believed that they had sailed over the edge of world civilization and would encounter savages. Face to face, they were beginning to realize that these charming people were as courteous and hospitable as any they had ever met. They were yet to discover that Japan was a highly civilized, cultured nation.

Early in the morning on Tuesday, July 12, Kayama went to the Americans and again asked them to go to Nagasaki. Through his intermediaries Perry stated that if the President's letter was not answered soon he would "consider his country insulted and will not hold himself accountable for the consequences. He expects a reply of some sort in a few days, and he will receive such reply nowhere but in this neighborhood.''

Kayama rushed back to Uraga to consult with officials, then returned that afternoon. He announced that a building would be erected on shore for a reception and a very important person would receive the letter.

Kayama and his companions then relaxed, especially after accepting drinks of whiskey and brandy. They became red-faced and merry, yet their manners remained elegant, their curiosity insatiable. Perry permitted them to tour the ship and examine its guns and engines.

Unlike the general population, Kayama's interpreters knew something about Western science and world

A Japanese view of Commodore Perry

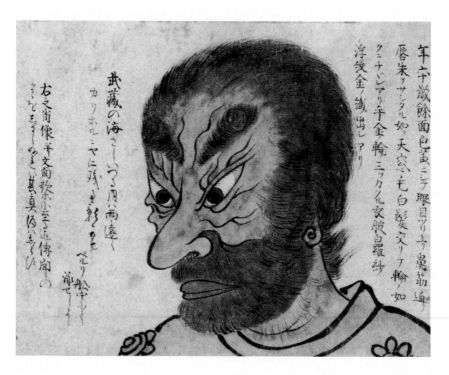

geography. Their knowledge of the Dutch and Chinese languages enabled them to learn facts about forbidden lands across the sea. They asked about roads that cut through mountains and about a railroad that was being built across the isthmus of Panama. When a globe was placed before them they immediately pointed to Washington and New York.

It was seven o'clock in the evening before the Japanese left the ship, bowing every step of the way. The Americans were impressed with their politeness, and noticed that when the Japanese were in their own boats enroute to shore, they were as formal, elegant, and dignified with each other as they had been with the Americans. Proper etiquette was not "company manners" but typical behavior.

On Wednesday, July 13, Kayama came aboard to exhibit a document from the Emperor. It authorized important officials to meet with Perry. The royal message, wrapped in velvet and encased in a sandalwood box, was treated with such reverence that Kayama would not allow anyone to touch it. Instead, the Americans were given a translation. The document specified that His Highness Toda, "Prince of Izu," and Ido, "Prince of Iwami," were authorized to receive the President's letter. These "princes" were actually the governors of Uraga.

Oriental duplicity? Not just Oriental! The Americans knew the art of bluffing, too. During the talks with Kayama they called Perry "admiral," because the title was more impressive than that of commodore, which is a lower rank.

Landing on Sacred Soil

Instead of using one of their permanent buildings, the Japanese erected a temporary wooden structure for their meeting with the Americans. It was located in a small village near Uraga.

At daybreak on Thursday, July 14, the *Susquehanna* and the *Mississippi* moved close to land, anchored, and aimed their guns at the shore. The men were prepared for battle in case their landing party was attacked.

Kayama came aboard as official host. He was dressed for the occasion in a costume made of multicolored silk, yellow velvet, and gold lace. Kayama may have looked magnificent by Japanese standards, but the Americans had to suppress their laughter. His trousers were so short and wide that the sailors thought they looked more like a petticoat.

All members of the crew were eager to set foot on Japanese soil, but since the ships had to be manned, they drew lots to determine who would go ashore. Fifteen launches carried about 100 marines, 100 sailors, and 40 musicians. Japanese guard boats flanked the Americans. As was customary, their oarsmen hissed as they rowed.

The American sailors and marines wore blue and white uniforms, officers were in full dress, and all were heavily armed with cutlasses and guns. As for "Admiral" Perry, his heavy uniform was buttoned to the throat despite the hot July weather. Tall and elegant, with sword at his side, he did indeed look like a Lord-High-Everything.

Perry proved to be a first-class showman, for he planned and staged a dramatic entrance. First, the marines formed two lines on the wharf. Then came sailors, marching to the lively music of two bands. Ships' cannons saluted when Commodore Perry disembarked. Bands played "Hail, Columbia" when he landed. Perry was flanked by two tall handsome black bodyguards, who proved to be sensational. The Japanese had never seen black men before.

The Americans could not have been more startled if they had traveled in a time machine to King Arthur's kingdom. The shore was a scene of feudal splendor. Thousands of Japanese soldiers encased in armor lined the beach. Some were pikemen. Others were archers, equipped with eight-foot bows. Two-sworded samurai warriors were everywhere. Lines of cavalry were stationed behind foot soldiers. Heraldic banners held high represented the daimyos to whom their soldiers owed allegiance. According to their tradition, warriors' faces had to look fierce. A few soldiers wore ferocious-looking masks that had been designed to scare enemies. The soldiers glared and glowered as the Americans marched by.

In the background villagers milled about, jumping up and craning their necks to get glimpses of the barbarians. The officers' uniforms with gleaming buttons and the wide epaulettes amused them. They never dreamed that clothing of this sort existed. Nor had they ever seen men with such long noses or with brown, blond, or red hair. And their size! The aliens were giants compared to Japanese men, who averaged five feet one inch. (Just as medieval

European knights were shorter than modern men, nineteenth-century Japanese soldiers were smaller than today's average Japanese male.)

The Audience Hall

The Commodore and his officers entered a canvas tent that served as an anteroom, then walked a carpeted path to the main hall. The walls were draped with huge purple silk banners displaying the imperial coat of arms. The floor was covered with red cloth.

The Americans did not know that ten samurai were underneath, concealed beneath the floor, ready for a signal to rush out and kill Perry and his aides.

As soon as Perry entered, the "princes" Ido and Toda rose from low stools and bowed. The Americans were seated on chairs that had been hastily taken from a nearby temple. Buddhist priests sat on these when they conducted funeral services. Only then did they dangle their legs from chairs, because the Japanese usually kneeled and sat back on their heels—a posture that Westerners still find difficult.

President Fillmore's letter was encased in a beautiful rosewood box with locks and hinges made of gold. When the Commodore signaled, two ship's boys carried the box to his bodyguards, who, in turn, placed the letter in a scarlet container supplied by the Japanese. A letter from Perry with Dutch and Chinese translations was also presented.

Kayama approached Prince Ido, got down on all fours, bowed his head to the floor, then received a Japanese document. He took it to the Commodore, then prostrated

The delivery of President Millard Fillmore's letter

himself once again before "His High and Mighty Mysteriousness."

Perry had not expected any written reply. His Dutch interpreter, Portman, explained that the document was merely an imperial receipt. It stated: "The letter of the President of the United States of North America and a copy are hereby received and will be delivered to the Emperor. . . . Therefore, as the letter has been received you can depart."

The entire procedure lasted about twenty minutes. Ido and Toda never uttered a word, because speaking with foreigners was against the law. A long silence was broken when Perry announced through his interpreters that he expected to leave in two or three days, and that he would return in the spring. "With all four vessels?" the Japanese interpreters asked.

"All of them," Perry replied, "and probably more, as these are only a portion of the squadron."

The fleet departed on July 17, three days after the meeting on shore, nine days after the arrival at Edo Bay.

Before the Americans sailed away, Kayama came on board bearing presents of food, fans, pipes, and soup bowls. In turn, Perry gave him calico, sugar, wine, and books. At first Kayama was reluctant to receive gifts. Owning foreign objects was forbidden. However, he couldn't resist. He concealed the books and bottles in his capacious gown. After bowing farewell to his American friends, he left with tears in his eyes. Kayama's mood became less sad after he entered his own boat. He knocked off the neck of a wine bottle and drank its contents.

Poor Kayama was punished. Ido destroyed his gifts and had him demoted because he had been too friendly with the Americans.

Perry was proud of his accomplishment. Nearly sixty years old, he had added to a long and distinguished career. As an officer in the U.S. Navy he had hunted pirates and slave traders. He had successfully commanded the largest American naval force during the Mexican War (1846–1848). He had succeeded in peace talks with Mexican leaders and African chiefs. He modernized the navy by insisting upon steam-powered warships. But he knew that his Japanese encounter was more significant than any of his former achievements. Both Russia and England had attempted to open Japanese ports for foreign ships and failed. Although Perry was unwelcome and overwhelmed in numbers, he had dared to land on the sacred soil of a hermit nation. He was the first Western ambassador to be received in Japan in over 200 years. How proud he was that he did not have to fire one shot!

Commodore Perry returned to Japan in February 1854 to negotiate a treaty which would grant the U.S. trading rights in Japanese ports. Again he staged a spectacular show for the Japanese. After the treaty was signed, gifts were exchanged. A miniature railroad given by the Americans was the hit of the show. Samurai took turns whirling around the short circle of track at the rate of twenty miles per hour, their loose robes flying in the wind as they clung to the passenger car's roof. They laughed and behaved as though they were riding a roller coaster. (Read the rest of the book to find out what the Japanese gave to the Americans.)

Meet the Author: **Rhoda Blumberg**

Before becoming an avid American history buff, Rhoda Blumberg wrote books about pets, monsters, witches, dragons, and UFOs. She enjoyed studying outer space for her book, *The First Travel Guide to the Moon*, and learning about the ocean for *The First Travel Guide to the Bottom of the Sea.*

The author calls her library card a "passport to adventure," because books enable her to travel through time and space, and witness exciting events of the past. Visiting 19th century feudal Japan with Commodore Perry was a unique experience, and writing about it was pure joy, because Ms. Blumberg likes to share her adventures with readers.

The author is at her typewriter almost every day. Her trash basket is often filled with discarded drafts of paragraphs and chapters that have to be rewritten. Writing is hard work that can be frustrating. Nevertheless, the joy of learning through research, and the pleasure of conveying information through writing give her tremendous satisfaction.

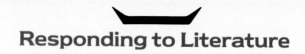

Responding to Literature

1. *Commodore Perry* was a runner-up, or Honor Book, for the Newbery Medal in 1986. If you were on the Newbery committee to select an award-winning book, what three things would you consider to be the most important?

2. In the nine days of Perry's visit, a great deal happened that was to change the history of two countries. Imagine that you are a newspaper reporter. Tell the important actions of the Americans and Japanese, beginning with Perry's arrival on July 8 and his departure on July 17.

3. Why did Commodore Perry succeed when so many people before him failed? Explain in a short paragraph.

4. Because neither side spoke the other's language, gestures and actions became very important. In what ways were they important to the Americans and to the Japanese?

5. What words would you choose to describe the American and Japanese reactions to each other? Then find the words the author uses and compare them.

6. Write a persuasive letter to the Emperor Komei requesting him to "open the doors" to his country.

A Moment of Wonder

(Japanese Haiku)

Two ducks swim to the shore
The quacking ducks and the blowing wind
Wrinkle the face of the water.

Hiroshige

The face of the dragonfly
Is practically nothing
But eyes.

Chisoku

What happiness
Crossing this summer river,
Sandals in hand!

Buson

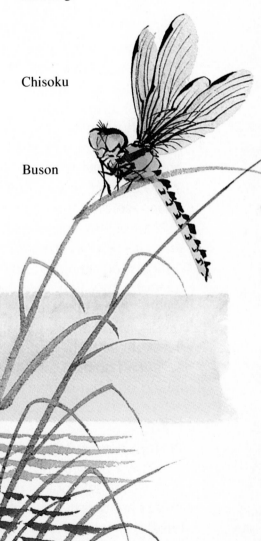

Appreciating Author's Craft

Thinking About Point of View in Nonfiction

Commodore Perry's trip is an important event in the history of the United States and Japan. In nonfiction accounts, the event from history is often looked at from two or more points of view. Point of view is the author's choice of narrator, or speaker. This choice affects the amount and kind of information the reader will be given. In this book, the author presents the American and Japanese points of view. The American and Japanese points of view are presented with historical accuracy. Both groups of people in the excerpt react to each other as Americans and Japanese of that time would have reacted.

Point of view may contain facts and opinions. As you read, it's always important to ask yourself if a statement is a fact or an opinion. Look at the example, "That night a meteor with a fiery tail streaked through the sky like a rocket. An omen from the gods!" The first statement is probably a fact. A rocketlike meteor did probably appear in the night sky. The second statement would not be the American opinion, or point of view, but a Japanese opinion, based on what people of that time thought.

Writing About Point of View in Nonfiction

You will be writing a summary of this selection. You will present the two points of view, the Japanese and the American, giving the facts and opinions as each side might have presented them. Also, you will write a conclusion as if

you were the author, trying to help a reader understand the two points of view. For example, you might say that "as a result of these incidents the Americans and the Japanese began to understand each other." (For ideas about writing, look at The Writer's Handbook.)

Prewriting To begin, read the sentences below from the selection which give two points of view. Decide from whose point of view each statement is made.

	American View	Japanese View
"Giant dragons puffing smoke," cried some. "Alien ships of fire," cried others.	☐	☐
The sailors were amused and dubbed the canvases "dungaree forts."	☐	☐

Copy these sentences and the boxes. Then with a partner add two more examples from the selection.

Writing Write a summary using the information you have gathered showing the Japanese and American points of view. As you write, include your own conclusions to help the reader understand the two points of view.

Revising Go over your draft. Then read your draft to your partner to make sure that you have included examples of two points of view. Revise your draft and write your final copy.

Presenting Put your summary up on a bulletin board for your classmates to read. Also look at the summaries of your classmates to see what they have written. Which summary is not accurate? What points do most of the summaries agree on?

Extending Your Reading

Expressing Yourself
Choose one or more of these activities:

Communicate Without Talking Pick an emotion such as fear, anger, or joy and act it out for a partner or for your class. When your emotion is guessed, ask what details your partner or your class used to come up with the right answer.

Draw a Mask Some Japanese soldiers wore masks to look fierce. Draw a life-size mask that looks frightening, or charming and friendly. Tell about the meaning of your mask.

Japanese Haiku The haiku on page 287 are short poems that originated in Japan. In haiku, word pictures suggest an idea or a feeling. Usually the word pictures are about some small marvel of nature. Haiku have three lines. Try your skill at composing a haiku. Illustrate your poem if you wish. (For more about haiku, see your Handbook.)

Japanese Music Find a record of traditional Japanese music and play it for your class. The traditional instruments include gongs, drums, flutes, and *samisens* (a banjolike instrument). Use this musical background to read a passage from this selection to your class.

More Books About Communication

Indian Talk: Hand Signals of the American Indians by Iron Eyes Cody. Naturegraph. The Plains Indians of America spoke many different languages. In order to communicate with each other, they developed a language based on hand signals. Iron Eyes Cody, a well-known film actor, demonstrates hundreds of signs used by Indians.

Yellow Bird and Me by Joyce Hansen. Clarion. When Doris starts to help the local silly guy Yellow Bird with his homework, she realizes he's not a "dummy." In fact, when he starts getting help for his learning disability, Yellow Bird turns out to be a surprise to Doris.

Desdemona: Twelve Going on Desperate by Beverly Keller. Lothrop. One calamity after another befalls Desdemona in this juvenile soap opera. She keeps running into Mark, the most attractive boy in school, just when she doesn't want to be seen with her embarrassingly short haircut. An evening with Mark at an art show turns out to be one of the most horrendous moments of her life, but also one of the nicest.

Words: A Book About Origins of Everyday Words and Phrases by Jane Sarnoff and Reynold Ruffins. Scribner's. Languages are constantly changing as people know them; for instance, do you know that the word *kangaroo* really means "I don't know"? This and many other words are traced back to their roots with many surprises along the way.

Exploring Mime by Mark Stolzenberg. Sterling. Mime is a silent way of telling a story with your face and body. With this book, you can learn how to make miming come alive.

The Sign of the Beaver

by Elizabeth George Speare

Introducing

The Sign of the Beaver

Matt Hallowell had been alone before, but never quite so alone as after his father left him to guard their family cabin in the wilderness. Matt was just thirteen years old, and as he stood looking out from the cabin he saw a vast wilderness stretched before him. What was it like to live in the wilderness in 1768?

The Maine Wilderness in 1768

Elizabeth George Speare's novel *The Sign of the Beaver* is historical fiction. That means the author has placed the story in the past at a specific time. One of Speare's purposes in writing this novel was to describe the setting and characters so accurately that you have the feeling you are in the wilderness in Maine in 1768. To do this, Speare had to find facts such as what a cabin of this time would be like and what many Indians felt about the new white settlers coming into Indian lands.

Speare also had to think about how the characters of the time might sound and the words they might use. For example, Matt refers to the young Indian, Attean (at·tē'un) as a *heathen* and a *savage* because people like Matt living

in the 1700s did not understand the culture of the Indians. Also, no one knows exactly how the Indians sounded as they learned English. The author has tried to show you that to the Indians, English is a foreign language. When, for example, the author has Attean ask, "You like go fish?" she is trying to help you understand that Attean is speaking a language that is not his own. (For more information on historical fiction, see the Handbook of Literary Terms.)

Thinking About Character Conflict

In literature, just as in real life, people sometimes don't get along with each other. They find they may not agree and sometimes they are in a real struggle or conflict. In *The Sign of the Beaver,* Speare has created two main characters who don't get along. Speare writes in such a way that you will learn about each of the characters as real people and probably wonder if they can ever work out their differences.

As you're reading this excerpt on your own, discover what Matt and Attean learn about each other.

The Sign of the Beaver

Matt felt pretty confident about his job of guarding the family cabin while his father went to fetch the rest of the family. He knew how to mark the days on his stick, how to tend the garden, and what had to be done to finish off the cabin for the winter. But two things happened which Matt could not have predicted.

First, a stranger named Ben showed up. Would Matt's father be upset if he didn't show hospitality to a stranger? Matt showed his good manners, invited the stranger for dinner and gave him a place to sleep by the fire. Matt tried to stay awake all night to keep an eye on things, but to his horror he dozed off. When he awoke, Ben was gone and so was his father's good rifle, the rifle that would have provided Matt with meat during the long summer.

Then, Matt went to fish, forgetting to bar the cabin door. Imagine Matt's surprise to come home and find the door hanging by its hinges and tracks of flour all over the cabin. At first Matt thought Ben had returned, but that was not the case. Matt had just gotten careless and a bear had come in and tipped over all his flour and eaten all his precious molasses. The long days with nothing sweet and no bread would seem even longer. As long as Matt could fish, he wouldn't starve, but the loss of his rifle and basic foods certainly lessened his chances of having anything good to eat. That's what started Matt thinking about bees and honey.

Day after day he kept remembering the bee tree. He and his father had discovered it weeks ago. High in a tree, at the swampy edge of the pond they had called Loon Pond, the bees were buzzing in and out of an old woodpecker hole. Matt had thought they were wild bees, but his father said no, there were no bees at all in America till the colonists brought them from England. This swarm must have escaped from one of the river towns. Bees were better left alone, Pa said.

He felt he could scarcely endure another meal of plain fish. He was hungry for a bit of something tasty. Knowing so well his fondness for molasses, his mother had persuaded them to carry that little keg all the way to Maine when his father would rather have gone without. She would have smiled to see him running his finger round and round the empty keg like a child and licking off the last drop the bear had missed. Now he couldn't stop thinking about that honey. It would be worth a sting or two just to have a taste of it. There couldn't be much danger in going up that tree and taking just a little—a cupful perhaps that the bees would never miss. One morning he made up his mind to try it, come what might.

It was an easy tree to climb, with branches as neatly placed as the rungs of a ladder. The bees did not seem to notice as he pulled himself higher and higher. Even when his head was on a level with the hole, they flew

lazily in and out, not paying him any mind. The hole
was small, not big enough for his hand and the spoon he
had brought with him. Peering in, he could just glimpse,
far inside, the golden mass of honeycomb. The bark all
around the hole was rotted and crumbling. Cautiously he
put his fingers on the edge and gave a slight tug. A good-
sized piece of bark broke off into his hand.

With it came the bees. With a furious buzzing they
came pouring from the broken hole. The humming grew
to a roar, like a great wind. Matt felt a sharp pain on his
neck, then another and another. The angry creatures
swarmed along his hands and bare arms, in his hair, on
his face.

How he got down out of that tree he never
remembered. Water! If he could reach water he could
escape them. Bellowing and waving his arms, he plunged
toward the pond. The bees were all around him. He
could not see through the whirling cloud of them. The
boggy ground sucked at his feet. He pulled one foot clear
out of his boot, went stumbling over sharp roots to the
water's edge, and flung himself forward. His foot caught
in a fallen branch and he wrenched it clear. Dazed with
pain, he sank down into the icy shelter of the water.

He came up choking. Just above the water the angry
bees circled. Twice more he ducked his head and held it
down till his lungs were bursting. He tried to swim out
into the pond but his feet were tangled in dragging
weeds. When he tried to jerk them free, a fierce pain ran
up his leg and he went under again, thrashing his arms
wildly.

Then something lifted him. His head came up from the
water and he gulped air into his aching lungs. He felt
strong arms around him. Half conscious, he dreamed that

his father was carrying him, and he did not wonder how this could be. Presently he knew he was lying on dry ground. Though his eyelids were swollen almost shut, he could see two figures bending over him—unreal, half-naked figures with dark faces. Then, as his wits began to return to him, he saw that they were Indians, an old man and a boy. The man's hands were reaching for his throat, and in panic Matt tried to jerk away.

"Not move," a deep voice ordered. "Bee needles have poison. Must get out."

Matt was too weak to struggle. He could not even lift his head. Now that he was out of the cold water, his skin seemed to be on fire from head to toe, yet he could not stop shivering. He had to lie helpless while the man's hands moved over his face and neck and body. Gradually he realized that they were gentle hands, probing and rubbing at one tender spot after another. His panic began to die away.

He could still not think clearly. Things seemed to keep fading before he could quite grasp them. He could not protest when the man lifted him again and carried him like a baby. It did not seem to matter where they were taking him, but shortly he found himself lying on his own bed in his own cabin. He was alone; the Indians had gone. He lay, too tired and sore to figure out how he came to be there, knowing only that the nightmare of whirling bees and choking water was past and that he was safe.

Some time passed. Then once again the Indian was bending over him, holding a wooden spoon against his lips. He swallowed in spite of himself, even when he found it was not food, but some bitter medicine. He was left alone again, and presently he slept.

Finally Matt woke and knew that he was well. His body was no longer on fire. He could open his eyes, and he saw that sunlight glinted through the chinks in the roof. All his familiar things were around him—the shelves with the pewter dishes, his jacket hanging on a peg. He felt as though he had been on a long journey and had come home. He must have slept through half a day and a night.

When the cabin door opened and the Indian entered, Matt hastily pulled himself up. Now, with clear eyes, he saw that there was nothing in the least strange about this man. He was dressed not so differently from Matt's own father, in a coat of some rough brown cloth and leggings fringed down the side. His face was smooth-shaven, and so was his whole head, except for one long black topknot. When he saw that Matt was awake, his stern face was lighted by a wide smile.

"Good." It was half word, half grunt. "White boy very sick. Now well."

Matt remembered his father's advice. "Good morning," he said respectfully.

The Indian pointed a hand at his own chest. "Saknis, family of beaver," he said. He seemed to be waiting.

"I'm Matthew Hallowell," Matt answered.

"Good. White man leave you here?"

"Just for a while," Matt told him. "He has gone to get my mother." It did not occur to him to lie to this old man as he had to Ben. Moreover, he knew that there was something he had to say. He tried to find the right words.

"I'm grateful to you," he said finally. "It was a very lucky thing you happened to find me."

"We watch. White boy very foolish to climb bee tree."

So, he had been right, Matt thought, that eyes were watching him from the forest. He was sure that the Indian had not asked him where he lived. They had brought him straight home to this cabin. Even though he knew it was his good fortune they'd been watching him yesterday, he still felt somewhat resentful of their spying. Abruptly he swung his feet to the floor, and winced as a sharp pain ran up his leg.

The Indian noticed, and moving closer he took Matt's ankle between his hands and pressed gently with his fingers.

"Is it broken?" Matt asked.

"*Nda*. Not broke. Mend soon. Sleep now. Not need medicine more."

The Indian had put something on the table as he came in. When he had gone, Matt hobbled over to see what it was and found a wooden bowl of stew, thick and greasy, flavored with some strange plant, wonderfully filling and strengthening. With it there was a cake of corn bread, coarser than his own but delicious.

The next day the Indian brought the boy with him.

"*Nkweniss*. You call grandson," he announced. "Attean."

The two boys stared at each other. The Indian boy's black eyes held no expression whatever. Unlike the old man, he was naked except for a breechcloth held up by a string at his waist. It passed between his legs and hung down like a little apron back and front. His heavy black hair fell straight to his shoulders.

"Attean same winter as white boy, maybe?" the man asked. He held up ten fingers and then four more.

"I'm thirteen," Matt answered, holding up his own fingers. At least, he excused himself, that would be true in another week.

The Indian boy did not speak a word. Quite plainly he had been brought here against his will. He stared about the cabin and seemed to despise everything he saw. He made Matt feel like a fool, sitting with his leg propped up on a stool. Matt steadied himself on his good leg and stood up.

Now he noticed that Saknis was holding out to him a rough sort of crutch. Matt wished he did not have to try it right now, with both of them watching him, but he could see that the man expected it. He managed a few steps, furious at his own clumsiness. He had never imagined how pesky a crutch could be. Moreover, although there was not the slightest change in the boy's face, Matt was sure that Attean was laughing at him. There was a nasty little gleam in the boy's eyes.

The moment they were gone, he seized the crutch in earnest, and very soon he could swing himself along at a good, brisk pace. Now he was able to get about outside the cabin, to check the corn patch and bring in firewood.

The trouble was, he had only one boot. The woolen stocking his mother had knit for him was wearing thin. On the rough ground it wore through in no time.

This too the Indian noticed, when he came with his grandson next morning. "No boot," he said, pointing.

"I lost it," Matt answered. "It came off in the mud when I ran." Once again he felt ridiculous under the Indian boy's black stare.

Three days later Saknis brought him a pair of moccasins. They were handsome and new, of moosehide, dark and glistening with grease, tied with stout thongs that were long enough to wrap about his ankles.

"Beaver woman make," Saknis said. "Better white man's boots. White boy see."

The Indian boy did not speak a word.

Matt took off his one boot and slipped on the moccasins. Indeed they were better! In fact they were wonderful. Not stiff like new leather boots. Not knobby or pinching anywhere. Light as nothing at all when he lifted his feet. No wonder Indians did not make a sound when they walked in the forest.

Shame suddenly flooded over Matt. This man had perhaps saved his life, had come bringing food and a crutch, and now these beautiful moccasins. It wasn't enough just to say an awkward thank you. He needed to give something in return. Not money. There were a few silver coins in the tin box, but something made him very sure that he could not offer money to this proud old man. He looked about him in despair. There was almost nothing of his own in the cabin.

Then he spied the two books on the shelf, the only two his father had been able to carry into the wilderness. One was the Bible. He dared not give away his father's Bible. The other book was his own, the only one he had ever possessed. *Robinson Crusoe*.[1] He had read it a dozen times and the thought of parting with it was painful, but it was the only thing he had to give. He hobbled across the room and took it down from the shelf and held it out to the Indian.

Saknis stared at it.

"It's for you," Matt said. "It's a gift. Please take it."

Saknis reached out and took the book in his hand. He turned it over and over slowly, his face showing not a sign of pleasure. Then he opened it and stood peering at

---

1. *Robinson Crusoe* refers to *The Life and Strange Adventures of Robinson Crusoe* by Daniel Defoe published in 1719 which was one of the few books enjoyed by young people in the 18th century.

the page. With shame, Matt saw that he was holding it upside down.

He couldn't read. Of course he couldn't. Matt should have known that. He had made a terrible mistake and embarrassed the good man. He had heard once that the one thing an Indian could never forgive was a hurt to his pride. He felt his own face burning.

But Saknis did not look embarrassed. His dark stare went from the book to Matt's face.

"White boy know signs?" he asked.

Matt was puzzled.

"White boy read what white man write here?"

"Yes," Matt admitted. "I can read it."

For a long moment the Indian studied the book. Then, astonishingly, that rare white smile flashed.

"Good," he grunted. "Saknis make treaty."

"A treaty?" Matt was even more puzzled.

"*Nkweniss* hunt. Bring white boy bird and rabbit. White boy teach Attean white man's signs."

"You mean—I should teach him to read?"

"Good. White boy teach Attean what book say."

Doubtfully, Matt looked from the old man to the boy, who stood silently listening. His heart sank. The scorn in the boy's face had turned to black anger.

"*Nda!*" The furious word exploded, the first word Matt had ever heard him speak. Half under his breath he muttered a string of incomprehensible words.

His grandfather's stern face did not change. He was undisturbed by the boy's defiance.

"Attean learn," he said. "White man come more and more to Indian land. White man not make treaty with pipe. White man make signs on paper, signs Indian not know. Indian put mark on paper to show him friend of white man. Then white man take land. Tell Indian cannot hunt on land. Attean learn to read white man's signs. Attean not give away hunting grounds."

The boy glowered at his grandfather, but he did not dare to speak again. With a black scowl, he stalked out of the cabin.

"Good," said Saknis calmly. He handed the book back to Matt. "Attean come *seba*—tomorrow."

Before he had his eyes open next morning, Matt knew that something was wrong with this day. When it came back to him he sat up with a groan. Attean! What had possessed him to give a book to an Indian? How could he possibly teach a savage to read?

He tried to think back to the time his mother had taught him his ABCs. He could plainly see that brown-covered primer she held in her hands. He had detested it. He had had to learn the short verses printed beside each letter.

> A   In Adam's fall
>   We sinned all.

That would hardly do. To be honest, he wasn't sure to this day just what it meant. He would feel mighty silly trying to explain it to a heathen. Then happily he recalled another book that had been sent to his sister, Sarah, from England, with a small picture to illustrate each letter. No nonsense about Adam. *A* was for *apple*. Sarah had been luckier than he.

But he had no way of making pictures, and there were

no apples here in the forest. What could he find for *A*
that an Indian would understand? He looked about the
cabin. *T* for *table*, though it was unlikely they'd ever get
as far as *T*. How about *A* for *arm*? That was simple
enough. *B*? His eye fell on the leg bone of the squirrel left
from last night's meal. The stub of a candle would do for
C. *D*? *Door* would be just the word for Attean. He
certainly could walk out of one fast enough, and would
again, no doubt, long before they got to *D*.

He doubted that Attean would come. Still, he had
better be ready. He stirred the fire, ate a chunk of the
cold Indian corn cake, and set about to prepare a
schoolroom. He shoved the two stools together and laid
Robinson Crusoe on the table. He did not have paper or
ink. He found a ribbon of birchbark in a corner and tore
off a strip and sharpened a stick to a point. Then he
waited.

Attean came, swinging a dead rabbit by the ears. He
slung it disdainfully on the table.

"Thank you," Matt said. "That's a big one. I won't need
anything else for several days."

His politeness brought no response.

"Sit here," he ordered. He hesitated. "I never thought as
how I'd have to teach anyone to read. But I have figured
a way to start."

Silently the boy sat down, as straight and rigid as a
cedar post. When Matt hunched himself onto the other
stool, the boy's scowl deepened. Plainly he did not like
having the white boy so close to him. Attean had no need
to be finicky, Matt thought. He smelled none too sweet
himself. The grease smeared on his body, even on his
hair, stunk up the whole cabin. It was supposed to keep
off the mosquitoes, he'd heard, but he thought he'd rather

Attean knocked the book from the table.

have the pesky insects himself. He drew a letter on the birch bark.

"This is the first letter," he explained, "A. A for *arm*."

He repeated this several times, pointing to his own arm. Attean kept to his stubborn, scornful silence. Matt set his jaw. He could be stubborn too, he decided. He opened *Robinson Crusoe*.

"We'll pick out the *A*'s on this page," he said, trying to control his impatience. He pointed. "Now you show me one."

Attean stared straight ahead of him in silence. Then, to Matt's astonishment, he grudgingly laid a grubby finger on a letter *A*.

"Good," said Matt, copying the word *Saknis* used so often. "Find another."

Suddenly the boy broke his silence. "White man's book foolish," he scoffed. "Write *arm, arm, arm* all over paper."

Puzzled at first, Matt saw his own mistake. "Hundreds of other words begin with *A*," he explained. "Or have *A* in them. And there are twenty-five more letters."

Attean scowled. "How long?" he demanded.

"What do you mean?"

"How long Attean learn signs in book?"

"It will take some time," Matt said. "There are a lot of long words in this book."

"One moon?"

"One month? Of course not. It might take a year."

With one swift jerk of his arm, Attean knocked the book from the table. Before Matt could speak, he was out of the cabin and gone.

"Reckon that's the end of the lessons," Matt said to himself. Cheerfully he began to skin the rabbit.

By the next morning he was half sorry the boy would not be coming again. He didn't know whether he was annoyed or relieved when Attean walked through the door without a sign of greeting and sat down at the table.

Matt decided to skip B for *bone*. In the night he had thought of a better way.

"This book isn't a treaty," he began. "It's a story. It's about a man who gets shipwrecked on a desert island. I'll read some of it out loud to show you."

He opened *Robinson Crusoe* at the first page and began to read.

I was born in the year 1632, in the city of York. . . .

He stopped. He remembered suddenly how the first time he had tried to read this book he had found that first page so dull he had come close to giving up right there. He had better skip the beginning and get on with the story if he wanted to catch Attean's attention.

"I'll read the part about the storm at sea," he said.

He had read the book so many times that he knew exactly where to find the right page. Taking a deep breath, as though he were struggling in the water himself, he chose the page where Robinson Crusoe was dashed from the lifeboat and swallowed up in the sea.

Nothing can describe the confusion of thought which I felt when I sunk into the water, for though I swam very well, yet I could not deliver myself from the waves so as to draw breath . . . for I saw the sea come after me as high as a great hill, and as furious as an enemy. . . .

Matt looked up from the page. There was not a flicker of interest in the boy's face. Had he understood a single word? Discouraged, he laid down the book. What did a storm at sea mean to a savage who had lived all his life in the forest?

"Well," he said lamely, "it gets better as you go along."

Once more Attean took him by surprise. "White man get out of water?" he asked.

"Oh yes," Matt said, delighted. "Everyone else on the ship is drowned. He gets thrown up all alone on an island."

The Indian nodded. He seemed satisfied.

"Shall I read more of it?"

Attean nodded again. "Go now," he said. "Come back *seba*."

The next morning there was no question of *B* for *bone*. Matt had the book open and waiting at the part he wanted to read.

"This is about the morning after the storm," he explained. "Robinson Crusoe looks out and sees that part of the ship hasn't sunk yet. He swims out and manages to save some things and carry them to shore." He began to read.

Once again it was impossible to tell whether Attean understood. Presently Matt slowed down. It was discouraging, reading to a wooden post. But Attean spoke at once.

"White man not smart like Indian," he said scornfully. "Indian not need thing from ship. Indian make all thing he need."

Disappointed and cross, Matt put the book down. They might as well get on with the alphabet. He drew a *B* on the birchbark.

After Attean had gone, Matt kept thinking about

Robinson Crusoe and all the useful things he had managed to salvage from that ship. He had found a carpenter's chest, for instance. Bags of nails. Two barrels of bullets. And a dozen hatchets—a dozen! Why, Matt and his father had come up here to Maine with one axe and an adz. They had cut down trees and built this whole cabin and the table and the stools without a single nail. Crusoe had found a hammock to sleep in instead of prickly hemlock boughs. He could see now how it must have sounded to Attean. Come to think of it, Robinson Crusoe had lived like a king on that desert island!

A few mornings later, at the end of the lesson, Matt delayed Attean.

"How did you kill that rabbit?" he asked, pointing to the offering Attean had thrown on the table. "There's no bullet hole in it."

"Indian not use bullet for rabbit," Attean answered scornfully.

"Then how? There's no hole at all."

For a moment it seemed that Attean would not bother to answer. Then the Indian shrugged. "Attean show," he said. "Come."

Matt was dumbfounded. It was the first sign the Indian had given of—well, of what exactly? He had not sounded friendly. But there was not time to puzzle this out right now. Attean was walking across the clearing, and he apparently expected Matt to follow. Pleased and curious, Matt hobbled after him, grateful that he no longer needed the crutch.

At the edge of the clearing the Indian stopped and

searched the ground. Presently he stooped down under a black spruce tree, poked into the dirt, and jerked up a long snakelike root. He drew from the leather pouch at his belt a curious sort of knife, the blade curved into a hook. With one sure stroke, he split one end of the root, then peeled off the bark by pulling at it with his teeth. He separated the whole length into two strands, which he spliced together by rolling them against his bare thigh. Next he searched about in the bushes till he found two forked saplings about three feet apart. He trimmed the twigs from these, drawing his knife toward his chest as Matt had been taught not to do. Then he cut a stout branch, and rested it lightly across the forks of his saplings. From the threadlike root he made a noose and suspended it from the stick so that it hung just above the ground. He worked without speaking, and it seemed to Matt that all this took him no time at all.

"Rabbit run into trap," he said finally. "Pull stick into bush, so white boy can kill."

"Golly," said Matt, filled with admiration. "I hadn't thought of making a snare. I didn't know you could make one without string or wire."

"Make more," Attean ordered, pointing into the woods. "Not too close."

After Attean had gone, Matt managed to make two more snares. They were clumsy things, and he was not too proud of them. Splitting a slippery root, he discovered, was not so easy as it had looked. He spoiled a number of them before he mastered the trick of splicing them together. They did not slide as easily as the one Attean had made, but they seemed strong enough.

Next morning he showed his traps to Attean. He had hoped for some sign of approval, but all he got was a

Matt managed to make two more snares.

grunt and a shrug. He knew that to Attean his work must look childish. However, on the third day one of his own snares had been upset, though the animal had got away. The day after that, to his joy, there was actually a partridge struggling to free itself in the bushes where the stick had caught. This time the grunt with which Attean rewarded him sounded very much like his grandfather's "Good." Silently the Indian watched as Matt reset the snare. Then they walked back to the cabin, Matt swinging his catch as nonchalantly as he had seen Attean do.

"You don't need to bring me any more food," he boasted. "I'll catch my own meat from now on."

Nevertheless, Attean continued to bring him some offering every morning. Not always fresh meat. He seemed to know exactly when Matt had finished the last scrap of rabbit or duck. Sometimes he brought a slab of corn cake, or a pouch full of nuts, once a small cake of maple sugar. Plainly he felt bound to keep the terms of his grandfather's treaty.

Matt stuck to his part of the bargain as well, though the lessons were an ordeal for them both. Matt knew well enough what a poor teacher he was. Sometimes it seemed that Attean was learning in spite of him. Once the Indian had resigned himself to mastering twenty-six letters, he took them in a gulp, scorning the childish *candle* and *door* and *table* that Matt had devised. Soon he was spelling out simple words. The real trouble was that Attean was contemptuous, that the whole matter of white man's words seemed to him nonsense. Impatiently they hurried through the lessons to get on with *Robinson Crusoe*. Matt suspected that the only reason Attean agreed to come back day after day was that he wanted to hear more of that story.

Skipping over the pages that sounded like sermons, Matt chose the sections he liked best himself. Now he came to the rescue of the man Friday. Attean sat quietly, and Matt almost forgot him in his own enjoyment of his favorite scene.

There was the mysterious footprint on the sand, the canoes drawn up on the lonely beach, and the strange, wild-looking men with two captives. One of the captives they mercilessly slaughtered. The fire was set blazing for a cannibal feast.

Then the second captive made a desperate escape, running straight to where Crusoe stood watching. Two savages pursued him with horrid yells. Matt glanced up from the book and saw that Attean's eyes were gleaming. He hurried on. No need to skip here. Crusoe struck a mighty blow at the first cannibal, knocking him senseless. Then, seeing that the other was fitting an arrow into his bow, he shot and killed him. Matt read on:

The poor savage who fled, but had stopped, though he saw both his enemies had fallen . . . yet was so frightened with the noise and fire of my piece, that he stood stock-still, and neither came forward nor went backward. . . . I hallooed again to him, and made signs to him to come forward, which he easily understood, and came a little way, then stopped again . . . he stood trembling as if he had been taken prisoner, and just about to be killed, as his two enemies were. I beckoned to him again to come to me, and gave him all signs of encouragement, that I could think of; and he came nearer and nearer, kneeling down every ten or twelve steps, in token of acknowledgment for saving his life. I smiled at him, and looked

*pleasantly, and beckoned to him to come still
nearer. At length he came close to me, and then he
kneeled down again, kissed the ground, and,
taking my foot, set it upon his head. This, it
seemed, was a token of swearing to be my slave
forever. . . .*

Attean sprang to his feet, a thundercloud wiping out all
pleasure from his face.

"*Nda!*" he shouted. "Not so."

Matt stopped, bewildered.

"Him never do that!"

"Never do what?"

"Never kneel down to white man!"

"But Crusoe had saved his life."

"Not kneel down," Attean repeated fiercely. "Not be
slave. Better die."

Matt opened his mouth to protest, but Attean gave him
no chance. In three steps he was out of the cabin.

Now he'll never come back, Matt thought. He sat
slowly turning over the pages. He had never questioned
that story. Like Robinson Crusoe, he had thought it
natural and right that the wild man should be the white
man's slave. Was there perhaps another possibility? The
thought was new and troubling.

He felt weak with relief when next morning Attean
walked stiffly into the cabin and sat down at the table.
Stumbling over himself, he set about the lesson. As soon
as he could, he picked up *Robinson Crusoe*. In the night
he had carefully thought out just what he was going to
say, if Attean ever gave him another chance. Now he had

Matt ran to overtake the Indian boy.

to talk fast, because he could see that Attean was set against hearing any more of this book.

"Let me go on," he pleaded. "It's different from now on. Friday—that's what Robinson Crusoe named him—doesn't kneel anymore."

"Not slave?"

"No," Matt lied. "After that they get to be—well—companions. They share everything together."

Ignoring the suspicion on Attean's face, Matt began hurriedly to read. He was thankful that he knew the book so well that he was able to see when trouble might be coming. One of the first words Crusoe taught his man Friday was the word *master*. Luckily he caught that one in time. And it was true, Crusoe and his new companion did go about together, sharing their adventures. Only, Matt thought, it would have been better perhaps if Friday hadn't been quite so thickheaded. After all, there must have been a thing or two about that desert island that a native who had lived there all his life could have taught Robinson Crusoe.

When Matt closed the book, Attean nodded. Then, as so many times before, he took Matt by surprise.

"You like go fish?" he asked.

"I sure would," Matt said gratefully.

Stopping to pick up his fish pole from beside the door, he ran to overtake the Indian boy, who strode ahead. He knew his grin was stretching from one ear to the other, but he couldn't hide his feelings as Attean did.

They walked some distance, Matt managing to keep pace with the Indian's swift stride, determined not to let Attean know that his ankle was aching. They seemed to be following no particular trail. Finally they came out on a part of the creek that Matt had not seen before. It was shallow here, studded with rocks and pebbles, so that the water, rippling over them, made little rapids or collected in quiet pools. Here Attean stopped, broke off a sapling, and instead of making a fish pole, drew his knife from his pouch and quickly shaved a sharp point, making a spear. Then he stepped gently into the stream. Matt stood watching.

Attean stood motionless, peering intently into a pool of clear water. All at once he stooped, darted his spear with one quick stroke, and came up with a glittering fish. He studied it for a moment. "Too small," he decided. To Matt's astonishment he spoke to the fish quite solemnly, a few incomprehensible words, then tossed it back into the stream. In a few moments he had speared another, which he judged large enough to keep.

"Do same," he ordered now, coming back to the bank. He handed Matt the spear.

He would just look ridiculous, Matt knew before he started. He waded in and stood up to his knees, looking down into the sliding water. Presently a fish darted past. At least he thought it was a fish. It was hard to tell which was shadow and which might be a fish. At any rate, it was gone before he got his spear into the water. Presently he saw another, this one quite definitely a fish, calmly drifting in the pool. He jabbed at it hopelessly. He was sure his stick actually touched the slippery thing. He lunged at it, lost his footing, and went down with a splash that would scare off any fish for miles around. When he came up dripping, he saw Attean watching him with a horrid grin.

Suddenly he felt hot, in spite of the icy water. Why had Attean brought him out here, anyway? Had Attean just wanted to show off his own cleverness, and to make

Matt look more clumsy than ever? Was this Attean's answer, in case Matt had any idea in his head about being a Robinson Crusoe? For a moment Matt glared back at Attean with a scowl as black as any Indian's. Then he wiped his nose with the back of his hand and sloshed back to the bank. He snatched up his own pole and line. He poked about under the wet leaves and found a good, juicy worm and fitted it to his hook.

"I'll do it my own way," he said. "I can catch plenty of fish with this, and that's what matters."

Attean sat on the bank and watched. To Matt's satisfaction, in no time there was a tug on the line, a strong one. An impressive-looking fish rose to the surface, thrashing fiercely. Matt gave a jerk, and the line came swinging out of the water so suddenly that he almost lost his footing again. It was empty.

"Fish broke line," Attean observed.

As if anyone couldn't see that! Furious at Attean, at the fish, and at himself, Matt examined the break, unable to face the Indian. He had lost more than a good fish. His hook had disappeared as well. The only hook he had.

Of course Attean noticed. Those black eyes never missed anything. "Make new hook," he suggested.

Without even getting to his feet, he reached out and broke a twig off a maple sapling. Out came the crooked knife again. In a few strokes he cut a piece as long as his little finger, carved a groove around the middle, and whittled both ends into sharp points. Now he stepped into the water and tied Matt's line expertly around the groove.

"Put on two worms," he said. "Cover up all hook."

He didn't offer to find the worms. Matt had lost all interest in fishing. He knew that somehow or other he would just provide more amusement for Attean. But he couldn't refuse.

He didn't have to wait long before another fish caught hold. This time he landed it neatly.

"Good," said Attean from the bank. "Big."

Matt was trying to get it off the line. "He swallowed the whole hook," he said.

"Better white man's hook," Attean said. "Turn around inside fish. Not get away."

Back on the bank Matt slit the fish and extracted the hook and his line. But the thin twig had broken in half.

"Easy make new hook," Attean said. "Make many hooks."

Of course. Looking down at the simple thing in his hand, Matt realized that he never again need worry about losing a hook. He could make a new one wherever he happened to be. It was another necessary thing that Attean had shown him, just as he had made the snare. He wasn't sure why Attean had bothered. But grudgingly he had to admit that Attean had proved to him once again that he didn't always have to depend on white man's tools.

All at once he was hungry. The sun was straight overhead, and it would be a long tramp back through the woods before he could cook his fish. Now he saw that Attean had the same thought.

The Indian was heaping up a small pile of pine needles and grass. He drew from his muskrat-skin pouch a piece of hard stone with bits of quartz embedded in it. Striking it with his knife, he soon had a spark, which he blew into a flame.

I could have done that myself, Matt thought. In fact he had done it many a time, but he had not realized that he could use a common stone as well as his flint.

He soon had a spark.

"Get fish ready," Attean ordered now, pointing to the two fish on the bank. Matt did not like his masterful tone, but he did as he was told. By the time he had the two fish split and gutted and washed in the creek, Attean had a fire blazing. Matt was curious to see how he would go about the cooking.

He watched as Attean cut two short branches, bending them first to make sure they were green. He trimmed and sharpened them rapidly. Then he thrust a pointed end into each fish from head to tail. A small green stick was set crosswise inside the fish to hold the sides apart. He handed one stick to Matt. One on each side of the fire, the two boys squatted and held their sticks to the blaze. From time to time Attean fed the fire with dry twigs. When the flesh was crisp and brown, they ate, still silently.

Matt licked his fingers. His resentment had vanished along with his hunger. "Golly," he said, "that was the best fish I ever ate."

"Good," said Attean. Across the fire he looked at Matt, and his eyes gleamed. He was laughing again, but somehow not with scorn.

"What did you say to that fish you threw back?" Matt was still curious.

"I say to him not to tell other fish," Attean said seriously. "Not scare away."

"You actually think a fish could understand?"

Attean shrugged. "Fish know many thing," he replied.

Matt sat pondering this strange idea. "Well, it seemed to work," he said finally. "At least the other fish came along."

A wide grin spread slowly across Attean's face. It was the first time Matt had seen him smile.

Matt may have thought that things had finally quieted down, but that was before he and Attean found an angry mother bear protecting her cubs. Through their tangle with the bear, Matt becomes involved in Attean's world and the life of the Beaver clan. You will want to discover what happens when the snows come and Attean's people must leave for other hunting grounds. Matt's parents are still not at the cabin. Matt, knowing that his ability to survive alone in the winter is doubtful, must still make the difficult decision of whether to leave with Attean or stay behind to await his parents. What would you decide if you were Matt?

Meet the Author: **Elizabeth George Speare**

Elizabeth George Speare tried to follow other people's advice when they warned her that good writers write only about what they really know. She tried writing about family memories, her children and their daily lives, but it didn't work. When, by chance, she discovered some fascinating historical records about a young, colonial New England woman, Speare found herself absorbed in a past that soon became as real to her as her own life. For Speare, it was almost like living a double life—spending her days by filling in the details of the life of her heroine and her evenings by sharing what she had discovered with her own family. The past was very real.

Speare did not live in colonial times, but she has lived in New England all her life. Her settings are places she has visited since she was a child. She has made her writing career an adventure in discovering the houses, the food, the clothing, and the subjects which filled the lives of the people she writes about. Speare's curiosity and imagination help a reader span the distance between a historical world that reaches across centuries to the present.

Elizabeth George Speare has won awards for her excellent contributions to literature and to historical fiction. You may enjoy reading her other outstanding books, *Calico Captive*, *The Bronze Bow*, and *The Witch of Blackbird Pond*.

Responding to Literature

1. *Robinson Crusoe* was published in 1719 and is still read and enjoyed today. Do you think *The Sign of the Beaver* will stand the test of time? Three hundred years from now, will young people still read it and enjoy it? Give reasons for your answer.

2. Saknis does not see Attean and Matt together for many weeks. Imagine that Saknis appears and asks the boys to tell him what has been happening. Take the part of either Matt or Attean. Explain to Saknis the most important things that have happened.

3. At the beginning of the selection, Attean's anger is so explosive it seems he can hardly stand being in the same room with Matt. By the end of the selection, the two boys are able to finally smile at each other. What do Matt and Attean learn about each other?

4. Elizabeth Speare is careful to include details that let you feel you are in the wilderness in 1780. What are four of those details from the selection that help you feel you are in that time and place?

5. It is said that if you give a person a fish, he may have a wonderful meal. If you teach a person *how* to fish, he will be able to eat for a lifetime. How does that saying apply to Matt and his ability to survive in the wilderness?

Direction

I was directed by my grandfather
To the East,
    so I might have the power of the bear;
To the South,
    so I might have the courage of the eagle;
To the West,
    so I might have the wisdom of the owl;
To the North,
    so I might have the craftiness of the fox;
To the Earth,
    so I might receive her fruit;
To the Sky,
    so I might lead a life of innocence.

Alonzo Lopez

Appreciating Author's Craft

Thinking About Character Conflict

When two stubborn characters are forced against their will to spend time together, there is conflict. Conflict is the struggle or clash between two opposing forces—in this case, two boys who have grown up in different cultures.

Speare shows you, not directly, but in a series of incidents, the conflict in the boys' relationship. Throughout the incidents, the tension remains. When Matt first tries to teach Attean the letter *A,* for example, Speare describes the tension this way:

> "This is the first letter," he explained. "*A. A* for *arm.*"
> He repeated this several times, pointing to his own arm. Attean kept to his stubborn, scornful silence. Matt set his jaw. He could be stubborn too, he decided.

The conflict between characters is important in a good story. Because Speare portrays the conflict so realistically, you may wonder if the boys will ever get along together.

Writing About Character Conflict

To illustrate character conflict, you can write a journal entry for Matt and for Attean giving their thoughts, facts, and ideas about the same incident. (For ideas about writing, look at The Writer's Handbook.)

Prewriting The chart shows one incident that led to conflict between Matt and Attean. Copy the chart and add two more examples.

Incident→Conflict	Matt's reaction	Attean's reaction
Matt makes traps to show to Attean	hopes for a sign of approval	grunts and shrugs

To begin work on your journal entries, review your chart. Then make up a new incident and decide what the characters would think, feel, notice, and how they would act. For example, suppose Matt and Attean are caught in a blizzard. How would each boy react to it? Add this information to your chart.

Writing Use the information you have added to the chart and write a journal entry for each boy, showing character conflict. The journal entries should be about the same incident, but one journal should present it from Matt's point of view and the other from Attean's point of view. Each journal entry should be two to three paragraphs. Date each entry.

Revising Read your draft to a partner and discuss how well the conflict is developed. Then revise your draft. Make changes so the conflict is strong. Then write your final copy.

Presenting Read your journal entries to your class, keeping the identity of each character a secret. See if your class can figure out whose journal the entry was from.

Extending Your Reading

Expressing Yourself

Choose one or more of these activities:

Do a Mime The author writes with such precise detail, you can figure out exactly how to do some of the things Matt and Attean do. Choose one of the examples of the skills Matt learns from Attean, such as making a fishhook or a snare. Work with a partner so that one of you reads the description and the other mimes the activity.

Conduct an Awards Ceremony Would you call *The Sign of the Beaver* a good example of historical fiction? Prepare a speech to recommend *The Sign of the Beaver* for a historical fiction award. If you decide it doesn't deserve the award, tell why.

Draw a Book Jacket Imagine that, like Matt, you are going off into the wilderness. You may choose only two books to take with you. What would they be? Draw book jackets for them and tell the class why you made those choices.

Present a Choral Reading Read the poem aloud on page 327 and think of how it applies to Attean. Then form a group and prepare a choral reading of the poem. Present the reading for your class.

More Books with Historical Settings

Constance: a Story of Early Plymouth by Patricia Clapp.
Lothrop. Teenaged Constance Hopkins, in a diary
spanning six years, tells about growing up among the first
settlers of the Plymouth Colony.

The Witch of Blackbird Pond by Elizabeth George Speare.
Houghton Mifflin. Kit Tyler finds more excitement than she
bargained for when she settles in what she regards as a
drab Connecticut town.

Tree of Freedom by Rebecca Caudill. Viking. A pioneer
family moves to Kentucky during the time of the
Revolutionary War. The author creates a memorable
portrait of their courage and spirit.

The Fair American by Elizabeth Coatsworth. Macmillan.
In 1789 Pierre escapes from France but not from the
dangers of the French Revolution. Scary sea adventures
await him and two young friends on a journey to America.

Young Fu of the Upper Yangtse by Elizabeth Foreman Lewis.
Holt. Thirteen-year-old Young Fu has much to explore when
he leaves his small town in the 1930s to become an
apprentice coppersmith in a big city.

HE PEOPLE COULD FLY

American Black Folktales
told by Virginia Hamilton
Illustrated by Leo and Diane Dillon

Introducing

THE PEOPLE COULD FLY

American Black Folktales

In the days before most people could read, they would gather at the end of the day and entertain each other by telling stories. The stories were more than entertainment; they were a way to pass on to others what was important in their lives. Down through the ages, many of these stories were "lost," or forgotten. Others, through the efforts of collectors such as author Virginia Hamilton, have come down to us as folktales, fables, myths, and legends. (For more about folktales, see your Handbook of Literary Terms.)

What It Meant to Be a Slave

In *The People Could Fly,* Virginia Hamilton collected the folktales told by American slaves during the time they were forbidden to read or write. Hamilton explains how the slaves expressed themselves through storytelling:

"Folktales take us back to the very beginnings of people's lives, to their hopes and their defeats. American black folktales originated with peoples, most of whom long ago were brought from Africa to this country against their will. These peoples were torn from their individual cultures as they left the past, their families and their social groups, and their languages and customs behind.

"The black peoples coming to America before the end of the Civil War entered as slaves, and they were separated and isolated by law because of their race. The African in

them was forcibly suppressed by the white slaveowners.
They were not supposed to speak their own languages. The
slaveowners made them speak American English but forbade
them to learn to read or write it. They were compelled to do
hard labor and exhorted never to run away. Alone and
helpless, the slaves lived under conditions as brutal as any
group of people has ever endured.

"It is amazing that the former Africans could ever smile and
laugh, let alone make up riddles and songs and jokes and
tell tales. As slaves, they were forced to live without
citizenship, without rights, as property—like horses and cows—
belonging to someone else. But no amount of hard labor
and suffering could suppress their powers of imagination."

The Theme of Freedom

Freedom may not be something you think about every day.
But if you suddenly lost it, you would probably realize that
freedom is as important to you as your life. This is the theme
of this collection of folktales. The events within the stories tell
of the attempts to gain that prize—freedom.

As you're reading these tales on your own, listen to the
"voice" of the storyteller and imagine how each story would
make you feel if you were a slave hearing the tale for the first
time.

THE PEOPLE COULD FLY

American Black Folktales

Carrying the Running-Aways

*N*ever had any idea of carryin the runnin-away slaves over the river. Even though I was right there on the plantation, right by that big river, it never got in my mind to do somethin like that. But one night the woman whose house I had gone courtin to said she knew a pretty girl wanted to cross the river and would I take her. Well, I met the girl and she was awful pretty. And soon the woman was tellin me how to get across, how to go, and when to leave.

Well, I had to think about it. But each day, that girl or the woman would come around, ask me would I row the girl across the river to a place called Ripley. Well, I finally said I would. And one night I went over to the woman's house. My owner trusted me and let me come and go as I pleased, long as I didn't try to read or write anythin. For writin and readin was forbidden to slaves.

Now, I had heard about the other side of the river from the other slaves. But I thought it was just like the side where we lived on the plantation. I thought there were slaves and masters over there, too, and overseers and rawhide whips they used on us. That's why I was so scared. I thought I'd land the girl over there and some overseer didn't know us would beat us for bein out at night. They could do that, you know.

Well, I did it. Oh, it was a long rowin time in the cold, with me worryin. But pretty soon I see a light way up high. Then I remembered the woman told me to watch for a light. Told me to row to the light, which is what I did. And when I got to it, there were two men. They reached down and grabbed the girl. Then one of the men took me by the arm. Said, "You about hungry?" And if he hadn't been holdin me, I would of fell out of that rowboat.

Well, that was my first trip. I was scared for a long time after that. But pretty soon I got over it, as other folks asked me to take them across the river. Two and three at a time, I'd take them. I got used to makin three or four trips every month.

Now it was funny. I never saw my passengers after that first girl. Because I took them on the nights when the moon was not showin, it was cloudy. And I always met them in the open or in a house with no light. So I never saw them, couldn't recognize them, and couldn't describe them. But I would say to them, "What you say?" And they would say the password. Sounded like "Menare." Seemed the word came from the Bible somewhere, but I don't know. And they would have to say that word before I took them across.

Well, there in Ripley was a man named Mr. Rankins, the rest was John, I think. He had a "station" there for escaping slaves. Ohio was a free state, I found out, so once they got across, Mr. Rankins would see to them. We went at night so we could continue back for more and to be sure no slave catchers would follow us there.

Mr. Rankins had a big light about thirty feet high up and it burned all night. It meant freedom for slaves if they could get to that bright flame.

I worked hard and almost got caught. I'd been rowin fugitives for almost four years. It was in 1863 and it was a night I carried twelve runnin-aways across the river to Mr. Rankins'. I stepped out of the boat back in Kentucky and they were after me. Don't know how they found out. But the slave catchers, didn't know them, were on my trail. I ran away from the plantation and all who I knew there. I lived in the fields and in the woods. Even in caves. Sometimes I slept up in the tree branches. Or in a hay pile. I couldn't get across the river now, it was watched so closely.

Finally, I did get across. Late one night me and my wife went. I had gone back to the plantation to get her. Mr. Rankins had him a bell by this time, along with the light. We were rowin and rowin. We could see the light and hear that bell, but it seemed we weren't gettin any closer. It took forever, it seemed. That was because we were so scared and it was so dark and we knew we could get caught and never get gone.

Well, we did get there. We pulled up there and went on to freedom. It was only a few months before all the slaves were freed.

We didn't stay on at Ripley. We went on to Detroit because I wasn't takin any chances. I have children and grandchildren now. Well, you know, the bigger ones don't care so much to hear about those times. But the little ones, well, they never get tired of hearin how their grandpa brought emancipation to loads of slaves he could touch and feel in the dark but never ever see.

Carrying the Running-Aways'' is a reality tale of freedom, a true slave narrative. The former slave who first told the tale was an actual person, Arnold Gragston, a slave in

Kentucky. His story of rowing runaways across the Ohio River represents thousands of such stories of escape to freedom.

The abolitionist who helped the runaways once they were across the river was John Rankin, a Presbyterian minister and a southerner who lived in Ripley, Ohio. The town is still there, situated on the great river. A rickety wood staircase leads up Liberty Hill from Ohio River bottom lands to the Underground "station" house of the Rankin family. From 1825 to 1865, more than two thousand slaves were sheltered at the house and guided on by the family. Today, the Rankin house is a State Memorial open to the public from April through October.

Another fugitive, Levi Perry, born a slave, crossed the Ohio River into freedom with his mother about 1854. They were rescued by John Rankin and were taken in and taken care of at the house with the light. Years later, every six months or so, Levi Perry would settle his ten children around him and he would begin: "Now listen, children. I want to tell you about slavery and how my mother and I ran away from it. So you'll know and never let it happen to you." This tale was told to me recently by my mother, Etta Belle Perry Hamilton, who is 92 years old and Levi Perry's oldest daughter.

Virginia Hamilton

Responding to Literature
The storyteller tells about being afraid to take his first runaway across the river to freedom. Yet, he spends almost four years helping many other slaves escape. Why do you think the storyteller continues to help the runaways before he and his wife finally cross the river to freedom?

The Talking Cooter

Say that Jim was a dreamer. He hoped someday to be a free man. But for now, he was a slave. Not far from the big house of the slaveowner was a pond. Jim liked to sit beside it and think. Someone had told him that animals used to talk. And Jim dreamed that someday some animal would talk to him and tell him how to get his freedom.

One day while Jim was right there by the pond, he spied a big cooter mud turtle at the edge of the water.

Jim picked up a pebble, threw it at the cooter, strikin him on his shell.

The cooter moved aside a little, stuck his head up, and said, "Don't do that again. Let's be frens. Would ya like to hear me play my fiddle?"

Jim was just shocked when the cooter spoke to him. He was most near to fallin over when the cooter took a teeny fiddle from under a stone and commenced to play it.

Jim sat there listenin and thought he just was dreamin. When he came out of his trance, the cooter had gone.

Then, every day, Jim walked over to the pond when his tasks were done. And each day, the cooter would greet him with, "Good mornin, fren. Do ya want to hear me play agin?"

And Jim had found his voice and his wits enough to say, "Yes, indeedy, I do. Good mornin to ya, too, Bruh Cooter."

343

And then the cooter played his fiddle, and he sang.

> *"Jim, you talk too much.*
> *Run along and find you freedom place."*

Now Jim was a dreamer, but he was a thinker, too. And he thought one day that if he let his owner meet the cooter, he might get his freedom that way. After all, a talkin cooter was a wonderful thing to hear. So Jim went on back to the plantation. He found the slaveowner, and he says, "Mas, I wanter tell you about this cooter down there at the pond."

"Well, what about it?" said the slaveowner.

"Mas," says Jim, "that cooter can talk. And he don't just talk. He taken out his fiddle and he play on it, pretty as you please."

"Oh, get out!" said the slaveowner. "You know that's not true."

"Tis too true," said Jim, as calm as he could. "He speak to me and play and sing for me nearly every day now."

The slaveowner had to laugh. "Well, then, Jim," he said, "if it's true, I'll give you your freedom. But if it's not true, I'm going to give you the worst whippin you ever had in your life."

"That's all right, Mas, I'll show you," said Jim. "I'll take you down there and you'll see for yourself."

So that's what Jim did. He took the slaveowner down to the pond. When they got there, there was no cooter to be seen.

"Huh," grunted the slaveowner. He had his whip in his hand and he snaked it good and hard, making a big, crackin sound.

"Good mornin," Jim said, loud, but not too loud. There was no answer. "Good mornin to ya, cooter," Jim said, a bit louder this time. No answer again.

"Well, I knew it," said the slaveowner. "Dang you, Jim, you fooled with me one time too many!" And he raised his whip to thrash Jim as hard as he could.

Just then, they heard music, a fiddle playin nearby. And right there the cooter came climbin out of the pond. He walked on his back legs and he had that fiddle tucked up under his chin like any ole fiddler. He was playin away on it, too.

"Good mornin," he said, and kept on playin. Then he commenced to sing:

> "Jim, I told you you talk too much.
> Run along find you freedom place."

Mebbe Jim did talk too much. But that was how he got his freedom.

The greatest dream or wish of the slave in the Southland was for freedom. Some of the slave tales show the slave indulging in a wish-fulfilling fantasy of gaining power over the owner and escaping from him. But it was rare that a slave won or was given freedom.

"The Talking Cooter" is one of many talking-animal tales with the motif of "the animal refuses to talk on demand." The talking animal is variously a talking turtle or tortoise or a talking mule. There are other variants, African versions, with talking skulls and bones.

Responding to Literature
How does fantasy play a part in Jim's gaining his freedom?

The People Could Fly

*T*hey say the people could fly. Say that long ago in Africa, some of the people knew magic. And they would walk up on the air like climbin up on a gate. And they flew like blackbirds over the fields. Black, shiny wings flappin against the blue up there.

Then, many of the people were captured for Slavery. The ones that could fly shed their wings. They couldn't take their wings across the water on the slave ships. Too crowded, don't you know.

The folks were full of misery, then. Got sick with the up and down of the sea. So they forgot about flyin when they could no longer breathe the sweet scent of Africa.

Say the people who could fly kept their power, although they shed their wings. They kept their secret magic in the land of slavery. They looked the same as the other people from Africa who had been coming over, who had dark skin. Say you couldn't tell anymore one who could fly from one who couldn't.

One such who could was an old man, call him Toby. And standin tall, yet afraid, was a young woman who once had wings. Call her Sarah. Now Sarah carried a babe tied to her back. She trembled to be so hard worked and scorned.

The slaves labored in the fields from sunup to sundown. The owner of the slaves callin himself their Master. Say he was a hard lump of clay. A hard, glinty coal. A hard rock pile, wouldn't be moved. His Overseer on horseback pointed out the slaves who were slowin down. So the one called Driver cracked his whip over the slow ones to make them move faster. That whip was a slice-open cut of pain. So they did move faster. Had to.

Sarah hoed and chopped the row as the babe on her back slept.

Say the child grew hungry. That babe started up bawling too loud. Sarah couldn't stop to feed it. Couldn't stop to soothe and quiet it down. She let it cry. She didn't want to. She had no heart to croon to it.

"Keep that thing quiet," called the Overseer. He pointed his finger at the babe. The woman scrunched low. The Driver cracked his whip across the babe anyhow. The babe hollered like any hurt child, and the woman fell to the earth.

The old man that was there, Toby, came and helped her to her feet.

"I must go soon," she told him.

"Soon," he said.

Sarah couldn't stand up straight any longer. She was too weak. The sun burned her face. The babe cried and cried, "Pity me, oh, pity me," say it sounded like. Sarah was so sad and starvin, she sat down in the row.

"Get up, you black cow," called the Overseer. He pointed his hand, and the Driver's whip snarled around Sarah's legs. Her sack dress tore into rags. Her legs bled onto the earth. She couldn't get up.

Toby was there where there was no one to help her and the babe.

"Now, before it's too late," panted Sarah. "Now, Father!"

"Yes, Daughter, the time is come," Toby answered. "Go, as you know how to go!"

He raised his arms, holding them out to her. *"Kum . . . yali, kum buba tambe,"* and more magic words, said so quickly, they sounded like whispers and sighs.

The young woman lifted one foot on the air. Then the other. She flew clumsily at first, with the child now held tightly in her arms. Then she felt the magic, the African mystery. Say she rose just as free as a bird. As light as a feather.

The Overseer rode after her, hollerin. Sarah flew over the fences. She flew over the woods. Tall trees could not snag her. Nor could the Overseer. She flew like an eagle now, until she was gone from sight. No one dared speak about it. Couldn't believe it. But it was, because they that was there saw that it was.

Say the next day was dead hot in the fields. A young man slave fell from the heat. The Driver come and whipped him. Toby come over and spoke words to the fallen one. The words of ancient Africa once heard are never remembered completely. The young man forgot them as soon as he heard them. They went way inside him. He got up and rolled over on the air. He rode it awhile. And he flew away.

Another and another fell from the heat. Toby was there. He cried out to the fallen and reached his arms out to them. *"Kum kunka yali, kum . . . tambe!"* Whispers and sighs. And they too rose on the air. They rode the hot breezes. The ones flyin were black and shinin sticks, wheelin above the head of the Overseer. They crossed the rows, the fields, the fences, the streams, and were away.

"Seize the old man!" cried the Overseer. "I heard him say the magic *words.* Seize him!"

The one callin himself Master come runnin. The Driver got his whip ready to curl around old Toby and tie him up. The slaveowner took his hip gun from its place. He meant to kill old, black Toby.

But Toby just laughed. Say he threw back his head and said, "Hee, hee! Don't you know who I am? Don't you know some

of us in this field?" He said it to their faces. "We are ones who fly!"

And he sighed the ancient words that were a dark promise. He said them all around to the others in the field under the whip, ". . . *buba yali . . . buba tambe. . . .*"

There was a great outcryin. The bent backs straightened up. Old and young who were called slaves and could fly joined hands. Say like they would ring-sing. But they didn't shuffle in a circle. They didn't sing. They rose on the air. They flew in a flock that was black against the heavenly blue. Black crows or black shadows. It didn't matter, they went so high. Way above the plantation, way over the slavery land. Say they flew away to *Free-dom.*

And the old man, old Toby, flew behind them, takin care of them. He wasn't cryin. He wasn't laughin. He was the seer. His gaze fell on the plantation where the slaves who could not fly waited.

"Take us with you!" Their looks spoke it but they were afraid to shout it. Toby couldn't take them with him. Hadn't the time to teach them to fly. They must wait for a chance to run.

"Goodie-bye!" The old man called Toby spoke to them, poor souls! And he was flyin gone.

So they say. The Overseer told it. The one called Master said it was a lie, a trick of the light. The Driver kept his mouth shut.

The slaves who could not fly told about the people who could fly to their children. When they were free. When they sat close before the fire in the free land, they told it. They did so love firelight and *Free-dom* and tellin.

They say that the children of the ones who could not fly told their children. And now, me, I have told it to you.

*T*he People Could Fly" is one of the most extraordinary, moving tales in black folklore. It almost makes us believe that the people *could* fly. There are numerous separate accounts of flying Africans and slaves in the black folktale literature. Such accounts are often combined with tales of slaves disappearing. A plausible explanation might be the slaves running away from slavery, slipping away while in the fields or under cover of darkness. In code language murmured from one slave to another, "Come fly away!" might have been the words used. Another explanation is the wish-fulfillment motif.

The magic hoe variant is often combined with the flying-African tale. A magic hoe is left still hoeing in an empty field after all the slaves have flown away. Magic with the hoe and other farm tools, and the power of disappearing, are often attributed to Gullah (Angolan) African slaves. Angolan slaves were thought by other slaves to have exceptional powers.

"The People Could Fly" is a detailed fantasy tale of suffering, of magic power exerted against the so-called Master and his underlings. Finally, it is a powerful testament to the millions of slaves who never had the opportunity to "fly" away. They remained slaves, as did their children. "The People Could Fly" was first told and retold by those who had only their imaginations to set them free.

Meet the Author: **Virginia Hamilton**

Virginia Hamilton's background provided the interest and authenticity for the folktales in this section. When her grandfather was a child, he and his mother became runaway slaves before the end of the Civil War and Emancipation. They settled in Yellow Springs, Ohio, which is located about seventy miles from the Ohio River and one of the most well-known stations in the Underground Railroad.

The youngest of five children, Hamilton talks about growing up in Yellow Springs, Ohio, surrounded by cousins, aunts, and uncles. "My mother's 'people' were . . . fond of telling tales and gossip about one another and even their ancestors. They were part of me from the time I understood that I belonged to all of them. My Uncle King told the best tall tales; my Aunt Leanna sang the finest sorrowful songs. My own mother could take a slice of fiction floating around the family and polish it into a saga. So could my father."

Hamilton received the Coretta Scott King Award in 1983 for *Sweet Whispers, Brother Rush,* which also received the John Newbery Honor Book, the Boston Globe—Horn Book and the Lewis Carroll Shelf Awards. In 1975, Virginia Hamilton became the first black author to receive the John Newbery Medal for her portrayal of a black teenager in *M. C. Higgins, the Great.*

RESPONDING TO LITERATURE

1. Think back over the characters you read about in each folktale. Try to remember the qualities you admired, such as courage or cleverness. What have these tales told you about black slaves in America that you didn't know before?

2. You have been chosen as class storyteller. Choose your favorite tale from *The People Could Fly* and tell it to your class. Ask your listeners if you have left anything out.

3. Imagine that you are a slave who is frightened into believing that there is no way, other than death, that your life will ever change. If you were hearing these tales for the first time, how would they make you feel about gaining freedom?

4. Folktales are stories created by common people and passed down by word of mouth. Why is it important to people today that folktales are collected and written down?

5. Virginia Hamilton has added notes after each folktale. For example, she tells that "Come fly away!" might have been a code language for slaves slipping away from slavery. What else did you learn from these notes that you didn't know before?

6. Think about the two poems you read on pages 355 and 356. How do they relate to the stories in this section?

Cross over the River

harriet tubman
coming down the river
black face
reflected in the water

harriet tubman
in a gunboat
singing

slaves on the shore
singing
there is a home
somewhere

Sam Cornish

Aunt Sue's Stories

Aunt Sue has a head full of stories.
Aunt Sue has a whole heart full of stories.
Summer nights on the front porch
Aunt Sue cuddles a brown-faced child to her bosom
And tells him stories.

Black slaves
Working in the hot sun,
And black slaves
Walking in the dewy night,
And black slaves
Singing sorrow songs on the banks of a mighty river
Mingle themselves softly
In the flow of old Aunt Sue's voice,
Mingle themselves softly
In the dark shadows that cross and recross
Aunt Sue's stories.

And the dark-faced child, listening,
Knows that Aunt Sue's stories are real stories.
He knows that Aunt Sue never got her stories
Out of any book at all,
But that they came
Right out of her own life.

The dark-faced child is quiet
Of a summer night
Listening to Aunt Sue's stories.

Langston Hughes

Appreciating Author's Craft

Thinking About Theme

There are probably times when you've wished that you could stay home from school, stay up as late as you like, and get up when you feel like it. Having the freedom to do what you want to do is the underlying meaning of each of these different wishes. In literature, the underlying meaning is called the theme. The theme of a story is not always stated in a sentence. The theme can be figured out by thinking about the goals of the characters, the events and actions in which the characters try to reach their goals, and the final outcome, which tells whether or not these goals are reached.

The author, Virginia Hamilton, has retold three folktales in which the theme is freedom. The goal of the characters is to be free. Their efforts and actions to gain freedom are different and usually very imaginative because gaining freedom seems so hopeless. For example, in "The Talking Cooter," Jim imagines a turtle that talks and plays the fiddle. Virginia Hamilton writes:

"Now Jim was a dreamer, but he was a thinker, too. And he thought one day that if he let his owner meet the cooter, he might get his freedom that way. After all, a talkin cooter was a wonderful thing to hear."

Writing About Theme

You can write your own tale in which you create an imaginative way to gain your freedom. For ideas about writing, look at The Writer's Handbook.

Prewriting To get started on your tale, copy the list below and complete it by identifying the imaginative way used in each tale as a method to achieve freedom.

Carrying the Running-Aways
escaping
_____

The Talking Cooter
_____

The People Could Fly
_____

Writing Imagine yourself in a situation from which you need to escape or be rescued, such as being trapped between floors in an elevator. Use the information on the list for ideas about how you can win your freedom. Then write a brief tale about how you get free. Explain the situation you are in, include your goal, how the goal can be achieved, and whether or not your goal is reached. Your tale should clearly illustrate the theme of freedom.

Revising Read your draft to a partner and discuss how clearly your theme of freedom is expressed. Make changes if you need to. Then proofread for errors and write your final copy.

Presenting Instead of reading your tale to your classmates, memorize it, wear a costume that suggests something about the situation in your tale, and present it as a storyteller.

EXTENDING YOUR READING

Expressing Yourself

Choose one or more of these activities:

Choreograph a Dance With a group of classmates, create an interpretive dance to tell the story of the selection called "The People Could Fly." Perform your dance in class. You may want to have your dance performed in silence, to the sound of drumming, or while someone reads the story.

Write a Poem In these selections, the people were "flying away" from slavery and "flying to" freedom. Ask some of your friends to tell you what they would like to fly from and to. Create a poem with several four-line stanzas. Start the first line of each stanza with "I'd fly away from," and the third line of each stanza with "I'd fly away to."

Make a Storyteller's Bag Write the names of some objects on slips of paper and put them in a paper bag. During a special class activity, pass the bag among your classmates who wish to participate and have them draw out the name of the object that they must use to tell a short story.

Put on a Play in the Dark Create a play describing the river crossings of one of the boats that were used to carry slaves to freedom in Ohio. Since the people in the boats could not see each other, you will have to put on your play in the dark, letting your words tell the story. For a special effect, use drumming sounds to stand for the sounds of the oars and of people's heartbeats.

More Books About Folklore

The Crest and the Hide by Harold Courlander. Coward, McCann & Geoghegan, Inc. All things are linked. If you kill all the frogs because their croaking keeps you awake at night, you will soon be overrun with mosquitoes and driven from your home. Here are twenty tales with messages for us from the Ashanti, Mensa, Swahili, Zulu, and other peoples of Africa.

Tales from Silver Lands by Charles J. Finger. Doubleday & Company, Inc. From the people of South America comes this collection of folktales inspired by tropical forests, high jagged mountains, and icy ocean depths. Read to find out why the hummingbird and the flamingo have such colorful feathers and what lies behind the wide wondering eyes of the seal.

The Magic Boat and Other Chinese Folk Stories by M. A. Jagendorf and Virginia Weng. Vanguard Press. There are over thirty brief, merry, wise, and witty folk stories from little-known ethnic regions of China in this book. Children turn into monkeys, women into waterfalls, and a man becomes a money tree. This is a magic passage to a mysterious land.

Someone Saw a Spider: Spider Facts and Folktales by Shirley Climo. Thomas Y. Crowell. Fascinating trivia is woven among the entertaining stories gathered from around the globe in the creepy collection. For instance, did you know that in real life, Little Miss Muffet's father, Dr. Thomas Muffet, told his patients to swallow spiders to cure illness? No wonder she was frightened away . . .

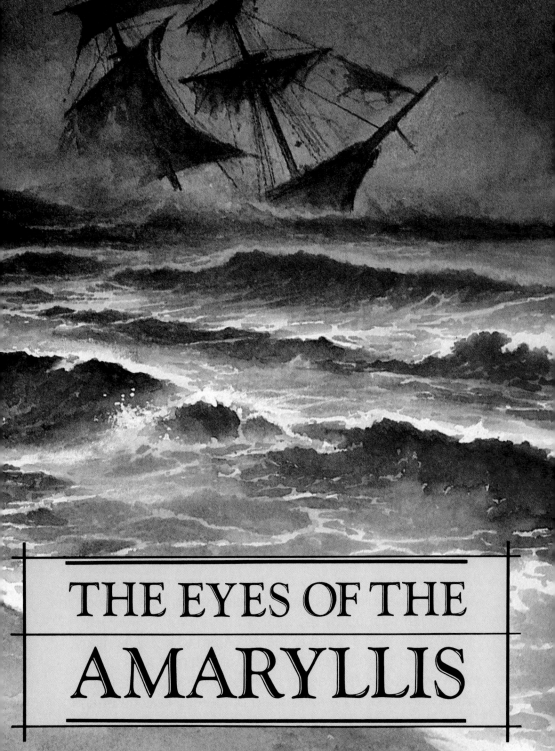

THE EYES OF THE
AMARYLLIS

by Natalie Babbitt

Introducing

THE EYES OF THE
AMARYLLIS

The ocean covers almost three-fourths of the earth's surface. It is so immense that you can sail on a ship for many days without seeing land. It is also very deep. In some areas, the bottom of the ocean lies more than six miles (ten kilometers) below the surface.

Very little is known about life in the sea and about the bottom of the sea. Each year, however, scientists are finding out more about the ocean's depths. Underwater cameras have now been able to photograph the sea creatures that live at the very bottom of the ocean.

Thinking About the Spell of the Sea

The sea casts a spell over everyone who sees it. A person can sit by the seashore, contented, just watching the waves roll up onto the shore. A walk on the beach can be exhilarating, also. You can find broken bits of shells, seaweed, pebbles, fish, and sometimes big logs of wood that have been cast up by the sea.

People who live close to the sea learn to know its many moods and learn to respect them. Sometimes the ocean is calm one day and a raging body of water the next. But whatever mood, a person has to be careful how he or she treats the ocean. The ocean is powerful and can easily claim your life.

The sea affects each person differently. In this story each character understands the sea in a different manner. George Read hates and fears the sea because it took his father's life. George's mother, Geneva Reade, understands and accepts the power of the sea, and has no fear. Young Geneva, or Jenny, as she is also known, looks at the sea for the first time and can "hear what the wind and sea are saying."

Thinking About Mood

Natalie Babbitt chooses her words carefully to convey the many moods of the sea. You can feel that you are there when Jenny sees the ocean for the first time. You know what it is like to walk on the beach. You can hear the sound of the waves. You are able to do this because of Natalie Babbitt's skillful choice of words. As you read the story, try to picture what the author has written for you.

As you're reading this novel on your own, find out how Jenny's visit to her Grandmother changes each member of the family.

THE EYES OF THE
AMARYLLIS

PROLOGUE
Seward's Warning

Listen, all you people lying lazy on the beach, is this what you imagine is the meaning of the sea? Oh, yes, it winks and sparkles as it sways beside you, spreading lacy foam along the sand, as dainty as a handkerchief. But can you really think that this is all it means? The foam, and these tender cowrie shells as pearly as a baby's toes? This purple featherweed floating up fine as the plume of an ostrich? That child in yellow, her face so grave beneath the brim of her linen hat? She sits there filling her bright tin bucket with those tiny shovelsful of sand, as cautious as a pharmacist measuring a dose, and watching her, you murmur to each other, "Sweet! How sweet!"

But listen. That is not the meaning of the sea. Less than a hundred and fifty years ago, on this very spot, out there where that row of rocky points thrusts up above the swells, a ship was lost. There, see? Where those herring gulls are wheeling down? It all looks much the same today: the rocks, and this beach that narrows to a pathway when the tide is in. But on that day at summer's end, the sky went dark, like twilight, with a shrieking wind, and the sea rose up tall as trees. Out there, where the gulls sit sunning now, it flung a ship against the rocks and swallowed her. It swallowed her whole, and every member of her crew. Captain, cargo, every inch of sail and rigging, gone in a single gulp, while the captain's wife stood helpless, watching. Up there, on that little bluff, that's where she stood, shrieking back at the wind, her son gone dumb with horror at her

side. And there was nothing to bury afterwards. Nothing. The sea had taken it all, and gave back not one plank or shred of canvas.

That is part of the meaning. But there's more. A little later, three months or four, a young man broke his heart over a foolish girl. Nothing to remark about in that, you think. But he was an artist, that young man. He had carved a figurehead for the Amaryllis, the ship that was swallowed, carved it in the likeness of the captain's wife—proud and handsome, with long red hair. Then he up and broke his heart over a foolish girl, and one morning very early, while the mist was still thick, he climbed into a dinghy and rowed himself straight out, out there well past the place where that sailboat skims along. He rowed out early in the morning, and he vanished. Oh, they found the dinghy later, just here, washed up, its oars stowed neat and dry inside. But he was not washed up, though they searched the shore for days. He was swallowed, they said at last, swallowed like the Amaryllis.

But he was not quite swallowed. Listen. That is the rest of the meaning of the sea. You lie here so unthinking—have you forgotten that the surface of the earth is three-fourths water? Those gulls out there, they know it better than you. The sea can swallow ships; and it can spit out whales upon the beach like watermelon seeds. It will take what it wants, and it will keep what it has taken, and you may not take away from it what it does not wish to give. Listen. No matter how old you grow or how important on the land, no matter how powerful or beautiful or rich, the sea does not care a straw for you. That frail grip you keep on the wisp of life that holds you upright— the sea can turn it loose in an instant. For life came first from the sea and

can be taken back. Listen. Your bodies, they are three-fourths water, like the surface of the earth. Ashes to ashes, the Bible says, and maybe so—but the ashes float on the water of you, like that purple featherweed floating on the tide. Even your tears are salt.

You do not listen. What if I told you that I was that carver of figureheads, the one they said was swallowed by the sea? The breeze in your ears, it carries my voice. But you only stretch on your fluffy towels and talk of present things, taking the sea for granted. So much the worse for you, then. My two Genevas listened, long ago, and understood.

1

"Well, Mother," said the big man uneasily, turning his hat round and round in his hands.

"Well, George," the old woman returned. Her voice was strong and brisk, but, for him, a little critical. She looked up at him from her wing chair by the sunny window and saw—her son, yes, but also a stranger, well into middle age, tall but stooped, with the pale skin and scratchy-looking clothes of an inland man of business. And she saw in him also what he had been: a happy, wild-haired boy running barefoot on the beach. The two were one and the same, no doubt, but she loved the man because she had loved the boy. For her, the boy had been much easier to love.

"So you've broken your ankle," the man said.

"So it seems," she answered. She looked down impatiently at her foot propped up on a hassock. It was thick with bandages and wooden splints, and beside it on the floor a crutch lay waiting. "It's a nuisance, but there you are. Where's my granddaughter? Where's my namesake?"

"She's out on the beach. She's—well, she's never seen the sea before, you know. I suppose she's . . . interested in having a look."

"Interested! Yes, I should imagine so." The old woman smiled faintly.

The man took a deep breath. "Look here, Mother, you know we've always wanted you to come and live with us in Springfield. Now that you're laid up and can't take care of yourself, it's a good time to leave this godforsaken place and come inland where we can look after you."

The old woman shook her head. "It's good of you, George, of course. But when I wrote to you, that wasn't what I had in mind at all. You've brought Geneva down to stay with me, haven't you? That was the plan, wasn't it? My ankle will mend, and when it does, I'll go on the same as I always have."

"I just don't understand it," her son exploded then. "All by yourself here, year after year! The sea pounding, day and night, the damp-ness, this blasted sand everywhere. And the wind! It never stops! I can hardly bear it for five minutes, and you've been listening to it for thirty years!"

"Fifty, George. You've forgotten. Your father and I, we came here fifty years ago."

"No, but I meant . . ."

"I know what you meant," she said. "You're thinking it's thirty years since the day your father was drowned."

The man gripped his hat more firmly. "All right, Mother, never mind that. Be sensible for once and come back with me. There's plenty of room for three in the buggy, and we can send a wagon later for your things. Surely you can't be so all-fired stubborn about it now, when you can scarcely hobble."

His mother shook her head again. "I don't need you, George. Not yet. It's not time yet. I'll come to you at Christmas, just as I've always done. But the rest of the year I belong right here. Geneva can take care of me till my ankle mends, and then you can come and fetch her."

"But, Mother!"

The old woman frowned at him and her eyes flashed. "George! Enough! We've had this argument a hundred times, and it bores me. You ran away from here a long time ago, and that's all right for you. But I will not budge an inch, not one inch, until . . ." She paused and looked away. Her anger seemed to leave her all at once, and she sighed. "George. Send Geneva in to me and then—go away, George. We only make each other cross."

At this the man seemed to sag a little. A look of pain crossed his face, and he turned half away from her, toward the door, though he watched her still. She was as handsome and vigorous as ever, her gray hair still streaked with red, her back straight as . . . a mast, he thought unwillingly, and then corrected it. Straight as a yardstick. A safer image.

She saw that he was watching her, and her face softened. "George. Dear boy, come and kiss me."

He went to her at once and knelt, and she put her arms around him and pulled him close. For a moment, the last long thirty years dissolved. They were mother and child again, she newly widowed, he newly fatherless, and they clung to each other. Then she loosened her hold and pushed him away gently. "Tell me," she said, smiling at him. "Geneva—what sort of child is she getting to be, do you think?"

"She's exactly like you," he said, sitting back on his heels.

The first Geneva Reade nodded and her eyes twinkled. "It's a

judgment on you, George. Well, send her in. And then go home to Springfield and leave me in peace."

The big man kissed his mother's cheek and stood up, putting on his hat. Then, at the door, he said carefully, "I should have thought, though, that you'd want to come away from this spot. I couldn't stand it, looking out there every day, remembering. I'd have gone mad by now."

"Mad?" said his mother. "Well, perhaps I am a little mad."

"Mother," he blurted then, turning back to her, "for the love of heaven, watch out for Jenny. She's all we've got. Don't let her—"

"Hang your clothes on a hickory limb, and don't go near the water," the old woman chanted, bobbing her head from side to side. And then she said, scornfully, "Don't worry. I'll keep her out of the sea. You weren't such a faintheart before your father died."

The man's face closed. "I'll be back in three weeks," he told her flatly. "To fetch Jenny home. And if you're not mended by then, you'll come and stay with us till you are, whether you want to or not."

"Goodbye, George," said his mother, dismissing him. "Have a pleasant ride home. We'll see you in a month or two."

"Three weeks, Mother. Not a moment longer."

"*Goodbye, George*," said the first Geneva Reade.

2

The journey that takes a traveler from inland places to the sea will
follow roads that stay, in themselves, exactly the same, but they seem
to change entirely. Carefree and busy, now leaf-shadowed, now blank
and blinding in the summer sunshine, they stretch ahead importantly
between green fields, and the air lies lightly on them. But by the time
they have come within three miles, then two, then one, of their
destination, they have turned submissive. The trees stand back and
stand thin, and scrub pines appear, ragged as molting birds. The
edges of the roads are lost now in drifts of sand, and the grass,
thinner, like the trees, is rough and tall, rising, kneeling, rising,
kneeling, as the breeze combs by.

There seems to be more sky here, a great deal more, so that the
traveler is made aware, perhaps for the first time, that he moves along
quite unprotected on the crust of the earth and might do well to move
with caution, lest all at once he fall off, fall up, endlessly, and
disappear. So he holds his gaze to the ground and finds that the air
has grown heavy with new, wet smells, and the roads and everything
around them look uncared-for. But this is not the case. They are
cared for with the closest attention—by the sea.

The second Geneva Reade had observed all this on the way to
Gran's house and was astonished by it in spite of the heavy presence
beside her in the buggy. Her father had not spoken a word for miles,
and he had allowed the horse to slow its pace to a clopping walk. His
clenched hands, wrapped in the reins, were white at the knuckles.
Jenny observed this, also, but she could not worry about it now. She

was going to see the ocean for the first time in her life.

To be away from home—to stay with Gran and help her while her ankle mended—this seemed a very grownup thing to do, and Jenny had boasted about it to her friends. But in truth she was a little alarmed about that part, though her grandmother, whom she had seen before only for the two weeks of the yearly Christmas season, had long been a figure of romance to her. Gran was not like other grandmothers, smelling of starch or mothballs, depending on the time of year, and spending their time watering their plants. Gran stood straight and proud. Her face and arms were sunburned. And though she talked and listened, there always seemed to be something else on her mind, something far more absorbing than Christmas conversation.

But Jenny did not care for household chores, and was not at all sure that somewhere in her lay hidden the makings of a bedside nurse. So it wasn't that part of her adventure that excited her. No, the real enticement was the ocean. But this she could not admit. She was the only one of her friends who had never been to the shore. Preposterous, when it was only thirty miles from Springfield! But her father had never let her come, had always refused to discuss it. He hardly ever went, himself, to see Gran at her house.

But now, because of Gran's ankle, all that had changed. She was going to see the ocean, and she had all she could do to keep from bouncing on the buggy's padded seat. When would the water show itself? Over the next rise? Now! The buggy started up—and then she

had gasped once and sat erect and very still.

For there it was, suddenly, the great Atlantic, so vast a thing that all of her imaginings could never have prepared her. It stretched away so far beyond the grassy plain that its sharp horizon curved to prove the roundness of the planet. In an instant she felt diminished, and with that new sensation came an unexpected sense of freedom. The breath she had caught and held slipped out in a long sigh, and she turned her head to see how her father was responding to the sight. But his face was rigid as a stone.

So she had turned back, and as the buggy rolled nearer, the coastline below them revealed itself slowly. A bay emerged and, far to the leftward tilt of its concavity, a tidy-looking town, with docks and the hulls of a few small ships. Then, as the buggy, reaching a fork, turned right, she saw that there were houses scattered all along the shore. Far to the right, however, they sat fewer and farther between until at last there was only one house, quite by itself, on a low bluff at the farthest edge of the bay, where the land curved slowly in and down and sank a heavy arm into the water.

"Is that Gran's house?" she had asked, pointing.

"Yes," said her father.

"That's where you lived when you were little?"

"Yes," he said shortly.

Her head filled at once with a thousand questions, but it was clear that he didn't want to talk. "I can ask Gran," she had thought to herself. "Later."

When the buggy rolled down and stopped at last beside the house, Jenny had climbed out slowly, her eyes turned to the beach. "Can I go and look?" she pleaded. "Before I go in to see Gran?"

"All right, I guess so," her father said. "But, Jenny, remember what I told you. Stay back from the water. Don't ever forget that it's dangerous." And then, taking down her satchel, he had gone to the door of the house, knocked once, and stepped inside.

The sea did not look dangerous. Jenny saw the whole of its low-tide shore behavior in one long glance—how it tipped and slopped, sifting the wet sand, stroking the beach with sliding foam. Well up on this beach, a straggling fringe of seaweed, like a scratchy penline, lay drying where the last high tide had stranded it, and here, too, intermingled, had been left abandoned pebbles by the million and broken bits of shell. Above the seaweed the toast-colored sand was loose and warm, and she longed to take off her shoes and stockings and dig her toes into it. Not now. Later. After her father had gone. Gran had promised her that if she, Jenny, were ever allowed to visit here, there would be much to do on the beach, things that could only be done correctly if one were barefoot.

Jenny took a cautious step over the seaweed line, down to where the sand was hard and wet, and at once a sly finger of foam slid up and curled around her ankle. She leapt back and the foam slipped away with a sigh, to be lost beneath the curl of the next small wave. Now new fingers of foam reached for her up the sand, and she retreated behind the seaweed reluctantly. Another wave, a soft thump, the

slide of foam, repeated over and over again. She watched it, amazed and faintly hypnotized, and the feeling of freedom that had come to her at first grew deeper. Wisps of her dark red hair, tied back so neatly at home by her mother blew about her face as the breeze swept past her, and suddenly it seemed as if she could hear it speaking. *True to yo-o-o-ou*, it whispered, and the foam answered: *Yes-s-s* (thump) *yes-s-s* (thump) *yes-s-s*.

"Jenny!"

She heard her father's voice behind her and, turning, plodded up across the sand to where he stood at the edge of the swaying grass.

"Jenny, look at you. You've soaked one foot already," he said despairingly. "Will you promise to stay safe, now? Will you be careful? I've kept you away from this place as long as I could, and—I know you're nearly grown, but still, it worries me to death to leave you here."

"I'll be careful, Papa," she said.

He put his hands on her shoulders and peered into her face, and then, dropping his hands, he shrugged. "Well, do your best to be useful to your grandmother. It's remarkable how she never seems to change, but still, she's getting on. You'll see. She's waiting for you—better go on in. I'll be back in three weeks."

"All right, Papa."

He left her, then, and climbed into the buggy, and as he urged the horse into a turn, she saw the stiffness of his shoulders ease, and he looked back at her almost cheerfully. "Goodbye!" he called.

She answered, "Goodbye," and added, to herself, "He's happy to be leaving." She watched him go and felt stranded and lonely, like the pebbles, but then she turned back for one more look at the sea and the lonely feeling fled away. For it seemed as if she had known this beach and loved it all her life, that she belonged here; that coming to this place, with its endless sky and water, was a kind of coming home.

3

"Quick, child, come and tell me," said Gran from her chair when Jenny went inside. "What did you find on the beach? Anything unusual?" And then she caught herself. "Dear me, listen to the old lady, ranting on without even saying hello." She held out her arms and Jenny went to her and gave her a hug of greeting.

"Well!" said Gran. "So here you are at last! Let me look at you." She sat back, folding her arms, and tilted her head solemnly. "Your father says you're just like me, and I know he thinks I'm stubborn and unreasonable. Are you?"

"I don't know," said Jenny, laughing. "I guess so, sometimes."

"You've still got my red hair," Gran observed, "but otherwise you've changed a little since Christmas. How old are you now?"

"Eleven," said Jenny. "Last February."

"Yes, and now it's the middle of August," said Gran. "So you're halfway to twelve. Not a child at all, really, though you mustn't expect me to stop calling you a child. I have a hard time remembering new things, sometimes. But I can remember the old things as if they happened yesterday. I met your grandfather for the first time when I was thirteen. Imagine that! He was twenty-one, and as handsome . . . well, as handsome as a walrus."

"A walrus!" said Jenny, laughing again. "Walruses aren't handsome."

"Well, now, that's a matter of taste," said Gran with a smile. "Your grandfather was a big man, heavyset, with a fine, big pair of mustaches. To me he was wonderfully handsome, and I fell in love with

him at once."

"When you were thirteen?"

"Yes, indeed."

"I'm not in love with anyone," said Jenny, "and no one's in love with me."

"Someone will be, someday," said Gran.

"Oh, no," said Jenny. "I don't expect it. I'm much too ugly."

"Ugly!" Gran exclaimed, throwing up a hand in mock dismay. "But, child, how can you be ugly when you look so much like me? Your grandfather fell in love with me, remember."

"When you were thirteen?"

"Oh, no, certainly not," said Gran. "Years later. He was a sailor— well, you know that, of course—and when he wasn't on a voyage he would come to Springfield to visit his sister. Your Great-aunt Jane. It was ten years later, when I was twenty-three and he was thirty-one— that's when he noticed me. Two years after that he had his own ship, and we were married and came to live right here, in this house." She looked about her with satisfaction at the tidy, low-ceilinged room with its simple chairs and tables, and its mantel full of odd bits of china. "Then—let's see. Your father was born six years after that, in the spring of '36, and then when he was fourteen, that's when the *Amaryllis* was . . . lost. Out there on the rocks in a terrible storm." She said this calmly enough, tipping her head to indicate the stretch of sea outside the window behind her, but a look of intensity came to her face and she leaned forward and put a hand on Jenny's arm. "You

went down to the beach just now?"

"Yes," said Jenny.

"Did you see anything? Anything at all?"

"Well," said Jenny, "I saw sand, and pebbles, and some long, stringy-looking weeds, and—the ocean, Gran! Oh, it's wonderful! It makes me feel . . ."

"Free!" said Gran triumphantly.

"Yes, that's it exactly," said Jenny, surprised. "How did you know?"

"How did I know?" said Gran. "What a question! It keeps me strong, that sense of freedom. And yet your father doesn't seem to feel it at all. Isn't that peculiar! But, child, was there nothing unusual on the beach? Nothing washed up?"

"What sort of thing?" asked Jenny, puzzled by the urgency in her grandmother's voice. "What are you looking for?"

"Never mind," said Gran, turning away from it. "Plenty of time for that later. Hand me the almanac on that table over there. I'll check the tides and then we'll have supper. Yes. Thank you, my dear. Now, let me see . . . here we are." She ran a fingertip down the page. "I thought so. High tide at 12:15 tonight. Good. Well! Now for supper."

"What shall I cook?" asked Jenny nervously. This was the part she had dreaded.

But Gran said, mercifully, "Cook? Why, nothing at all! What an idea!" She bent and picked up the crutch, and then, pulling herself up onto her good leg, she stood tall and straight and glared at her

granddaughter. "I'm not an invalid, you know. And I don't intend to sit here and be fussed over. I shall do the cooking."

"But, Gran, I thought—"

"Never mind what you thought. Follow me. You can set the table, and fetch and carry now and then, but that's not why I sent for you."

Jenny tried hard to disguise her relief, but Gran, looking at her narrowly, recognized it anyway. "You don't like to cook?"

"No," said Jenny. "Not very much."

"Neither do I," said Gran. "We shall do as little of it as we possibly can without starving. Come along."

In the dining room, over the mantel, hung a drawing of a ship. "That's the *Amaryllis*," said Gran as they sat down to eat. "A brig, she was, a big two-master. A beautiful thing to see. Your grandfather owned her, and he was her captain, too. He sailed her up and down the coast from Maine to the Caribbean."

"Did you ever go along?" asked Jenny.

"No, I never did. Women aren't welcome on trading ships, you know, and anyway, I had your father to care for. No, I stayed right here. And yet in a way I did go along. Look more closely there. Do you see the figurehead? Go and look."

Jenny got up from her chair and went to peer at the picture. "It's a woman," she reported, "and she's holding some kind of flower in her hands."

"It's a likeness of me," said Gran proudly. "That's an amaryllis I'm holding. A big red lily from the islands. Your grandfather thought they were very handsome, and he always said they reminded him of me. A romantic notion, but that's the way he was. So he named the ship after them, and put me on the prow. He tried time and again to bring me one—an amaryllis—but they always died on the way. Sometimes he'd be gone for months at a time, you see. It's a long way down to the islands."

"You couldn't have had much time with him," said Jenny, coming back to the table. "If he was gone so much. Weren't you lonely?"

"One gets used to it," said Gran. "But when the *Amaryllis* was due, I would go out to the bluff there and watch for it, and then we'd have such lovely parties when he was home again."

"My father comes home at the same time every day," said Jenny. "Five-thirty, when he's closed up the store."

"I know," said Gran, without interest. "It sounds very dull."

Jenny thought so, too, now. It seemed unbearably dull. But she added, in unconscious imitation, "Still, one gets used to it."

"I suppose so," said Gran.

Supper was nearly over when suddenly Gran put down her fork. She lifted her head, holding out a hand in a signal for silence. "Shh!" she whispered. "There! Do you hear it?"

Jenny listened. Nothing came to her ears but the breeze and the

slap of waves. She looked at Gran questioningly. "What? What should I hear?"

"The tide," said Gran. "It's turned." She stared at Jenny and her eyes were blank, as if she'd forgotten for an instant that she was not alone. Then she was herself again, but with a difference. Something in her concentration had shifted, some inner curtain dropping while another opened. "Finish your supper," she said. "Then we'll clear away and go out to the beach."

4

Leaning on her crutch, with Jenny at her other side to steady her, Gran stumped across the swaying grass to the little bluff that thrust out before the house. On three sides of it, the land dropped steeply four feet or so to the beach, so that it formed a small point, and here there was an old wooden bench. Gran eased herself down onto it and settled her bundled ankle out in front of her with a grimace of pain.

"You shouldn't go about on it so much," said Jenny.

"I have a doctor to tell me what to do," said Gran indifferently. "And if I don't pay attention to him, what makes you think I'll pay attention to you? Now, be a good child and sit here beside me. It will be dark soon. We've only an hour before bedtime, and I want to talk to you."

Jenny sat down and waited, but Gran was silent, leaning forward, staring out to sea. The sun, dropping rapidly behind them, seemed to be drawing the daylight with it like a veil, revealing behind the blue, as it slid away, the endlessness of space. A star appeared, and before them the green-brown waves took on an iridescence and spilled a sort of glow along the sand.

"At this time of day," said Gran at last, "it looks different. There almost seems to be a light . . . coming up from the bottom."

Jenny had to lean close to hear her grandmother's words, for the breeze had quickened and was whispering again in her ears. "The wind almost talks, doesn't it?" she said shyly.

Gran, at this, turned and looked at her closely. "So you hear it, too? Good. I was hoping for it. Give me your hand."

Gran's sun-browned hand was dry and strong, hard in spite of the rumpled skin at her wrist and knuckles. But her long fingers, holding Jenny's, were trembling slightly. Jenny looked down and saw how different this hand was from her mother's, so soft and padded and white. "It's important to look after your hands," her mother always said. "A lady doesn't go about with ragged fingernails, dear, and get her skin all chapped. You must learn to take more care. Your hands look so . . . *used*, Jenny. Like a boy's." Now Jenny saw that her hands were like Gran's, and for the first time she was proud of them. Oh, they were younger, to be sure. But very like.

"Pay close attention, Geneva," said Gran. "There's very little time. We must go to bed soon, and sleep, if we're to be fresh again by midnight."

"Midnight?" Jenny echoed.

"Certainly," said Gran. "We must be up again at midnight."

"But why?"

"High tide, child," said Gran, and then she stiffened.

"Hist! Look there."

Jenny, startled, turned her head in the direction of Gran's gaze, and saw the figure of a man trudging slowly toward them along the shadowed beach. It was impossible to see his features, for his head was bowed, but Jenny could tell that he was rather small and hunched. He wore a dark, short coat of some heavy material, and his hands were plunged deep into his pockets. Then, as he came abreast of them, below the little bluff, he halted and looked up, and in the last

gleam of daylight, Jenny saw a bearded face, ruined and rutted, with quiet but watchful eyes. "Good evening, Mrs. Reade," he said to Gran, and his voice had the same insistent rustle as the wind.

"Good evening, Seward," said Gran, and her fingers gave Jenny's a brief, unconscious squeeze.

The man stood looking at Gran for a moment, and then his gaze shifted to Jenny and his eyebrows lifted. But he said nothing more, and, dropping his head again, he moved off slowly down the beach, disappearing at last in the gloom.

"Who was that?" asked Jenny.

"Then you saw him, too," said Gran, and there was evident relief in her voice.

"Yes, of course I saw him," said Jenny. "What do you mean? How could I not have seen him?"

"Never mind," said Gran. "Now. There's very little time." Her fingers tightened once more on her granddaughter's. "Geneva, listen carefully. Do you believe in things you can't explain?"

Jenny sat silent, considering. No one had ever asked her such a question before. At last she said, "Like things in fairy tales?"

"No, child," said Gran. "I mean—that all the daily things we do, and all the things we can touch and see in this world, are only one part of what's there, and that there's another world around us all the time that's mostly hidden from us. Do you ever think such things?"

"Well," said Jenny, confused and a little uncomfortable, but pleased, too, that Gran should speak to her this way. "Well, I think

so. Yes, sometimes. Especially at night. But it's kind of scary."

"Ah!" said Gran. "Then you don't see quite what I mean. To me it's not 'scary' at all. Why should things we can't explain have to be frightening?"

"I don't know," said Jenny, "but they are. Sometimes, at night, I'm afraid to hang my hand down over the edge of the bed, be-cause . . . well . . ."

"Because you're afraid something will grab it from under the bed!" said Gran, finishing the thought for her. "I know. Everyone has that notion sometimes. But that's our imagination, Geneva. I'm not talking about imagined things. I'm talking about . . . well, never mind. I'll just have to take a chance and hope you'll understand. You did see Seward just now, after all . . ." Her voice trailed off, but before Jenny could speak, she began again. "At high tide, child, I want you to come down here to the beach and search. I've done it by myself for thirty years, and then, last week, I stumbled in the sand and broke my silly ankle, and now, with that and this blasted crutch, I can't get about well enough. Not to do it properly. That's why I sent for you, Geneva. I'm depending on you to help me. You must come and search, and if you find anything, you must bring it back at once. You must get there first, before Seward."

"Seward? The man who just went by?" said Jenny.

"Yes. He goes for miles along the beach," said Gran, "and picks things up."

"But who is he?"

Gran ignored this question. "I'll give you a lantern at midnight. Then you must come out and search."

"But what am I to look for?" Jenny cried. "I don't understand at all."

Gran drew her hand away and laced her own fingers tightly together. There was a long pause, and then: "For thirty years," she said, "I've waited for a sign from my darling. It will come, it *will*, on the high tide someday. Any day now, surely. But someone must be here to find it. You must be my legs now, and my eyes, on the beach. To think of its coming, and my not even seeing it! No, Geneva, you must find it for me."

"A sign? From my grandfather? Oh, Gran!" said Jenny, dumfounded. "Gran, how?"

"When I tell you," said Gran, "you mustn't think I've gone mad." It was nearly dark, but Jenny could see that her grandmother's eyes burned brightly, her heavy brows drawn down into a furrow. "I've never talked of this to anyone before. But now it appears I must. Dear child, the *Amaryllis*, and all the swallowed ships . . . I know it seems impossible, and yet it's true. Seward told me. At first I didn't believe him, but then, when I saw how things were, I knew. He watches me. He has to, poor soul—he hasn't any choice. And he knows I'm waiting for a sign. Geneva, namesake, after the *Amaryllis* sank, I walked on the beach for weeks. I wanted something back—a button,

a length of rope, anything to make the sinking real. Because it was so strange, Geneva, so strange to stand here and watch the ship go down in such a gulp, so near to shore, and then—for there to be nothing! Do you see how strange it was? It was as if there had never been a ship at all, and no beloved husband—as if my happy life with him had only been a dream that was over suddenly and I had waked from it to find that it had never even happened."

"But, Gran," said Jenny, "you had my father, didn't you? Why wasn't he a good reminder?"

"George?" said Gran, surprised. "Yes, yes, there was George. But he was so . . . he didn't make the difference I needed. So I walked on the beach and waited for something, some sign to hold on to. But Nicholas Irving had been drowned, too, at almost the same time, and nothing had been found of him, either. It seemed as if the sea was taking everything, and giving nothing back."

"Who was Nicholas Irving?" Jenny asked.

"Poor Nicholas!" said Gran. "So gifted. He carved the figurehead for the *Amaryllis,* and made that drawing in the dining room. He could do things with a pen or a bit of wood or plaster that were wonderful to see. He drowned himself, they said." Gran's voice turned careful for a moment. "I don't know. That's another story. But, Geneva, some time after that, one night, Seward came to me on the beach, and when he told me—when we walked and talked—he told me things, and at last I understood. And I knew that there *would* be a sign sent back to me and that I must wait and watch for it."

"Then you mean," said Jenny, "that my grandfather's ship is down there somewhere, and that something is bound to be washed ashore sometime?"

"No, Geneva," said Gran, and her eyes burned bright again. "I mean that there will be a *sign*. Not by accident, but on purpose. From him. Because the sea swallowed ships, it keeps them at the bottom to guard its treasures. And all the drowned sailors are there, Geneva, all the poor drowned sailors, sailing the ships forever at the bottom of the sea."

5

Upstairs, in the room that had been her father's, Jenny leaned against the big four-poster bed and blinked. She hardly recognized herself against these strange new backgrounds. She had often thought of herself as a character in a story—a story where nothing ever happened. But now it was as if she had been lifted bodily into a new story—Gran's—where everything was different. Out there on the beach, Gran had talked to her as if they were two women, not a grandmother and a child, and Gran expected her to understand.

But what would her father say? He had told her that Gran was getting on. He had said that Jenny would "see." Did he know, then, about this waiting for a sign? No, somehow Jenny knew he didn't. And all at once she feared that, if he were to know, he would decide that Gran *was* mad. He had not wanted Jenny to come here. And he might never have allowed it at all if he had known about the waiting. Would he have come, instead, by himself, and taken Gran away? But taken her where?

There was a building at home, a large, square building of yellow brick, standing in a barren treeless yard inside an iron fence. There were rows and rows of narrow windows, blank and silent, and some of them were barred. Remembering that building, Jenny shuddered. They had passed it many times, she and her friends, passed it on purpose, taking the long way home from school to scare themselves with what they hoped and feared to see. Or hear. For the building was a madhouse. If her father thought that Gran was mad, would he put her there, behind those silent windows? No, he wouldn't do a thing

like that. That was Springfield. Here, things were different.

Then, as she leaned against her father's bed, the music at the back of her thoughts—the music of the rising tide—pushed through and commanded her attention. She went to the window and looked down at the beach. The water was black now, much blacker than the star-strewn sky, and it looked thick, almost solid, like gelatin. But the foam still glowed with an inner light that made it seem a different substance from the spilling waves, like a magic kind of lace on a black satin skirt.

A skirt, with lace. People always talked about the sea as if it were a "she," while Father Neptune was a "he." But the sea was real, and Neptune only a made-up figure, silly, really, with his trident and his curly beard. Silly to think of a trident, a fork—for that was all it was—as a weapon for a ruler of the sea. You couldn't calm those waves, or stir them up, for that matter, with a fork. Gran had called the sea an "it." Yes, that was better. It was far too big to be a he or a she. It was beyond such small distinctions. And it did not have a ruler; it was a rule all by itself.

She opened the window, and the cool, wet breeze rushed in. Behind her, in a sconce above the bureau, the flames of the candles leaned and flickered, so that her shadow shifted. She sighed and, closing the window, wandered over to the washstand. There was a mirror there, with a bone frame and handle, and she picked it up and stared at her reflection. It, at least, looked just the same as always. "I'm ugly," she told herself, studying the heavy brows, too heavy; the

narrow nose, too narrow; the pale white skin, too pale, with too many freckles. She had always gone along content with her face. It hadn't seemed important in the least. But lately she had begun to suspect, with sorrow, that a face might be very important. And hers, her face, was ugly. Would always be ugly. There was nothing to be done for it.

"Still, my hair is all right," she allowed herself. "It's the only nice thing about me." She had decided that she would never cut it. Not a single strand. Someday, when she was sixteen, she would be old enough to twist it up, away from her neck, and wear it in a heavy coil on the back of her head. Like her mother. Like Gran. Gran's hair must have looked like this when she was young. There was lots of red in it still. Red was unusual. Special. Like Gran herself.

From somewhere downstairs, a clock chimed ten. Jenny struggled out of her clothes—her rumpled dress, her stockings, her petticoat, her bloomers—and pulled a cotton nightgown over her head. "My father slept in this bed when he was little," she told herself, climbing in, but it was impossible to see him as someone her own size, so she gave it up and snuggled down under the covers. After all, he had always been a man to her, always old, always married to her mother. It was impossible to imagine him young, growing up, falling in love like someone in a play. Of course they loved each other, her father and mother. Of course they did. But they didn't talk about it, as Gran had. Gran had declared, "Your grandfather fell in love with *me*," and later, on the beach, she had said, in a different sort of voice, "For

thirty years I've waited for a sign from my darling." My darling! Jenny's father and mother did not call each other "my darling." Jenny lay staring in the candlelight, and all at once decided that she would do anything for Gran. Whatever she was asked to do. And then, with the music of the sea in her ears, she fell asleep.

It seemed as if she'd only dozed a moment before she woke to hear Gran calling her. "Geneva! Get up! High tide." Dazed, she stumbled out of bed, found her shoes, pulled them on without thinking, and shrugged into her dressing gown. Downstairs, Gran waited at the door, a lantern dangling from one hand, the other gripping her crutch. She was still dressed, and Jenny said, "Gran! You haven't been to bed!"

"I slept in my chair here," said Gran, "in the parlor. Come, quickly. You must get down to the beach."

Outside, the noise of the water was deafening, and Jenny could see in the dimness that the waves were high now, surging forward, tumbling over with a crash that flogged the beach, almost made it quake. The foam spilled up and slid away in a rapid rush of bubbles, spreading nearly to the foot of the little bluff, so that the beach was narrowed to a slender strip of damp, cold sand.

It had been gentle and playful before, this ocean, but now it was dark, magnificent, alarming. Jenny hesitated, apprehensive, but Gran did not seem to notice. Instead, she moved on firmly, out to the

wooden bench. "Quick!" she urged, over the roar of the wind and water. "There! Along the tide line! Now, before Seward comes! Search all along the edges of the foam. Anything you find, *anything,* bring it to me at once."

Jenny took the lantern and slid down the bluff to the beach. She paused as the rolling water seized her feet and dragged at them, and for a moment she was filled with dread. But then, in her ears, the wind rose up distinct from the noise of the water. It called to her, and a strange new rising feeling of excitement filled her, driving out the fear. She plunged off through the foam, her shoes a sodden wreck at once, her nightgown and wrapper soaked and plastered to her legs. The lantern, swinging high from her lifted hand, rocked a golden arc of light across the streaming sand, and she forgot to notice how cold the water was, how rasping when it flung its load of broken shell and seaweed around her ankles. She was aware only of freedom and exhilaration. Springfield—what was that? Buggies and school and being careful—what were they? Gran did not say, "Be careful," because Gran was not afraid. Here they were all one thing, she, and Gran, the wild, dark rushing water, and the wind. Up and back she went along the beach, passing the bluff a dozen times, searching through the fringes of the tide. She wanted now, more than anything else, to believe in the sign and to find it. For Gran.

But there was nothing. And at last, spent and disappointed, she waded back to the bluff and stood below it, shivering now from cold. "There's nothing, Gran. Nothing at all."

"Yes," said Gran. "The tide is turning back. Might as well come in now, and go to bed."

Inside the house, Gran paused and looked at her and Jenny saw that her concentration had shifted back. Gran was her afternoon self, her usual self, again. "Why, bless me, child, you're soaked to the skin! And your shoes—why ever did you wear your shoes? But, of course. You didn't realize—how foolish of me. Go and towel off. Have you another nightgown? Put it on, and I'll go light the fire and make some tea."

Upstairs, Jenny piled her dripping clothes thoughtlessly into the basin on the washstand and rubbed herself dry. And then, warm again, wrapped in the towel, she picked up the bone-handled mirror once more and peered at her face. The pale white skin was rosy now, and the eyes that stared back at her under those heavy brows were shining. "Gran isn't mad," she reassured this new reflection. "She's just—well, she's got the sea in her, somehow. I can feel it, too. Everything feels different here. I'm different. Oh, I wish I could stay forever!"

6

When Jenny woke up in the morning, she climbed out of bed and went at once to the window. The beaming sea lay far out, at low tide, much as it had the afternoon before, and it sparkled in the early sunshine, flicking tiny, blinding flashes of light into the air. The horizon, impossibly far away, invited her. The soft breeze invited her. This was a mermaid morning—a morning for sitting on the rocks and combing your long red hair. She was enchanted by it, and found that the feeling of freedom was stronger than ever. Why, she had walked on the beach last night, when the sea was up and roaring, and no one had said, "You mustn't." No one had said, "It's dangerous." Imagine! Gran was taking it for granted that she could take care of herself. And all at once she felt stronger here, at the edge of this other world, than she ever had in Springfield.

But what about the *Amaryllis* and the sign? What about the man on the beach? All right. There were things she didn't understand. But this morning they didn't seem to matter. It was enough that Gran understood them. Gran needed her to do the searching now. Well, she would do it. In Springfield, to get up in the middle of the night on such an errand would be outrageous. But this was not Springfield. This was a different place. Gran's place.

And so, as the pattern of her days and nights took hold, Springfield receded to a distant blur. It began to seem that she had always lived here by the sea, had always watched for the turning of the tide. She had come to this house on a Saturday afternoon, and on Sunday she could run as free along the beach as her father had those long, long

years before, shoeless, joyful, and at home. These first few days were bright and hot, the sea a wide green smile. She collected little shells and, once, a sturdy clam who lived for a day in a bucket of sand and sea water, spitting occasionally like a miniature geyser, before she put him back.

Each day the tide came in a little later, advancing slowly, so that by Thursday she was out with Gran long after midnight and again late in the afternoon. Sometimes, when the wind was up, the waves were tall, and sometimes they rolled in gently, like breathing, deep and slow. But there was never anything to find, nothing whatever washed up except the seaweed and the outcast pebbles. And soon the search began to seem to her to be a sort of game she played with the sea, she and Gran, twice every day, the way some people play at reading cards for prophecies, caught by belief and disbelief like a pin between two magnets. But believing didn't matter with games, and anyway, by Thursday, the night sky was turning to dawn when the time came for the search, and the high tides of the daylight hours were frothy and warm with sunshine. The sea was a good-humored presence, a play-mate, and not at all mysterious.

In between, they talked, she and Gran. Gran took her through the house and showed her everything, opening drawers and chests and wardrobes. For the house was full of treasures: a fluffy boll of cotton from Antigua; a brittle red lobster's claw from Maine; a huge, rough, curling shell from Puerto Rico that had a flaring ear lined with shiny pink as delicate as china; a little pig from Haiti, carved from satin-

wood; a length of gaudy cloth from Trinidad; a snuff box from New York City with a picture on it of Martin Van Buren, an old campaign souvenir. And with each treasure came stories from Gran that filled Jenny's head with rich, exotic pictures of the color and slow heat of the Caribbean, the noise and bustle of the northern American ports.

In one of the trunks there was a miniature tin trumpet and a wooden cannon, toys that had been her father's when he was young. She lingered over them, delighted to find that the trumpet still gave out a reedy bleat when she blew it. But Gran had no stories to go with these treasures. She only said, "George was such an active child. How he loved the sea when he was little!"

"He doesn't love it now," said Jenny. "Why not, Gran?"

Gran's face took on a shadow. "He was there with me the day the *Amaryllis* sank. He adored his father, and I suppose he just never got over it. He went away to Springfield soon after, and didn't even try to understand." She put the trumpet and cannon back into the trunk and took out an object wrapped in paper. "Here. Look at this. Isn't this remarkable?"

The object, unwrapped, turned out to be a plaster sea gull, its wings arched, ready for flight. But as Jenny turned it round in her hands, it looked like a wave, too, with dipping curls of foam. "Is it meant to be a bird," she asked, "or . . ."

"Good for you!" said Gran. "It's both. It's lots of things. Nicholas Irving made it. It was a model for a bigger piece, a statue he tried to carve once from marble. Poor Nicholas! Bring it downstairs if you

like. I haven't looked at it for years. Anyway, it's time for lunch."

This had been Friday morning. The first week was coming to an end, and Jenny, stuffed with wind and sea, was sunburned and deeply contented. The days had been richer than any she had ever known, and except for occasional reminders of some old quarrel between Gran and her father, she was completely happy. But after lunch on this Friday, the sky turned heavy. It began to drizzle, and as so often happens when the weather changes, the mood changed, too, helped along by a visitor who soured the calm of Gran's house like a drop of vinegar in cream.

Jenny answered the knock at the door, and was surprised to find, instead of the egg man or the greengrocer, a woman dressed in the very height of fashion: a tailored suit of dark, ribbed silk, its skirt draped in rich folds over her hips, and ending in an underskirt of pleated yellow that just brushed the tops of smart black-leather boots. "And who have we here, I wonder?" said the woman, as if all outdoors belonged to her and Jenny had just knocked at *her* door to be let out into it.

"I'm Geneva Reade," said Jenny, suddenly aware of her own bare feet and untidy gingham pinafore. "Did you want to see my grand-mother?"

"Grandmother!" exclaimed the woman. She laughed, tilting her head so that the yellow plume on her black felt hat bobbed and waved. Her face, though it was no longer young, was extremely

403

pretty: a round face, dimpled, framed in becoming waves of gray-brown hair drawn back over small, neat ears. "A grandmother? But, of course. It *has* been that long."

"Who's there?" called Gran from the kitchen.

"Hello, Geneva," the woman called back, as she came in, furling her black umbrella. "You'll never guess! Come here at once and see!"

Gran came stumping into the parlor and stopped dead. "Isabel! Heaven help me, it's Isabel Cooper, isn't it?"

"Right and wrong," said the woman gaily. "Isabel Owen for a good long time now. What *have* you done to yourself, Geneva? Sprained your ankle?"

"Broke it," said Gran. "What in the world are you doing here?"

"We're on our way down to Greenville, my dear. But Harley had some tiresome business or other to do in town, so I said, 'Harley, I'll just go and see some of my old friends,' so he dropped me here. He'll only be a short time, but I did so want to see you, Geneva, before we went our way. Why, it's been ages and ages!"

"Sit down, Isabel," said Gran without enthusiasm, lowering herself into her own chair. "This is my namesake, George's daughter. Geneva, this is Mrs.—uh—Owen, did you say? I used to know her long ago, when she lived here in town."

"How do you do," said Jenny, bobbing a small curtsy in her best Springfield manner.

"George's child!" said the woman. "I declare! I can't imagine little George all grown up. Geneva, she's the image of you,

404

the very image."

"Yes, she is," said Gran complacently. "She's here to help me while my ankle mends."

"I see," said Mrs. Owen, and instantly lost interest in Jenny, who sat down across the room to watch this fascinating visitor. "Geneva, you've hardly changed at all. I'd have known you anywhere. Why, it's amazing how well you've kept over the years."

"One foot in the grave," said Gran. "You've kept well yourself, I see."

"Yes, but, my dear, I *am* a ways behind you, after all. Twenty-five years younger, at least, if my memory serves."

"Twenty," said Gran, "but never mind. We're both past our prime."

The woman frowned briefly, and then turned sunny again. "Oh, well," she said carelessly, "whatever *that* may mean. I'm sure I don't think of myself as one whit different from what I used to be. Happy times, Geneva, the old days here!"

"Yes, you were quite a belle," said Gran dryly.

The woman dimpled. "I was, rather, wasn't I! But, Geneva, here you are still, while I've been out and doing. How ever have you kept yourself amused in this boring old place? I'm sure I couldn't wait to get away!"

"Why should I leave?" said Gran. "This is my home."

"Of course," said Mrs. Owen, turning solemn on the instant. "The Captain. Forgive me. You know, I was just sure you'd never marry

again. Here you sit, and unless I'm mistaken, you haven't changed a thing in this room since the Captain . . . that is—"

"No," said Gran. "Nothing's been changed. Why should I change it? I like it this way."

The woman rose from her chair and wandered about the room, picking things up, looking at them, putting them down again. "I remember that teapot," she said, pointing to the china on the mantelpiece. "You let my mother borrow it once, and I came down to get it for her. Remember? It was the day of my sixteenth birthday party, and the hired girl had broken *our* teapot that very morning. Dear me! It seems like yesterday."

"Close to forty years ago," said Gran, "if it's a day."

"I'm sure I don't know why you keep harping on exact numbers of years, Geneva," said Mrs. Owen. "It's such a tiresome habit. Dear me, what's this?" She paused at a side table where, before lunch, Jenny had set down the plaster sea gull that looked like a wave. "Geneva, what in the world is this old thing?"

"Do you mean to tell me, Isabel," said Gran, her ironic enjoyment of this visitor drying up on the instant, "that you don't remember? Of course you do. I can't imagine why you bother to pretend you don't. That's Nicholas Irving's work, as you very well know—the model he made for the statue."

"Nicholas Irving? Oh. Dear me. Of course. Now I remember. What a funny duck he was. Yes, I do remember something about a statue."

"I should think you would," said Gran. "Don't try to play your little

games with me, missy. You remember it perfectly well, and now that I come to think of it, I dare say that's why you came here today—to see if you'd been forgiven at last. A guilty conscience can be very troublesome, I've heard."

"Well, you're entirely wrong about that, Geneva," said the woman resentfully. "I don't in the least feel guilty. But I might have guessed you'd still be blaming me for what happened to Nicholas."

"He loved you, heaven help him," said Gran, "and you let him think you loved him back. He was making that statue for *you,* and then you laughed at it, Isabel. You laughed, and broke his heart."

"Well, I'm sure it wasn't *my* fault if he cared for me," said Mrs. Owen, her round face puckering a little. "*I* couldn't help it. Lots of boys cared for me, and *they* didn't go and drown themselves."

"Nicholas wasn't 'lots of boys,'" said Gran. "Nicholas was special."

"I'm sure you see it that way, Geneva," said the woman, "but I couldn't go and marry *everyone,* now, could I? Anyway, Nicholas was so . . . solemn. Oh, I liked him at first, but after a while he just got too . . . well, too solemn, as I say. About as much fun as an old sheep. And I never could see what that silly statue had to do with anything."

Gran started to speak, stopped, and turned to look at Jenny, who was sitting open-mouthed, listening. "Geneva," she said, "I'd very much appreciate it if you'd go up to your room for a while. I'll call you down later."

"But, Gran!" Jenny protested, and then, seeing the look in her

grandmother's eye, she said, almost meekly, "All right." She went out into the hall and up the stairs, as slowly as she dared, but there was silence in the parlor, and once in her room, when the conversation started up again, she could hear nothing more than a murmur from the two women. After a time, however, their voices rose suddenly and the words were audible.

"Listen to the pot calling the kettle black!" cried the visitor. "You're a fine one, Geneva Reade, to talk about sparing a person's feelings! Everyone knows how you neglected that boy of yours after the Captain drowned. Why, you never cared a straw for George. It was just the Captain, the Captain, always the Captain, until—"

"Leave this house, Isabel Cooper," Gran thundered, "and never come back. I don't ever want to see you again."

Crisp footsteps in the hall, and then: "But, Geneva, it's raining outside, and Harley isn't back yet. You can't expect me to—"

"Yes, I can," said Gran, and Jenny could imagine the grim expression on her grandmother's face. "Goodbye, Isabel."

The sound of the door opening and closing. A moment of silence. Next the thump as Gran's crutch swung her back to the parlor. Then nothing but the rain and the slosh of waves. But Jenny sat on her father's bed, and the visitor's words hung in her ears, so that she did not hear anything else. "You never cared a straw for George." Could it be true? And all at once the little tin trumpet seemed the saddest thing in the world to her. What chance had its thin sound ever had, trying to be heard above the tide?

7

When Jenny came downstairs again, she found Gran standing at the window behind her chair, staring out at the sea. Searching for something to say, Jenny managed at last, "She's not very nice, that woman who was here."

"No," said Gran, without turning around. "She isn't, and wasn't. The face of an angel, even now, but in no way like an angel otherwise."

"Did Nicholas Irving really drown himself because of her?" asked Jenny.

"So they say," said Gran. She came away from the window and sat down in her chair. She looked exhausted. "Geneva, people do strange things for love sometimes. You're old enough to realize that."

A silence fell between them. Jenny fingered a fold of her pinafore, and then she said, with difficulty, "Gran, didn't you love my father?"

"You mustn't think such things," said Gran stiffly. "Forget you ever heard it. That woman—Isabel—she's a fool. She understands nothing at all. The only thing she cares about is what others think of her. To people like that, the rest of the world is there just to hold up a mirror for them to see their own reflection in. She never understood poor Nicholas, and she doesn't understand anything about your father and me. He's my son. Of course I love him. We don't agree on certain things, that's all. Put it out of your mind." She turned away and took up the almanac. "High tide at five o'clock. An hour from now," she announced, staring down at the page. Then she closed the almanac and laid it aside. "This rain is going to be with us for a while,

Geneva," she said. "You'll need something to keep you dry. Go upstairs to the back bedroom and look in the bottom of that big trunk, the one where we found the sea gull. I think there's an old oilskin there somewhere that your father had when he was about your age. And a sou'wester, too."

Upstairs, Jenny knelt before the trunk and lifted its great domed lid. The trumpet and the cannon were lying on top of the accumulation inside, but she did not pick them up again. Instead, she thrust a hand down under the layers of odds and ends, searching for the slick feel of the oilskin. At last she found it and, as carefully as she could, began to pull it up and out, trying not to disturb the things resting on top of it. But this appeared to be impossible, and as she gave the oilskin a final yank to free it, it brought up with it, caught in the stiffness of a too-long-folded sleeve, a small, square leather box which tumbled out onto the floor.

She left the oilskin dangling from the trunk and, picking up the box, tried to open it. There was a little metal knob sticking out of its front side and this she pressed firmly. At first nothing happened, but a stronger jab released an inner catch, and the lid sprang open. The box was lined with purple velvet, and there, resting in a depression that fit it exactly, lay a wafer-thin gold pocket watch. It was a handsome thing, much more handsome than the watches for sale in her father's store, the kind he carried himself: of some metal that was silver-colored but not silver, and thick as a thumb. Jenny eased the

gold watch out of its nest and turned it over. The back was engraved with curling vines and leaves, and in the center a small square, left plain, was marked with the single initial *R*.

Jenny had often opened the back of her father's watch to look at the works, so intricate, fitted so precisely into their round, neat skull. She pried this one open now with a fingernail, and peered in. And then her eye fell on the inside of the lifted back, and she saw that it, too, was engraved:

MORGAN READE 1818
GEORGE MORGAN READE 1857

George Morgan Reade. That was her father! She stood up, tucking the stiff, creased oilskin under her arm, and went downstairs, the watch cupped carefully in one palm. "Gran," she said, going into the parlor, "look what I found! It's got my father's name in it."

Gran had been studying the almanac again, and looked up from it vaguely, as if it were an effort to bring herself out of her thoughts. But when Jenny put the watch into her hand, her eyes cleared. "Dear heaven!" she exclaimed. "It's your grandfather's watch."

"But it has Papa's name in it, too," said Jenny. "Look—it's on the inside of the lid."

Gran opened the back and stared at the names engraved there. "Yes. I remember now. Your grandfather got this watch on his twenty-first birthday, from *his* father. But he never carried it with him when

he went to sea. He used to say it was too special, that it might get lost or stolen, and that he wanted to save it for . . . George. For George's twenty-first birthday. He had the name and date put in long before, to be ready."

"But Gran! Papa's way past twenty-one by now. Why didn't you ever give it to him?"

"I forgot," said Gran. "I clean forgot all about it. When the time came, your father had been a long time in Springfield. I remember sending him a letter, to wish him a happy birthday, but I just plain forgot about this."

"It would've meant a lot to Papa, I expect, to have it," said Jenny disapprovingly. "You should've remembered."

"Now you're angry," said Gran, and the tired look came back to her face.

"Well, I just don't understand it," said Jenny. "What's the trouble with you and Papa, anyway?"

"Geneva, dear child," said Gran, "I don't know how to explain it to you, or even if I should try. But—well—your father, he's a fine man, but he just doesn't see. After the *Amaryllis* went down, he kept saying to me, 'It's over.' And he wanted me to move back to Springfield and start a new life. But I didn't want a new life. I wanted this one, and I didn't believe it was over. I wanted to stay here where I could be close to . . . the ship, where I could wait. Your grandfather and I—what we felt for each other doesn't just stop. Remember what we talked about the first night you were here? There's another world around us,

Geneva, around us all the time, and here I can be closer to it. But your father—he doesn't sense the other world around him; he doesn't see that things don't end. If he did, he wouldn't be so frightened. Ever since his father drowned, he's been terrified of endings. He thinks of the sea the way other people think of graveyards, and he can't stand this place because it keeps reminding him. That's why he ran away—to run away from endings. He was very young, and some people thought I was wrong to allow the separation. But what could I have done? He couldn't stay here, and I couldn't leave."

She paused and ran a fingertip over the names engraved inside the lid of the gold watch. And then she said, "This watch, now—it's like a sign in itself, isn't it? A sign from father to son. The numbers stand on the face in an endless circle, and the hands will keep going round and round when we wind it up. But George wouldn't have seen it like that. He'd only have seen an old watch that had stopped—time come to an end—and he wouldn't have wanted to have it. Do you understand?"

Jenny stood staring at Gran, and could feel herself pulled between them, her father and her grandmother. "I don't know," she said.

Gran stared back at her and then she pulled herself up out of her chair and stood tall. "Enough," she said. "Come. High tide."

And so, another useless search, another supper. But things felt very different. The rain continued, filling in the chinks of silence that *would* fall between them, Gran and Jenny, no matter how hard they

413

tried to keep a conversation going. Bedtime came as a welcome relief, and Jenny, protected by an earnest wish not to think about the watch, and the little tin trumpet, and the ugly words of the pretty Mrs. Owen, went to sleep almost at once.

When Gran next called her, Jenny woke to find that the windows of her room were touched faintly with light, the pale beginnings of dawn. There was scarcely a breath of wind. She went to the window and saw that the sea had been transformed. It was hung with a thin fog, against which the rain still fell, straight down, with a whispering sound, hushed and dim. Downstairs, Gran was waiting with the oilskin and Jenny put it on obediently, but they both moved quietly, as if there were someone or something near that must not be awakened or disturbed. "We won't need the lantern," said Gran in a low voice. "It's almost light. Geneva, I have a feeling that perhaps, this time. . . Come, let's go out and begin."

The beach was ghostly, muffled, in the silvery half-light. The warm rain was so fine that it was almost a mist, but it raised tiny knobs on the surface of the swelling water, water that rolled so gently it did not crest, but merely flattened, sighing, on the sand, sliding far up to the bottom of the bluff with only the barest film of bubbles. The far horizon had vanished in the fog, and the swells seemed to be coming in from nowhere, only to this place and nowhere else, glinting with that same pale silver light that was part dawn, part fog,

part rain. Jenny started off along the dark strip of sand with her hands deep in the pockets of the oilskin, feeling as if she were still asleep and dreaming, carrying the dream along around her.

For the fog gave way ahead and closed behind her as she went, and the now-familiar landmarks, as they swam into focus, looked strange: the boulder, gleaming now with rain; the withered scrub-pine stump decked with moisture-beaded spiderwebs; the rotted dock, its far end faint in fog out over the water; and finally another bluff that marked the limit of that arm of the search, soft now, its rough grass leaning and heavy with raindrops. She paused here, blinking, her cheeks wet under the brim of the old sou'wester. She could feel the silence and the waiting everywhere. And then she turned and started back.

She had reached the scrub-pine stump again when she saw it: a dark something floating just within her sight, where the sea faded into the fog. It rose and fell on the soundless, shifting water, and with each swell it was brought a little closer to shore, a little closer to where she stood. "Driftwood," she suggested to herself, but it did not look like driftwood. Its shape seemed too regular, too smooth. As she stood there, her eyes wide, straining to see more clearly, the wind lifted and the rain began to fall a little harder, digging tiny pockmarks in the sand. Riding a taller swell, the object rolled, submerged, bobbed up again, and Jenny saw a touch of color on its surface. "It isn't driftwood," she said aloud. "It's—something else."

The object, floating now in sight, now lost between the swells,

came nearer and nearer. Suddenly Jenny could wait no longer. She waded out, deeper and deeper, until at last she stood in water to her waist. Heaves of sea lifted the oilskin up around her and dragged at her, but her eyes were fixed on the object, and at last it washed into her reaching arms. Clutching it, she struggled back to shore, and stood there in the rain, holding the thing, staring down at it.

It was made of wood and it was heavy with years of seeping water, but she saw at once what it was, in spite of its softened planes and curves, its barely visible residue of paint. She was holding in her arms the carved head of a woman, split at an angle across the lower face so that only a portion of the mouth remained. But the eyes, under heavy brows, were lidded and calm, the nose long and narrow, the section of mouth curved upward in a smile. And the hair, swept down from the brow in deep-carved strands, still held bright fragments of dark red color.

Staring at the head, Jenny swallowed hard. And then she began to run down the beach, clumsy in the flapping oilskin, her heels thudding over the firm, wet sand, holding the wooden head tight against her chest. "Gran!" she cried. "Gran! I've got something!" The fog opened out ahead of her, and at last she could see her grandmother standing on the little bluff, a dim shape under a big umbrella. "Gran!" she cried again.

"Quick!" came Gran's voice. "Quick! Oh, Lord it's come! Yes, *yes*, child, bring it to me!"

Jenny arrived breathless at the bottom of the bluff and struggled up, and Gran, dropping her crutch, flinging aside the umbrella, reached out and seized the wooden head. She took one look at it and sank down on the old bench, clasping the head to her bosom, rocking back and forth. "Geneva," she cried, "do you know what this is? Do you see? It's my head, from the ship! Heaven he praised, he's sent me a sign at last!" Her voice broke and she began to weep, her words coming slow between deep, gasping breaths. "It's the figurehead, Geneva—from my darling—from the *Amaryllis*—sent up from the bottom of the sea."

And the wind, rising, whispered around them: *True to you-o-o-ou.*

8

The rest of that day, and the next and the next, were as confused and cloudy as the first days had been calm and bright. Outside, the sky hung low, clouds drifting over clouds, and the rain fell softly, continuously, turning the sea and beach into a blur. Inside, Gran was feverish. She would talk, excitedly, and then lapse into silence, drop off to sleep for a moment, and wake to talk again. Jenny did not know what to do with her, and a vague alarm moved in to tremble in her stomach. The head from the *Amaryllis* lay on the table beside Gran's chair in the parlor, and the calm smile on its carved face was more like the Gran Jenny knew than this agitated woman who sat, stood, stumped about, sat again, dozed exhausted, doing none of these for more than five minutes at a time, it seemed.

Jenny took over the cooking, producing from Gran's unfamiliar stores peculiar meals whose inharmonious parts were never ready at the same moment, never ready to the same degree of doneness; and she carried them in to the parlor on a tray, but Gran would scarcely touch them. "Geneva," she would say, "did I ever tell you the story of how—" and would begin a tale told once so far that hour and twice the hour before, of her life in the old days with the Captain. For she called him "the Captain" now, not "your grandfather," and she talked of nothing, no one, else, putting out her hand again and again to touch the wooden head. And then, in the middle of the story, her voice would fade and she would fall asleep, her head bowed down on her chest.

It was clear from the brightness of her eyes and the flush on her cheeks that she was ill. But Jenny did not know how to find the doctor and was in any case afraid to leave her grandmother alone while she went out to look, for she feared that now, in addition to the fever, Gran might really be going mad. The building in Springfield, the one with the dark, barred windows, was never far from her thoughts. "If the doctor comes," she worried, "he'll see how it is with her. He'll send for my father and they'll take her away." And so she waited helplessly.

But at the end of the third day, late in the afternoon, she tiptoed in to the parlor from the kitchen and found that Gran was truly asleep at last, her breathing deep and regular. The flush was gone from her face, and her hands lay relaxed in her lap. The fever, at least, had passed. Weak with relief, Jenny smoothed the quilt over her grand-mother's knees, tucking it under, and sank down on a footstool near the window. Outside, the rain still fell, the swells still spilled across the sodden beach, and Jenny realized that she had not left the house since the day of the discovery. There had been no watching for the tides, no searching up and back along the sand. There was, of course, no need for searching now.

Then, for the first time, she turned and looked—really looked—at the wooden head lying on the table next to her. Reaching out a hand, she ran her fingertips over its water-softened cheek. The surface, drying a little in the warmth of the lamp beside it, felt fuzzy,

and the fragments of red paint in the deep-carved strands of hair were curling here and there, turning up their edges as they, too, dried in the lamplight. The head was real. There could be no doubt about that. The place where it had split from the rest of the body was lighter in color, and rougher, as if the break were recent: the wood was raw, not mellowed yet by the constant caress of salt water.

Yes, the head was real. It had been part of the *Amaryllis,* and now it was here. It had come—here. A queer coincidence. Perhaps. But it was here. Gran stirred in her sleep and her mouth curved into a smile, and Jenny saw how much her Grandmother's face still looked like this younger, wooden face carved so long ago—strong, handsome, a very good face. And all at once she remembered something the terrible and pretty Mrs. Owen had said to Gran: "She's the image of you, Geneva—the very image."

The very image? Did she, too, then, have a very good face? After all? Not ugly? Would someone, some shadowy someone, love her someday the way her grandfather had loved Gran? Or perhaps still loved Gran from . . . wherever he was? Unexpectedly, she found that she was blushing. "That's silly," she said aloud, and stood up, moved about the room, plumping pillows, bustling, embarrassed. But her heart had a new lightness, and the trembling in her stomach had disappeared.

Gran woke in the morning, after the third long night in her chair, pale but refreshed. "What are we doing down here in the parlor?" she

demanded as Jenny, sitting up from her own sleep on the sofa, greeted her. "Good grief, I'm stiff as a board."

"You've been sick, Gran," said Jenny. "I was so worried—how do you feel?"

"Well, now let's see," said Gran doubtfully, patting herself here and there. "I seem to be all right, but I'm hungry as a bear. Yes, I remember now. Foolish old woman, to stand so long outside in the rain. And yet"—she turned to gaze at the wooden head—"it wasn't entirely foolish."

They were quiet then. Jenny came to stand by Gran, and they both looked at the head, which smiled back serenely. "I knew it would happen," said Gran, "and it did." She put a gentle hand on her granddaughter's arm. "Geneva," she said, "remember this: nothing is impossible."

There followed three lighthearted days, in spite of the steady rain cocooning them, lighthearted for Jenny because Gran was all right again, better, in fact, than she had been before; lighthearted for Gran because her dearest wish had been granted. All of her old intensity, her obsession with the tides, was gone, to uncover, by its absence, a great capacity for pleasure.

She taught Jenny how to play German whist; they read aloud; they made salt-water taffy. A new trunk was opened, revealing hats and dresses in the opulent style of the 1830's and 40's, and for hours they

played at dressing up. Gran pulled out one tall-brimmed bonnet with plumes and ribbons and ruffled white lace, and, clapping it on her head, went to see herself in a mirror. "Well, it looked all right in its heyday," she said, laughing at her reflection. "Or in *my* heyday, I should say. Wait. I know. Come with me." She stumped to the parlor and, picking up the wooden head, placed the bonnet over the carved hair lovingly. "That's the way it looked, more or less." The head smiled indulgently. "No," said Gran, removing the bonnet and laying the head back, gently, in its place. "What's the matter with me? Blasphemy, almost. But your grandfather gave me this bonnet. How he would laugh to see the figurehead wearing it! He was a great laugher, that man. Everything amused him."

Jenny remembered, then, her father's sober face. "Gran," she said slowly, "if Papa could see the head, would it make him feel better? Would it make him love the sea again, and not be so afraid?"

Gran turned and looked at her. "When he comes for you, the end of next week," she said thoughtfully, "we'll show it to him. And give him the watch. And see."

And so it came to a Friday again, and still the rain fell. The beach had a drowned, abandoned look, and in the afternoon Jenny, growing restless, put on the old oilskin and ventured out to look around. She had entirely lost track of the tides, but the sea seemed to her to have sunk beyond even its farthest point, slapping sullenly at the

hard, ridged sand. Below the line of soggy seaweed, she found a sharp trail of new clawprints, like little forks, etched cleanly in the sand, and following them she spotted at last the sea gull responsible, waddling discontentedly some distance ahead. His feathers looked bedraggled and askew, like an old shirt, ragged and none too clean. But when he heard her approaching, he opened perfect wings and, transformed, lifted into the air, beating off above the water, powerful and sure. Somehow his flight from her made her feel alien and wistful. She hung her head and started back along the empty beach, higher up, above the tide line. It seemed, now, to be a kind of trespassing to mark the smoother sand, where the gull had walked, with feet that did not belong there.

It was because of this higher route home that she noticed the deep prints of a man's heavy boots, stretching ahead of her near the edge of the sand where the wet grass leaned. The rims of the prints were softened from the rain, no longer crisp, as the gull's prints had been, so Jenny knew that the man who had made them had come along sometime before. But still she felt queer to see them there. Abruptly, she lost the sense that she was the intruder here. Instead, it now began to feel as if she herself—and Gran—had been intruded upon, on this sand that was theirs alone. She hurried back to the house and said to Gran, "There's been a man walking on our beach."

And Gran, putting down her mending, frowned and said, "Seward."

9

At supper Gran said musingly, "I wonder if Seward knows the head has come."

"But how could he?" Jenny asked, surprised. "And, Gran, I don't see why he should care about it, anyway. Unless," she added quickly, "if he's your friend and would be glad to see you happy."

"He's not exactly . . . a friend," said Gran.

"Oh," said Jenny. A vague apprehension filled her and she asked, a little timidly, "Is he a bad person?"

Gran looked hard at her, as if she were trying to see inside her head. "Geneva," she said, "it's not a question of good or bad. It's a question of whether he's . . ." She paused.

"Whether he's what?" asked Jenny, frowning, fearful of what the answer would be.

"Finish your supper," said Gran. "We'll talk in the parlor afterwards. I can see I'd better tell you the whole story."

The parlor, with the lamps turned up and a fresh fire popping in the grate, should have been cozy and secure, but Jenny sat nervously on the sofa, opposite Gran's chair, and folded her hands. "I feel the way I do at home when we tell ghost stories," she said as her grandmother eased herself down and laid the crutch on the floor.

"Well," said Gran, lifting her eyebrows, "in a way that's what we're going to do."

"I don't believe in ghosts, though," said Jenny. "Do you?"

"I don't know," said Gran. "I didn't when I was your age, but

now . . . Geneva, you see that the sign has come, don't you?"

"Yes," said Jenny, "but . . ."

"I know," said Gran. "You believe it's accidental. Well, perhaps you're right, perhaps not. Nevertheless, the head from the *Amaryllis* has come home after thirty years, and it lies here on this table, in plain sight. And there's something more about it you didn't notice, being unfamiliar with such things. It's got no barnacles on it, and no signs of rotting. Keep that in mind, Geneva, while I talk."

She settled her ankle more comfortably on the hassock and leaned back. "Do you remember that I told you about Nicholas Irving, and how he drowned himself not long after the *Amaryllis* sank?"

"Yes," said Jenny. "Because of that woman who was here."

"Isabel Cooper," said Gran. "Yes. Because at first she pretended to be fond of him, but then, later, she laughed at him to his face, laughed at his work and at his love for her. We thought at first, when he disappeared, that he'd gone away—inland, perhaps, or down the coast. It wasn't until two days later that his dinghy was found, washed up. Without him in it. Still some people thought it had drifted loose by itself and that Nicholas was holed up somewhere, licking his wounds. But he didn't come back, and at last some of his friends went to his workshop to see if he'd left any messages or clues. They found all his tools lying about, and another figurehead for some other ship, only half finished. His clothes were there, food stores, everything. And the marble statue he'd been working on, it was still there, too, but it looked as if he'd tried to smash it. It was all chipped and scarred

with chisel marks." She sighed. "He was . . . temperamental. Another man might have squared his shoulders and gone ahead with his life in spite of being unlucky in love, but not Nicholas. He was completely addled over Isabel."

"Well," said Jenny, "I guess she was very pretty."

"Yes, she was," Gran returned, "but Nicholas should have known that wasn't much all by itself. 'Pretty' doesn't mean 'good,' you know, Geneva. Real life isn't like fairy tales. 'Pretty' simply means that by accident you've got things arranged on your outside in an extra-pleasing manner. It doesn't tell a thing about your inside. Still, Nicholas was temperamental, as I said, emotional, the way they say all artists are, and beauty was important to him. But we were very fond of him. He came here often. He was almost ten years older than your father, but he was rather like a son to us, and sometimes when your grandfather was off on a voyage, he'd come and read to George and me, or take a hand of whist. He was a good boy, and very, very gifted." She sighed again, remembering, and shook her head. "His friends found a note in his workshop. It said, 'I can't go on. Look for me in the sea.'"

"That's sad!" said Jenny, much moved by this romantic tale.

"It's absurd," Gran contradicted severely. "A terrible, terrible waste, and all for nothing."

"Still," said Jenny dreamily, liking the story anyway, "I feel sorry for him."

"It's not a happy story, certainly," said Gran, the hardness of her tone melting away. "A month or two after his disappearance—his drowning—whatever—one night when I was walking on the beach—remember, I was newly widowed then, and half crazy with it, heaven help me—I was walking on the beach, it was one of those nights when the moon is very bright, and I was wandering along, worried about George, who'd gone away to Springfield to live with your Great-aunt Jane, and I was longing for something from the *Amaryllis*, thinking about the sinking, trying to figure it out, when all at once I noticed a man coming toward me. He looked familiar, somehow, his clothes and his way of walking, and I cried out, 'Nicholas!' And it *was* Nicholas, but he was different."

"Different how?" asked Jenny, fearful again of the reply.

"It was his eyes, mostly. They didn't have that fiery light in them any more," said Gran. "They were quiet. And he had a beard, too. He tried to ignore me, to go on past me, but I spoke to him again, and he stopped and said, as if he were a stranger, 'Not Nicholas, ma'am. My name is Seward.'"

"Seward!" Jenny exclaimed.

"Yes," said Gran. "And for a moment I thought I'd made a mistake. But he raised his hand up to his beard and I saw the scar on his thumb where his chisel had slipped once long before when he was working. No, it was Nicholas, all right, and I said so. So we walked together and he told me . . ."

"What?" Jenny urged.

"Geneva, you may believe it or not, just as you choose. *I* believed it, and I'll tell you why in a minute. He told me he'd rowed the dinghy out, far out to sea, the night of the day that Isabel laughed at him. And he stowed the oars, stood up, and flung himself overboard. He was so determined to drown that when he sank he opened his mouth and tried to breathe the water into his lungs, but in the next moment he came to the surface again and began to choke. In that moment he forgot about Isabel and wanted to stay alive after all, so he looked around for the dinghy, but it was gone."

"Gone?" said Jenny, breathless. "You mean, disappeared?"

"So he told me," said Gran. "He began trying to swim, but found that he couldn't, somehow, and instead he sank again and kept on sinking, in spite of kicking and trying to come back up. He described the water to me and voices, talking to him, pulling him down and down. And all he could think of was how much he didn't want to drown. He tried to speak to the voices, and found that he could, and he argued with them all the way to the bottom. Yes. He went all the way to the bottom. And he told me, Geneva, that when he got to the bottom, he saw the *Amaryllis.*"

"Oh, Gran!" said Jenny, forgetting for the moment that she was supposed to be making up her mind about all this.

"Yes," said Gran. "It was the *Amaryllis,* and it was moving over the sea bottom. Its lamps were lit and there were men working on the deck, though he told me he was too far away to see who they were."

"But how did he know it was the *Amaryllis,* if he was so far away?" asked Jenny.

"Why," said Gran, "he recognized the figurehead. There was light, he told me, coming from the face, from the eyes, and he recognized it, even through the blur of the water. And all the time the voices kept talking to him and he kept arguing, saying he didn't want to stay down there, and at last it seemed as if a bargain had been struck, and the next thing he knew, he was lying on the beach in the dark, and he was completely dry. As if he'd never been in the water at all. And he told me that he knew he wasn't Nicholas Irving any more, but someone—something—else; that he would be called Seward now because it meant 'guardian of the sea.' And he realized that he'd promised, in exchange for being returned, to walk along the beaches and give back to the sea anything that it valued—that was the word, 'valued'—that had somehow been washed ashore. And that if he didn't keep his promise, he'd be brought back down to the bottom of the sea again and kept there."

"Drowned after all," said Jenny.

"Yes," said Gran. "Drowned after all. And then he told me that he knew, as clearly as if he'd been told—in fact, he believed he had been told—that your grandfather wanted more than anything else to send a sign to me—that his desire was very strong—and that he, Seward, would have to watch and make sure that, if a sign was sent, it was something I'd be allowed to keep."

Jenny frowned, trying to picture the scene underwater. "He really saw the ship on the bottom," she said.

"Yes," said Gran. "Sailing. Keeping watch. The sea bottom was covered with treasure, he told me, and there were lots of wrecked ships, too, great ruined hulls, lying down there forsaken, full of holes and rotting away. But the *Amaryllis,* and all the ships with figureheads, are kept whole and clean, he said, to sail on the bottom and guard the treasure."

All at once Jenny could not accept the story. Springfield asserted itself, and she said, "I don't believe it."

"You don't?"

"No. It's crazy. That man—Seward, or whoever he is—he must have dreamed it."

"Very well," said Gran calmly. "There's one last piece to the story. As we stood there on the sand in the moonlight, talking, two of your grandfather's friends came down from the grass above us. One of them took my arm and said, 'Geneva, come back with us. We've been looking for you. You know the Captain wouldn't want you to wander out here night after night all by yourself.' And I turned around to them and I said, 'But I'm not by myself,' and they said, in this pitying sort of way, 'Come with us now. You must try to get hold of yourself.' I turned back, and Seward had walked away, on down the beach. 'No,' I said, 'I want to stay here and talk to Nicholas,' and I called to him to come back. And one of the men said, 'Geneva, please, there's no one there.'"

"You mean they didn't see him?" said Jenny.

"No," said Gran, "they didn't see him. But I couldn't see him, either, very well, by that time, he'd gone so far. So I thought, well, perhaps they just hadn't noticed him, so I pointed to the row of footprints he'd made as he walked away. They were very clear in the moonlight. And I said, 'Look. See the footprints? I haven't been alone. It was Nicholas, and we've been walking.' And then one of the men put his arm around me and said, 'Geneva, you're exhausted and you're making yourself sick. There aren't any footprints there.'"

"But, Gran!" Jenny began, eyes wide.

"Wait," Gran interrupted. "Seward—or Nicholas—has been walking this beach for thirty years, and no one's ever seen him but me. Him *or* his footprints. Not then, on that night, or at any time thereafter."

They sat staring at each other in silence. At last Jenny said, "But Gran, *I* saw him—and I saw his footprints, too."

"Yes, child," said Gran. "You did."

10

Later Jenny lay in bed, eyes wide and staring into the dark. She kept thinking about Seward, but she did not want to think about him. If the rain would only stop, if the sun would shine tomorrow, everything would seem a great deal more reasonable. This place, this house—she saw more clearly than ever, now, that it stood at the edge of another world, at the edge where the things she understood and the things beyond her understanding began to merge and blur. That other world—it brought on transformations, and its blurring edge was marked by the hemline of the sea.

Still, even the sea seemed simple in the sunshine. Funny how clear, bright daylight made you laugh at phantoms. They vanished, fled away like smoke, under the sun's round, candid eye. Yes, that was the thing: sunshine to light the corners.

But there was no sunshine next morning. The rain had stopped at last, but the sky was still hung with gray, against which new humps of vapor hurried by, changing their shapes and rolling as they went. After breakfast, Gran turned the pages of the almanac and read, aloud:

Final days of August
Usher in September.
Autumn equinox ahead—
Stormy seas. Remember.

"Stormy seas!" said Jenny, discouraged. "Does that mean it's going to rain again?"

"It's coming into that time of year, Geneva," said Gran. "Always bad weather at the equinox. Is it getting on your nerves?"

"A little," said Jenny.

"I know," said Gran. "Moss in the bones. Still, I like it, somehow."

"Better than when the sun is out?"

"Yes, I really do. It's much more interesting, I've always thought. Come, let's bake a cake. That should cheer you up."

Jenny cracked the eggs—twelve of them, a whole dozen days of labor for some unknown, dedicated hen—and beat their slippery whites into a rigid cloud of foam. She had beaten egg whites often before, but now she saw the process as yet another transformation. She sifted the flour, measured the sugar, watched as Gran folded everything into a batter smooth and pale as thickened cream. Transformations again. And the humble dailiness of these activities only increased the knowledge that, at some undetermined point, her world had slid away a final barrier and allowed that other world to merge with it at last, like the fog moving in from nowhere, into the air she breathed, changing its flavor, giving it a richness it had not had before. Like the scent of the angel-food cake drifting out from the oven to fill the house with promises. Like the head on the parlor table.

While the cake was baking, she found herself wandering again and again to the dining room to look at the drawing of the *Amaryllis*, with its wind-belled sails and thrusting prow, the figurehead tilting un-

afraid over a frill of splitting waves, chin lifted to the wide and blank horizon. She tried to picture the ship sailing like this on the sea bottom, and found that she *could* picture it—could easily imagine the heavy silence of the deep, deep water, the schools of little fish flitting soundlessly before the prow, the dim green wavering light surrounding it. And she could see, too, rotting chests and boxes, lids askew, the rocks and sandy bottom glinting here and there with scattered treasures. She could picture all this, and more: the shadowy figures on the deck, one of them surely the grandfather she had never seen, striding effortlessly up and down. Phantoms. But real. And wonderful. Why not?

Why not. There was no answer for "why not," except to say "why not, indeed." And so, at last, accepting everything, she said to Gran at lunch, "Will Seward want you to give back the head?"

"I don't know," said Gran. "I've been asking myself that very question. But if he doesn't know I have it . . . Geneva, perhaps I should put it away somewhere for a while. Just in case." And the deed was done at once, the head nested deep in a drawer of the lowboy in the dining room, the drawer locked, the key dropped into the china teapot on the parlor mantelpiece. "Now," said Gran, "if he should come here—which is very unlikely—he won't discover it. I think we shall be safe. Have another piece of cake. Why, bless my soul, look there! The sun's come out!"

It was true. The house brimmed suddenly with light—hard, yellow

light—as if a curtain had been swept aside. From the parlor window after lunch, Jenny saw a sky wiped clean, and polished to a glittering blue. The tide was in, but the sea still seemed sullen, thumping fretfully no more than halfway up the sand as the breeze puffed, dropped, puffed again. She craned her neck to look both ways along the beach, and that was when she saw him—Seward, plodding along, still some distance away, headed in their direction.

Her first thought was: He walks here even when the sun shines! And then: "Gran!" she called. "Come look. He's on the beach again."

Gran came in from the kitchen, where she'd been setting a pot of beans to soak, and stumped up to the window. By this time, Seward had made his way a great deal closer and his face was lifted. He was looking toward the house.

"Speak of the Devil, and he'll appear," said Gran.

Jenny understood for the first time what this expression really meant, and she shivered a little. "Do you think he's coming to the house?" she whispered, as if she feared he'd hear her through the glass.

"He never has before," said Gran. "He'll pass on by, no doubt."

But he did not pass on by. When he arrived at the bluff, he turned and, coming up the sand beside it, paused, pulling at his beard.

"Stand back," Gran murmured. "He'll see us. He's coming in." She moved away from the window, and Jenny, turning too, saw that she stood very straight beside her chair, her chin up. "We'll tell him

nothing, Geneva," she said. "Whatever he asks, we'll tell him nothing. There. There's his knock. Let him in, child."

If Seward was a ghost, he was a very solid one, a rather short man, only a few inches taller than Jenny, but stocky, wearing the same coat she had seen him in before. His tousled hair and beard were damp and beaded with sea spray, and the rough-skinned folds and pouches of his face made him look as if he'd spent a dozen lifetimes on the beach. He wiped his sandy boots carefully before he came in, and he stood in the parlor a little awkwardly, keeping his hands in his pockets. He looked about the room, and when his quiet eyes found the plaster sea gull, they flickered briefly and then were quiet once more. "I'm sorry to intrude on you this way, Mrs. Reade," he said, and Jenny thought again how much his low voice sounded like the breeze.

"You're welcome here," said Gran stiffly.

"Something has come," he said.

Gran's fingers tightened on her crutch. "I don't know what you mean," she said.

"It's valued," he said, ignoring her words. He spoke without severity, without any emotion at all. "You must give it back at once."

"I don't know what you mean," Gran repeated. "Nothing has come."

There was a pause, and then his gaze moved to Jenny. "She must give it back, miss," he said.

Jenny found herself unable to speak. She could only stand there clutching the skirt of her pinafore, staring at him.

At last he said, "I'll come again." He turned and stood at the door, waiting. Jenny went and opened it, and he stepped over the sill into the wind, his hair lifting and fluttering. Jenny noticed, then, that much of it was white. "Goodbye, Mrs. Reade," he said without looking back.

"Goodbye, Seward," said Gran with the same stiffness in her voice.

Jenny shut the door behind him and went to the window to watch him move away. Gran said, "He shan't have it." And all the easy calm of the last few days was gone. "I've waited too long. I'll never give it up."

"How did he know?" asked Jenny, feeling again a trembling in her stomach. "What will he do?"

"I don't know," said Gran, "but he shan't have it. If he comes back, Geneva, you're not to let him in."

11

Early in the evening, after supper, Gran said, "I want to go out and have a look around. Let's go sit on the bench for a while."

"But what if Seward comes back?" Jenny asked her nervously. "What if he's out there now?"

"If he is, he is," said Gran defiantly. "I'm not going to shut myself up in this house because of him. I haven't been out for a week, and I need a breath of air. Get the oilskin, Geneva. The bench will still be damp and we'll need something to sit on."

Outside, settled on the bench, the two sat for a long time without speaking. Gran kept her back straight, standing the crutch upright against her knees, gazing up and down the beach, but there was no one to be seen walking there. Waves came rolling in smoothly, in even rows that smacked the whole length of the beach at once till the sand seemed to ring with them. There was no wind at all.

"Gran," Jenny said at last, "doesn't the sky look funny!" She had been studying it, and had thought at first that it was promising another sunny day tomorrow, but now she was not so sure. From far to the south, high feathers of cloud were fanning up and out from what appeared to be a single point on the horizon, and behind the house they were stained to brilliant orange and scarlet as the sun dropped. "Gran," said Jenny, "look! The clouds are coming in a great big V."

Gran looked up, and her eyes narrowed. After a pause, she said,

"Yes. I've seen it like that before. There's a storm somewhere out to sea. Maybe even a hurricane. It's the time of year for it."

"A hurricane!" Jenny exclaimed, and all at once she was dismayed. They heard of such things in Springfield from time to time, and had even felt the fringes of the worst ones in the form of lashing rains and wind. Her father—how pale and quiet he would be until the storm was over! She remembered standing beside him at a window when she was much smaller, watching the raindrops drive against the pane, and he had said, not really to her, "It's a terrible way to go, out at sea in such a storm." And she had thought at the time that by "go" he had meant, simply, "travel," and could not understand the dread she sensed in him. Now she understood it very well, and felt the dread herself. The *Amaryllis* had been lost in a hurricane, and he had stood here, right here where she was sitting now, and watched it all happen. And couldn't do a thing to stop it. "A hurricane!" she repeated. "Will it come here?"

"Perhaps," said Gran, "but I don't think so. They very rarely do. We might get the edges, if there is one, but that's all." Her manner was casual, but there was something behind it that Jenny couldn't read—something hard.

"The air is so quiet." said Jenny uneasily. "There isn't any wind at all."

"Not now," said Gran, "but it may pick up. You mustn't let it frighten you, Geneva. Weather is only weather. It comes and goes."

Jenny was amazed by this response. She stared at Gran, and then she said, "But, Gran, how can you say that when you know what the sea can do?"

"*What* can it do, Geneva?" Gran asked, and her voice was harsh. "Rise up? Swallow ships? Wash away a town? Yes, it can do all that. It can take your life, your love, everything you have that you care for. So. What should *you* do? Run away from it, as your father did? Run to Springfield and hide in a closet so you don't have to hear it or see it, or even think of it? That doesn't make it go away. It's still here, doing what it pleases. So you stay and try to keep what's left to you. You wait it out. You fight it and survive it. Lots of storms have blown across this bay, blown and gone, and I'm still here. Strong as ever. I'm not afraid of it, and never was." She sat breathing hard for a moment and then she said, in a cooler voice, "You mustn't be afraid of it, either."

Jenny was silent, her grandmother's scorn for her father burning deep inside her. Gran seemed like a rock there next to her. Invincible. And unforgiving. There was something fine in her defiance, but something heartless, too. Jenny wondered if she herself could be a rock, but looking out at the water, she doubted it. The sea was full of transformations. It was very wide, and very deep. And she was very small.

"Come," said Gran at last, pulling herself up. "We'll go inside now."

In the time that remained till bedtime, as they sat in the parlor, each with her own book open in her lap, the breeze came back gradually, first in little puffs and gusts, and then in longer sweeps that whined at the corners of the house. Gran looked up, listened, and laid her book aside. "Geneva," she said, "we've left the oilskin out on the bench. I can hear it flapping. Go out and get it, child, before it blows away."

"Yes, Gran," said Jenny. She went outside and stood in front of the house for a moment. It was growing dark very rapidly, and the sea, though it had been lying far out before, was rising, in those long, smooth swells, at a pace that seemed unusual even to Jenny's inexperienced eye. She hurried to the bench and took up the oilskin, and then, turning, she stopped short and gasped. Seward was standing on the grass between her and the house.

"Good evening, miss," he said.

"G-good evening," Jenny stammered.

"I said I'd come again," he reminded her. "I didn't mean to startle you."

Jenny stared at him, not knowing what to say. Gran had told her she mustn't let him into the house, but what if he insisted?

"Tell her for me," he said, as if he could read her thought, "that she must give it back at once."

"She won't though," Jenny blurted, forgetting that she was to tell him nothing. "She said so."

"She must," said Seward. "It's valued. The ship can't find its way along the bottom without its eyes. Explain to her. She must give it back now, before it's too late."

Jenny's breath caught. "Oh, please," she begged, "what do you mean? What will happen?"

"If she doesn't give it back," said Seward in that voice without emotion, "the sea will come and take it." He turned away. "Tell her," he said over his shoulder, and then he disappeared into the dark.

But, inside Gran set her jaw and said, "Never. No matter what. Does he think I waited half a lifetime just to give up now? Don't be afraid, Geneva. Go to bed." She sat up straight in her chair, her eyes bright and hard, gripping the crutch across her knees like a weapon. "I shall stay down here tonight," she said, "and wait."

12

All night the hurricane—for there was a hurricane—wheeled slowly north. Its eye rode far offshore, but its sweeping arms of wind and rain clawed at the nearest beaches, and the sea rose up before it in great, spreading welts that raced for miles ahead, rolling in to land in the measured waves Jenny had seen at evening.

It had begun a week before, this hurricane, on the very day of the arrival of the sign, begun as a petulance deep in the Caribbean. But as it swung in an upward arc to the west and north, its indignation grew, the speed of its winds increased until at last, arriving in mid-coastal waters, it had spun itself into a rage. It was small, no more than forty miles across, but deadly: round its eye the winds were whirling ninety miles an hour. It paused at dawn and hung for an hour, and then, as if its orders had been heard, its target sighted, it veered abruptly westward toward the coast, and the sea ran on ahead in a frenzy of excitement.

All night Jenny had slept in fits and starts, aware of the booming rhythm of the waves. Then, after hours of tossing, she was brought bolt upright by a sudden Niagara of rain. At the same moment a blast of wind slammed at the house, a wind that did not pass off but kept on coming, its voice rising steadily. The light was so dim that she could barely see, and could not guess what time it was. Alarmed, she slipped out of bed, pulled on her clothes, and crept downstairs, holding tight to the banister. The clock in the lower hall said eight o'clock. Morning! But it seemed more like the onset of the night.

She peered into the parlor and saw that Gran was sitting rigid in her chair, wide awake, still gripping the crutch across her knees. "Gran," Jenny quavered, "is this it? Has the hurricane come?"

"Yes," said Gran. "It's here. It's just beginning."

"Oh, Gran, what shall we do?" wailed Jenny.

"We shall wait!" Gran rapped out. "It's only a storm. Only a storm, Geneva! We shall sit here and wait it out."

Jenny was drawn almost against her will to the window, and what she saw there dizzied her. Under the darkened sky, the sea was white, running sidewise, exploding in sheets of spray against the long arm of the land that formed their end of the little bay. Clots of foam fled by through the air like rushing phantoms, and the water was so high that the beach had vanished. Rain was flung past the window horizontally, so that it was hard to tell the place where it ended and the sea began. Everything was water. And noise. For the voice of the wind kept rising steadily. Jenny shrank back from the window. "Oh, Gran!" she whispered.

"It's only a storm, I tell you," Gran insisted. Her face was stony. "Go put the kettle on for tea."

Jenny went to the kitchen and took up the kettle. She was trembling so much that it rattled in her hand, and she could not get the pump to work. She leaned against the metal sink and worked the handle up and down, up and down, but nothing came. Helplessly, she went back to the parlor. "There's no water!" she exclaimed.

Gran laughed at this, a harsh, unnatural laugh. "No water!" she echoed. "Milk, then. And bread. We must keep up our strength."

They sat in the parlor with their bread and milk, but Jenny could scarcely swallow. She wanted to cover her ears, to run away, but there was nowhere to run. That other world she had accepted, that world that lay beyond the edges of the sea, had loomed up and now was blotting out, shouldering out, drowning out the real world altogether. The parlor, the house, and everything in it seemed altered—thin and unfamiliar—as if the order she depended on had warped and might collapse at any moment. She wanted to cry, but Gran's fierce expression kept her from it. Her grandmother sat with narrowed eyes and ate slowly, refusing to acknowledge the rising bellow of the wind, ignoring the spray dashed in around the windows, down the complaining chimney, under the bolted door. The house trembled, Jenny trembled, the whole world trembled. Gran alone was firm.

Outside, the wind increased. Impossible, and yet its voice grew stronger, till the roaring was almost intolerable. Jenny doubled over on the sofa, her arms around her head, but still she dared not cry. And then, after a time, Gran seemed to notice her and said, "Geneva. Sit up." Her voice was steely. "Take away the plates and glasses. Now."

Jenny got to her feet somehow, and did as she was told. "I *won't* cry," she told herself over and over. "I won't let her see me cry."

When she came back to the parlor, Gran said to her, "Bring me the head." Without a word, Jenny took the key from the china teapot, opened the drawer in the dining room, lifted out the wooden head, brought it to Gran. Gran took it and settled it in her lap, pushing the crutch off onto the floor. "Now," she said, "go and sit down. And wait."

Perched again on the sofa, Jenny wrung her hands and fought back tears. There was nothing else to do but sit and wait, while the storm shrieked on, all around the house. Outside, the sea rose higher and came searching almost to the top of the little bluff. Sit and wait—it can't go on forever—there isn't that much wind and water in the world. Jenny's thoughts presented these alternatives to nightmare, but other thoughts rejected them: sit and wait for the sea to come and take us—take the wooden head and me and Gran and everything.

And then, after a screaming eternity, the clock in the hall began to strike, a faint, feeble sound against the wind—bong, bong, bong, all the way up to ten. And as if the tenth stroke were a signal, the storm stopped. Suddenly. The rain stopped, the wind stopped, the room was full of dazzling sunlight. Jenny thought, "We're dead. We've gone to heaven." Her ears rang with the silence. She looked at Gran, but her grandmother sat as stiffly upright as before. "Gran!" she cried. "Is it over? How can it be over all at once like that?"

"It's *half* over," said Gran. "We're in the eye. It will only last a few minutes." She did not take her hands from the wooden head in her lap. She did not stir at all.

450

Jenny got up from the sofa and ventured again to the window. The sea had risen just over the top of the bluff and now, instead of rushing sidewise to the arm of land beside them, it raged like boiling water in a great pot, tumbling, churning, rushing in every direction at once, smashing against itself and casting up bursts of glittering spray. The sky overhead was a brilliant blue, with only a few loose clouds to mottle it.

But Jenny saw with horror that before them and encircling them was a towering wall of thick, black clouds, closing them in, rising from the water like the sides of a chasm, miles into the air—a chasm from which there could be no escape. She could see the topmost edges of the wall, folded back smoothly against the sky. And she could see that it was moving, its far arc gliding toward them across the furious sea.

Gran did not get up to look. She stayed where she was, her hands on the wooden head, and she said, "It will start again soon."

Jenny stood hypnotized at the window, watching as the walls of black came onward. Gradually, the room grew dimmer, the dazzling patch of sky was curtained out. And then the clouds engulfed them. Instantly, the wind began again, shrieking louder than ever, and the world outside was lost in new sheets of rain that swept in the opposite direction now, northward toward the town at the other end of the bay.

This shift seemed to catch the house off-guard. There was a crash high over their heads, and a sluice of water spread into the parlor

from the fireplace, like blood streaming from a wound. "Why, the chimney's gone!" Gran exclaimed. She sounded shocked, surprised. The sudden breaching of her fortress seemed to jar her own determination; she bent a little in her chair, gripping the wooden head, and her voice had lost a fraction of its metal.

Jenny sensed the loss and it chilled her, for she had been drawing her own slim courage from Gran. She moved backward from the window and stood distracted in the middle of the room, her hands tight over her ears now to cut the screeching wind. She had no notion what to do. Her mind was numb, her bones like jelly, and it seemed as if only the locking of her muscles could hold her upright. From the kitchen came another crash, a sound of shattering glass, and at once the house was full of wind. A lamp toppled, the curtains rose up like banners. And with a noise like a cork popping from a bottle the front door burst its bolt and was flung wide open. It hung flapping from one twisted hinge, and in the next moment the sea came over the sill.

It purled into the parlor silently, a foam-flecked, spreading puddle, soaking the braided rug, reaching across the floor. It looked harmless, a simple spill from a pitcher, easy to mop away. But Gran shrank back in her chair. She lifted the wooden head from her lap and held it close in her arms while the water rippled toward her. A low wave rushed at the doorsill and the puddle deepened, spreading rapidly, sliding around her feet, and Jenny's feet, until an inch stood on the floor, from wall to wall, and still Gran sat transfixed. The wind

screamed round and round the house and rushed in through the breaches in a triumph, bringing with it salty flakes of spray. The water on the floor rose slowly, with little currents of its own that beckoned backward toward the gaping doorway even while it rippled in.

Jenny could stand it no longer. "Give the head back, Gran!" she shrilled. "Give it back!" But she could hardly hear her own voice against the wind, and she began to sob, explosively, all efforts to control her tears gone flying.

Then Gran was pushing up from her chair. Her crutch had drifted out of reach, but she stood erect without it. "All *right!*" she cried, but she was not speaking to Jenny. Her face was dark, her jaw thrust out. "All *right!*" she cried again. "All *right!*" She began to wade across the room, moving firmly in spite of her bundled foot.

Jenny's sobs caught in her throat. "Gran!" she gasped. "What are you doing?"

But Gran did not hear her, did not reply. She moved forward, the drenched hem of her skirt trailing out behind her. She came to the doorway and without a pause went out into the storm.

Jenny splashed after her. At the battered door, she shouted, "Gran! Be careful! Just drop it into the water, Gran, and then come . . ." But the shout died in her throat, for all at once it was clear that Gran did not mean to come back. She was pushing forward, leaning against the wind, out toward the flooded bluff, and she showed no signs of dropping the wooden head. Her hair tore loose

from its pins and twists and streamed out sidewise. "Gran!" shrieked Jenny. "Gran, no. Come back!"

But Gran could not have heard, for the wind shrieked louder, and the waves were dragging at her knees. She staggered, her arms flew out, and the head, released at last, fell free. And as it fell, the sea rose up and swallowed it. She paused. And then she found her balance once again and struggled on, nearer to the margin of the bluff. Jenny, near fainting, floundered over the doorsill. "Gran!" she shouted. "Wait!"

Then: a miracle. A hand grasped her shoulder from behind, a voice boomed out above the wind: "Jenny! Go back." It was her father— drenched, his hair wild, his jaw thrust out like Gran's. He lifted her and set her back inside the doorway. And then he plunged out into the wind and water, and seized Gran in the final instant, just as she sagged and was dropping into the sea.

13

Tea. Strong, hot, with lots of sugar. It warmed away the cold of Jenny's heart as the blankets wrapped around her warmed away the shivers in her legs. She sat upstairs, in Gran's room, sipping, and watched as her father ministered to his mother. He had cut away the sodden bandages and splints from her ankle, stripped away her dripping dress and petticoats, and bundled her into bed. Then he had gone downstairs, sloshed to the kitchen, coaxed water from the balky pump. He had managed somehow to kindle a fire in the stove, had boiled water in the kettle. He was amazing. And now he was spooning the tea into Gran as if he were feeding a little child, except that her cup had been sharpened with brandy. She lay quietly, accepting it. She had not said a word.

The hurricane was gone. It had whirled directly over them, moved inland, and was breaking up against the hills and trees. "Just another rainstorm by now," said Jenny's father when she asked him. "Noisy and wet, but mostly harmless. You had the worst of it here."

"But, Papa," she said, "how did you know to come?"

"I sat there in the store," he told her, "and I watched the barometers go down and down and down. Finally I couldn't stand it any longer. I hitched up the buggy and I came."

Jenny held her hand over her tea and felt the rising steam turn to dew against her palm. She was thinking about her father—coming out in the storm, coming to the sea. "Papa," she asked him, "where's the buggy now? Where's the horse?"

"I haven't any idea," he said. "After a while the wind got so bad

that limbs were cracking and there were twigs flying everywhere. The horse kept shying, and at last he reared and broke the traces. He ran off, and there I was, sitting like a dummy in the buggy all alone, with rain blowing in my face. So I just climbed out and came the rest of the way on foot." He seemed, himself, amazed at this, even while he told about it.

"On foot!" Jenny exclaimed. "How far?"

"I really don't know," he answered. "A few miles."

"That must have been terrible!" said Jenny, her eyes round. "When Gran went out, I thought the wind would blow her over!"

"I didn't really think about it much," he said. "All I wanted to do was come to the two of you. Why, for all I knew, the house had flooded and you might be . . . well, never mind. It didn't happen. I got here in time."

They were quiet then. He set aside Gran's spoon and teacup, and smoothed a red-gray strand of hair away from her cheek. She sighed and closed her eyes, and he murmured to Jenny, "Come, we'll let her sleep a little now."

In her bedroom, in *his* bedroom, they sat together on the edge of the bed, and he took her hand and held it. Jenny thought about the sign—the wooden head—and wondered if he'd understand when he knew.

"You've had a bad time," he sat at last.

"Oh, no!" she protested. "Not until today! Before the storm, it

456

was—fine, mostly. Papa, do you remember a woman named Isabel Cooper?"

"Hmmm," he said. "No, I don't think so. Why?"

"Well, but do you remember a man named Nicholas?"

"Yes," he said, "if you mean Nicholas Irving, the one who carved the figurehead for the *Amaryllis*. He was like a big brother to me there for a while. Why, he taught me how to swim! But that was a long time ago, Jenny. Has Gran been talking about him?"

"Yes," said Jenny. "She's talked a lot about the old days. Nicholas Irving was in love with Isabel Cooper, but she didn't like him. That's why he tried to drown himself."

"Ah!" said her father. "Yes, I remember now. A terrible thing. Isn't it amazing what people will do for love!" He paused, and his serious expression turned into a smile. "Why, some people will even go out in a buggy in the worst storm of the age!"

"And come to the sea, even if they don't like it," Jenny added wisely.

"Yes," he said. "And come to the sea."

After a moment, she asked, "Were you scared, Papa?"

He lifted her hand and moved her fingers about, as if he was amazed at how well they worked. "You know," he said, "I didn't even stop to think about it. I just . . . got into the buggy and came."

"You were brave, the way you went and rescued Gran," said Jenny admiringly. "Maybe you won't be scared ever again after this."

There was a pause, and then he said, "Maybe not."

Jenny hopped down off the bed. "Wait here, Papa," she said. "I want to show you something." She hurried into the back bedroom and returned with the little tin trumpet and the wooden cannon. "Look, Papa. Look what we found in the trunk!"

Her father took the toys and stared at them in astonishment. "Good Lord. Why, I remember these. Imagine her saving them all this time!" He sat there thinking, and then he said, "Jenny, what was Gran doing, out there in the storm like that?"

Jenny looked at him soberly. "It's hard to explain, Papa. Wait. I've got one more thing to show you." She hurried out again and went to Gran's room. Gran was dozing, her face slack against the pillow. Jenny tiptoed in, went to the highboy in the corner, and took the gold watch from the drawer where Gran had told her to put it for safekeeping. Back in her father's room, she laid it gently in his hand. "It's for you," she said. "Grandfather had it all engraved and every-thing. For your twenty-first birthday. But Gran forgot." Then she added quickly, "But she's very sorry. Look inside the lid, Papa. Open it."

Her father lifted the thin back carefully and stared at the engrav-ing. "Oh!" he whispered. Then, in a steadier voice: "Jenny, how incredible! Why, it's almost like a message, isn't it? After all these years!"

Jenny drew a deep breath. "Papa," she said, "do you believe in things you can't explain?"

He looked at her, puzzled, and then he said slowly. "Yes, I guess I do. Sometimes. Here, especially."

And so she told him everything.

Later, when the story was done, Jenny leaned her head against her father's shoulder and sighed. "But, you know, Papa, she waited so long—and now she doesn't have anything."

"But she does!" said her father. "She has us, just as she always did. Maybe she'll see that, now." He picked up the little tin trumpet and blew into it. The thin bleat sounded loud in the quiet, and he put it down quickly, but it was too late. From the next room a voice called.

"George?"

They went to the door of Gran's room and saw that she was sitting up in bed. "Well, George," she said. She sounded very tired.

"Well, Mother," he returned.

"Dear boy," she said to him, "come and kiss me."

They ate their supper upstairs in Gran's room, a supper thrown together, by Jenny and her father, any old way in the ruined kitchen. But Gran had very little appetite. She sat propped up with pillows, and she kept moving her foot under the covers.

"How does it feel?" Jenny asked.

"Light without all those bandages," she said. "But whether it's mended or not, I really can't tell."

"Well," said Jenny's father, "either way, you'd better come back to Springfield, at least until we can get someone to clean up the mess downstairs."

"Is it very bad?" she asked him.

"I'm afraid so," he said. "The wind smashed the kitchen window and blew everything all around, the front door's almost off, the chimney's gone entirely. And the floor—some of the boards are bound to warp. It may take weeks to dry."

"It's been a good house," said Gran. "It just couldn't quite hold out. I couldn't hold out, either, George. We're old, this house and I."

"And yet," he said, "you can mend, both of you."

"No," said Gran. "We can be patched up, stuck back together one way or another, perhaps, but it wouldn't last for long. You've been urging me to come and stay in Springfield for years, George. I think the time has come for me to do it now."

"We've always wanted you," he said, "but only if you really wanted to come."

She shrugged. "I'm tired," she said. "I think I'll go to sleep now."

"I'll find a horse and buggy first thing in the morning," he told her, spreading up her covers. "We'll get an early start."

"All right," she said, and closed her eyes.

Jenny went up to the bed and leaned down to kiss her grandmother's cheek. "Good night, Gran," she said.

And Gran said, "Good night . . . Jenny."

14

In the morning, Jenny woke to soft sunshine. She climbed out of bed and crossed to the window. Below, the beach was clean and smooth, and the sea lay smiling and slopping contentedly far down the sand. Just offshore, a gull was wheeling against the bright blue sky. "Yesterday," Jenny reminded herself, "there was a hurricane!" But it was hard to remember now. Until she remembered Gran. "We're all going home today," she murmured, and in spite of the warm sunlight, she was filled with sadness.

She was pulling on her clothes when her father appeared in the doorway. "Well, lazybones," he said, "it's about time you were up. I've been to town already and brought back a first-rate horse and buggy. Pack your things. We'll be leaving soon."

"How's Gran?" she asked him.

"She's ready," he said. "We've both had breakfast. There's milk and bread and an orange for you downstairs. Come along. I'm anxious to get started. Your mother will be worried to death."

"I'll be ready in a minute," she said.

Downstairs, it would have been impossible to forget the storm. The parlor had a dismal look and a damp, unnatural smell. Water stood in the corners, and there was wet sand crusted everywhere. From the blown-in kitchen window a light breeze stirred the limp curtains and passed on out through the space where the front door had been propped against a side of the gaping doorframe. The clock in the hall

had stopped. Jenny took up her orange and, peeling it as she went, wandered sadly through the rooms. The life had gone from the house. It looked defeated.

She paused in the dining room and, sucking her orange, looked at the picture of the ship. It hung a little crooked now, but here, at least, there was spirit still. The ship was so beautiful, a crisp, strong, winged thing, the figurehead intact and calm, with the big red blossom cradled in its hands. It had a presence, an unshakable intent; it seemed almost, this morning, to leap from the frame and sail into the room. Jenny could feel its force. She lowered the orange from her mouth and stood puzzled, staring.

"Jenny!" her father called. "We're ready. Come along."

She backed away from the picture reluctantly and, turning, went through the parlor to the door. Her father was carrying Gran in his arms, crossing the strip of grass to the rented buggy. Gran's face was quiet, closed. The horse stood waiting, jingling his harness. Jenny went out across the doorsill and hesitated for a moment. The air was warm and soft and the sea sparkled, tossing up tiny whitecaps. It was very still, and yet—somewhere there was an urgency. "Just a minute," Jenny said to her father. She felt drawn strongly to the beach. She ran down across the sand, down to the water's edge, and looked out.

The flashes of sunlight reflected from the sea were blinding. She rubbed her eyes to free them of the dancing red spots that filled them and made them water. And then she began to walk along the edges of

the low, ruffling waves, down the empty beach in a final tracing of the searches of the week before, still responding to the urgency that seemed to be drawing her.

Coming at last to the scrub-pine stump, she stopped and looked out again. And caught her breath. No more than ten yards out, a small bright object floated on the swells. No, it was only the flashing of the sun in her eyes again. But something seemed to stay beyond her blinking, something reddish-orange, a vibrant spot of color that rode forward on the water. The breeze increased and the object took on dimensions, sailing nearer and nearer, and then, with a final lift of wave, it was slipped across the foam to her feet.

It was a blossom, not made of wood, but real, with six wide, curling petals, and a long white fragile stamen arching out from its cone-shaped heart. A lily, just like the one in the picture. A big red lily from the islands—an amaryllis.

Jenny bent and lifted it up, cupping it in her hands. And then she turned. "Gran!" she cried. "Oh, *Gran!*" She ran back along the beach to the bluff and crossed, up the sand, holding the blossom out before her. "Gran!" she cried again.

As she ran, Gran rose up in the buggy—rose up and then climbed down and went to meet her, striding with long, strong steps. They came together and Gran seized the blossom. Color seemed to flood from it up into her face. And as she stood there, tears running down her cheeks, the breeze came up and whispered once more: *True to yo-o-o-ou..*

Later, as the buggy rolled away, Gran said briskly to her son, "We may have to lay a new floor, George, but that shouldn't be too difficult. And the chimney can be built back up with the same old bricks."

"I can do a lot of the work myself," he said. "We'll rest up at home for a day or two and then bring everybody back and get started. I need a vacation, anyway. Exercise. Do you know I haven't been swimming in years?"

"I know," said Gran. "You're white as a clam."

As their talk went on, Jenny sat looking backward at the battered house dropping away behind them. And then she saw a short, dark figure standing on the beach. He was looking after them, and on an impulse Jenny lifted an arm and waved. He stood motionless, and then he turned and walked away down the beach, but his step seemed lighter to her, now, than it had before. As he disappeared, the sea flashed its wide green smile and answered her wave with a careless toss of foam. She leaned far out of the buggy and shouted to it, "We're coming back!" And then she settled herself in her seat and put a hand into the pocket of her pinafore. There was sand in the pocket, and she chased it around the thready inside seam with her fingertips, humming under her breath.

The buggy topped the rise and rolled on under a stand of trees, and after a while came to a fence along the road, behind which a few cows were grazing peacefully. There was a boy at work in the grass, picking up the litter of twigs and small branches scattered by the vanished storm, and as the buggy passed him, he straightened and stared at Jenny with wide-eyed admiration. She ignored him, holding her chin high, and said to herself, "That's silly." But she retied the ribbon that held back her hair, settling its bow more carefully, and smiled all the way to Springfield.

Meet the Author: **Natalie Babbitt**

Natalie Babbitt has been in love with books all her life. As a child, she read endlessly, mostly fairy tales and Greek myths, and her mother and father read to her as well.

Ms. Babbitt has also had a love affair with the alphabet ever since she was a child. She writes: "The alphabet is still a miracle to me—how those twenty-six funny shapes can group themselves in endlessly different ways to make words with endlessly different meanings. . .

"My mother and I used to play a game called Anagrams where you made words out of letters printed on small, tidy squares of thick cardboard. Every once in a while, one would drop on the floor, and Dingo, our dog, would chew it. We didn't mind so much if it was a J or a Q because those were hard letters to use, but it was bad if an E or an S got chewed. Still, we just let them dry out and used them anyway, rumpled though they were with tooth marks.

"Now my daughter, Lucy, and I play Boggle whenever we're together. The letters for this game are printed on wooden cubes, and Rosie, the dog we have now, isn't much interested in them. I think dogs like the taste of paper better—Rosie always enjoys a paper napkin for a snack if she can sneak one. But whether they're printed on cardboard or wood or on the pages of a book, for me it's the same fascination over and over—those twenty-six funny shapes and the magical things they can do with each other."

Responding to Literature

1. In the prologue, Seward begins by asking, "Listen, all you people lying lazy on the beach, is this what you imagine is the meaning of the sea?" Do you think the story changed your understanding of the sea? Explain your answer.

2. Jenny is away from her Springfield home for only a few weeks, but a great deal has happened. Imagine that when she returns home, she sits down to tell her mother of her stay at Gran's. Tell the important events Jenny would explain to her mother.

3. Jenny, her father, and Gran leave together in the buggy at the end of the story. But each character is in some way different from the person he or she was in the beginning of the story. Explain how Jenny, her father, and Gran have changed.

4. Before the hurricane hits, Jenny thinks that Gran's house "stood at the edge of another world, at the edge where the things she understood and the things beyond her understanding began to merge and blur." Give two examples of events in the story that belong to the other world beyond Jenny's understanding.

5. Gran asks Jenny early in the story if she believes in things she cannot explain. Tell of a story or event you have heard that is an example of something that cannot be easily explained.

The Noise of Waters

All day I hear the noise of waters
    Making moan,
Sad as the sea-bird is, when going
    Forth alone,
He hears the winds cry to the waters'
    Monotone.

The grey winds, the cold winds are blowing
    Where I go.
I hear the noise of many waters
    Far below.
All day, all night, I hear them flowing
    To and fro.

James Joyce

The Sea

The sea is a hungry dog,
Giant and gray.
He rolls on the beach all day.
With his clashing teeth and shaggy jaws

Hour upon hour he gnaws
The rumbling, tumbling stones,
And "Bones, bones, bones, bones!"
The giant sea-dog moans,
Licking his greasy paws.

And when the night wind roars
And the moon rocks in the stormy cloud,
He bounds to his feet and snuffs and sniffs,
Shaking his wet sides over the cliffs,
And howls and hollos long and loud.

But on quiet days in May or June,
When even the grasses on the dune
Play no more their reedy tune,
With his head between his paws
He lies on the sandy shores,
So quiet, so quiet, he scarcely snores.

James Reeves

Appreciating Author's Craft

Reading *The Eyes of the* Amaryllis, you might experience a feeling of suspense, excitement, or mystery. The author's choice of setting, objects, details, and words all help create the mood. Turn to page 414, the second paragraph, and read. Think about the feeling you get reading about Jenny's walk on the beach before she finds the figurehead.

The ghostly, unreal atmosphere of the beach is the perfect setting for a sign from a ghost ship at the bottom of the sea. This setting affects Jenny in such a way that she isn't quite sure if she is in a real or dream world. Natalie Babbitt chooses her setting, details, and words so carefully that you can move with Jenny in the mysterious mists of Gran's beach.

Writing a Book Review

You will write a book review about *The Eyes of the* Amaryllis, focusing on how skillfully the author helps establish mood through the choice of words. (For ideas about writing, look at The Writer's Handbook.)

Prewriting Turn to page 398 to Jenny's first search on the beach. What kind of feelings do you get when you read the passage? What are some of the sights, sounds, and actions that contribute to the mood? What words help you see, hear, and feel the setting?

On the chart on the next page are listed some of the words that establish mood on page 398. At the right are listed some possible feelings that you might have about this page. Copy this chart on a piece of paper. For the pages indicated, make a list of mood words and your feelings created by these words.

Mood Words	Possible Feelings
page 398	
rolling water seized her feet and dragged at them	suspense frightening excitement mystery
filled with dread	
freedom and exhilaration	
wild, dark, rushing water	
Pages 400–401	
Pages 447–448	

Writing For your book review, begin with your opinion of the novel, which will serve as a topic sentence. Then briefly summarize the plot. The rest of your review should be about how the author uses words to create a mood and your feelings created by these words. For example, when you are writing about pages 447–448, you could draw attention to words such as "the sea was exploding in sheets of spray" and "the voice of the wind kept rising steadily." You could write that these words helped you feel the power of the wind and the sea.

Revising Read through your draft with your chart alongside you. Then write the final copy of your book review.

Presenting Read your review to someone who hasn't read the novel to see if your review convinces him or her to read the novel.

Extending Your Reading

Expressing Yourself
Choose one or more of these activities:

Research Sailing Ships Go to the library to find pictures of sailing ships from the nineteenth century. Try to find one that is two masted like the *Amaryllis*. Share your discoveries with the class.

Draw a Ghost Ship Turn to pages 430–431 to read the description of the *Amaryllis* as Nicholas Irving saw it. Use the description and your own imagination to draw the ship at the bottom of the sea.

Listening to Music Ask your teacher or librarian to help you find a recording or cassette tape of Claude Debussy's *La Mer.* Play the recording for your classmates. Listen to the music once with your eyes closed. Then listen to it again and write down words which describe what you imagine. Share your ideas with your classmates.

Chart the Amaryllis's Journey Find a map which includes North America and the Caribbean Sea. Place a mark on the *Amaryllis*'s ports of call: Antigua, Maine, Puerto Rico, Haiti, Trinidad, and New York City.

Poetry Anthology The poems on pages 470–471 are about the wind. Compile a short collection of poetry about wind, rain, or snow, and let your classmates read it.

More Books About Fantasy

The Wolves of Willoughby Chase by Joan Aiken. Doubleday. Fierce wolves running around the countryside and a great English country house with a secret passage provide the background for this gripping tale about nineteenth-century England. Two young cousins are left in the care of an evil, scheming governess. Little do they know what terrifying adventures await them.

A Stranger Came Ashore by Mollie Hunter. Harper. On the night of a fierce storm there is a shipwreck in the waters around the Shetland Islands. Rain and wind sweep a stranger into the life of the Henderson family. The stranger is Finn Learson, a young handsome man who *seems* to be the only survivor of the wreck. When the terrible truth about the stranger is revealed, young Robbie has to act quickly to save his sister in this suspenseful thriller.

Mrs. Frisby and the Rats of NIMH by Robert C. O'Brien. Atheneum. Mrs. Frisby, a widowed mouse with four children, is faced with a problem. Needing help, she goes to a wise old owl, and through him meets the rats of NIMH, who are not ordinary rats. How these rats are able to help Mrs. Frisby makes engrossing reading.

The White Mountains by John Christopher. Macmillan. Machine creatures called Tripods control the earth in this exciting story of the twenty-first century. When children reach fourteen years of age, they undergo an operation called Capping, which puts them under the domination of the Tripods. Three boys, learning that free people live in the White Mountains, decide to escape before they are capped. Many adventures lay before them.

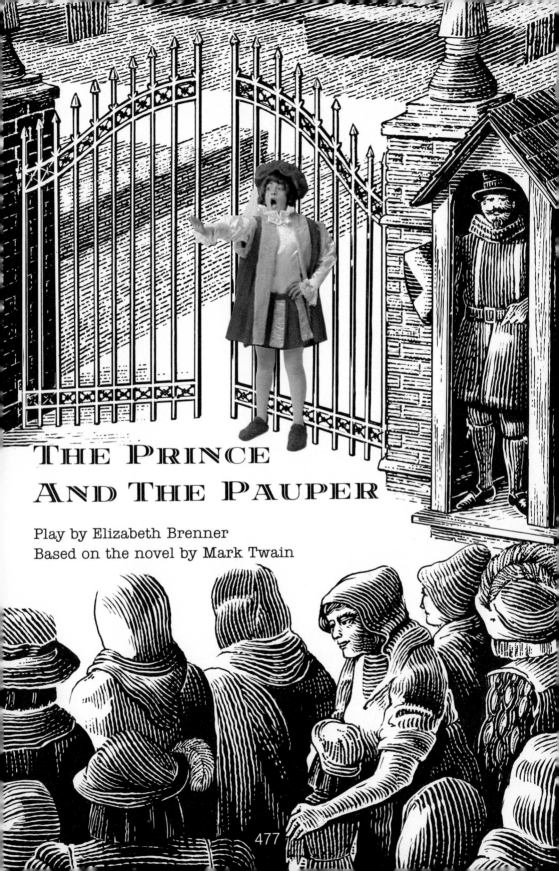

The Prince
And The Pauper

Play by Elizabeth Brenner
Based on the novel by Mark Twain

Introducing

The Prince And The Pauper

When Mark Twain wrote his novels over a hundred years ago, he never dreamed they would become so popular. Most of his writings are still in print today. *The Adventures of Huckleberry Finn* appeals to readers of all ages. Young people especially like *The Adventures of Tom Sawyer* and *The Prince and the Pauper*.

Many of Twain's books have been made into plays, musicals, cartoons, and films. Twain was the first American to write in a style that sounds like real speech. People today still know the names of the wonderful characters in his stories. The adventures of Twain's characters make people laugh but think about serious things as well.

What Makes Mark Twain Fun to Read?

Much of Twain's writing shows his great sense of humor. In *The Prince and the Pauper*, Twain uses a kind of humor called role reversal where one character pretends to be or is mistaken for someone else. The audience knows about the switch, but the fun is in seeing how the other characters in the story react.

Twain also conveys humor through the use of language.

The Pauper talks like an ordinary boy even when he has become a prince. The Prince always talks and acts in a regal manner. The other characters, not knowing the situation, think the Prince and the Pauper are both mad.

You might find some of the expressions humorous too. Twain is writing about old England and so he uses such quaint expressions as "Call back your wandering memory" and "Do you mark the resemblance?"

Thinking About Setting

Setting is the time and place of the events in a story. Sometimes setting is not very important, but in this play, based on Mark Twain's work, visualizing the setting adds to our understanding of the plot. As you read this play, you can make your own mental pictures of the characters in action in their settings. To help you set a scene, a narrator describes the setting and some of the action.

As you are reading this play on your own, find out what changes the Prince and the Pauper make in their lives and how the changes affect each one.

The Prince And The Pauper

CLASSIC

by Mark Twain
adapted by Elizabeth Brenner

(16 boys, 5 girls, and the narrator)

CHARACTERS

NARRATOR	HUGO ⎫ friends of John Canty
TOM CANTY, a poor boy who looks like the prince	RUFFLER ⎭
	TWO GUARDS, palace guards
PRINCE EDWARD, a young English prince	TWO WOMEN ⎫ part of crowd
LORD ST. JOHN ⎫ advisors to the king	TWO MEN ⎭
EARL OF HERTFORD ⎭ and prince	PAGE
JOHN CANTY, Tom's father	COOK
MOTHER, Tom's mother	GROOM
GAMMER CANTY, Tom's grandmother	BUTLER ⎬ Attendants of the Court
	LORD
	LADY

NARRATOR: This play takes place in the early sixteenth century. The setting is outside the gate of Westminster Palace. Two guards march to their stations while a crowd moves in on both sides. The crowd is talking about the royal family.

1st WOMAN: Perhaps the King himself will come outside today.

2nd WOMAN: You hope for too much. If only I could get a glimpse of the young Prince! They say he is very handsome.

1st MAN: I hear the King is ill. He'll not show himself this afternoon.

1st WOMAN: I saw the royal Princess only last Sunday. She grows more beautiful every day.

2nd MAN: Look out, young fellow. Standing there is not a safe occupation for the likes of you.

TOM: *(Excitedly)*: The Prince! I can see the Prince!

1st GUARD: Mind your manners, you young beggar!

TOM: Let me go! Let me go!

1st MAN *(Quickly)*: Look, the Prince is here!

2nd MAN: The Prince has come out of the palace grounds!

PRINCE *(Indignantly)*: Guards! How dare you treat a poor lad like that! How dare you use my father's lowest subject so! Release him! Open the gates and let him in. Away with you! *(In a kindly voice)* Lad, you look tired and hungry; you have been ill-treated. Come with me.

NARRATOR: A few minutes later, we find ourselves in the chamber of the Prince. Tom is sitting at a table spread with all kinds of food. He looks at it with awe as he eats. The Prince walks about the room, talking to Tom.

PRINCE: Good. Now that I've dismissed my attendants, we can talk. What is your name?

TOM: Tom Canty, if it pleases you, sir.

PRINCE: 'Tis an odd name. Where do you live?

TOM: Offal Court, in the city, sir.

PRINCE: Offal Court! Another odd name. Have you parents?

TOM: I have two parents and Gammer Canty, my grandmother, besides; but I do not care so much for her, if I may say so, sir. I also have sisters, Nan and Bet.

PRINCE: Is your grandmother not kind to you?

TOM: She has, I fear, a wicked heart, and is not kind to me or to anyone else.

PRINCE: Does she mistreat you?

TOM: There are times when she beats me, sir.

PRINCE: Beats you—and you so frail and small. To the Tower[1] with her!

---

1. Tower of London: where many persons of royal and noble blood were held prisoner.

TOM: Sir, you forget our low station. The Tower is only for great criminals.

PRINCE: So it is. I shall have to think of some other punishment for her. Is your father kind to you?

TOM: No worse than my grandmother, sir, but my mother is good to me, as are my sisters.

PRINCE: Well, that is better! Tell me more about your life at Offal Court. What do you do for fun there?

TOM: Oh, we do have a good time there, except when we are hungry. There are Punch and Judy shows,[2] and dancing monkeys!

PRINCE: Yes, yes, go on!

TOM: We boys of Offal Court have sparring matches and races, and in the summer we wade and swim in the canals and the river.

PRINCE: It would be worth my father's kingdom to enjoy that just once!

TOM: We dance and sing around the Maypole,[3] and roll in the mud sometimes, too.

PRINCE: Oh, say no more! If only I could wear clothes like yours just once and run barefoot through mud—I think I would give up my crown for that!

TOM: If I could wear such fine clothes as yours just once—

---

2. Punch and Judy shows: a puppet show in which Punch quarrels violently with his wife Judy.

3. Maypole: a high pole decorated with flowers or ribbons, used as part of May Day festivities.

PRINCE	*(Quickly)*: Would you really like that? Then it shall be. I'll call the servants to clear away the table. While they do that, you and I shall go into the next room and exchange clothing. *(Calls)* Page!
PAGE:	Yes, Your Highness?
PRINCE:	Tell the First Groom of the Chamber, the Lord Chief Butler, and the Lord Head Cook to come and clear away this table.
PAGE:	Yes, Your Highness.
PRINCE:	Quickly, lad, follow me. Now's our chance. My attendants will be occupied and will not find us.
NARRATOR:	A moment later, the royal servants enter and clear the dining table. While they are busy, Tom and the Prince leave the room. When the boys re-enter, they have exchanged clothing. They run over and stare first into the mirror, then at each other.
PRINCE:	What do you make of this, Tom Canty?
TOM:	Your worship, do not make me answer. It is not right that a person of my station say such a thing.
PRINCE:	Then *I* will say it. You have the same hair, the same eyes, the same voice and manner, the same stature, the same face as I. Now that we have exchanged clothing, there's no one who could tell us apart. Where did you get that bruise on your hand?
TOM:	It is nothing, sir. The poor guard at the gate—
PRINCE:	That was a cruel thing to do. I'll speak to him at once. Do not move until I return. That is a command.

NARRATOR: The Prince, in Tom's clothing, goes to the main gate. The guards, thinking he is Tom, laugh and push him into the street.

1st GUARD: Away with you, beggar!

2nd GUARD: That's what you get for making trouble for us with the Prince, you pauper.

PRINCE: I am the Prince of Wales, and you will be hanged for laying a hand on me.

1st GUARD *(Mockingly)*: I salute your gracious Highness. *(Angrily)* Be off, you crazy rubbish! And you too, old man! What do you want?

JOHN CANTY: I want the lad. So there you are, Tom, out gawking at royalty and haven't begged a farthing for me, I warrant. If it be so, I'll break all the bones in your body, or I'm not John Canty.

PRINCE: So you're his father. Then you will fetch him away and restore me to the palace.

JOHN: *His* father? I am *your* father, and I'll pound that lesson into you, I will.

PRINCE: Do not joke or delay any longer. Take me to the King, my father, and he shall make you rich. Believe me—I am indeed the Prince of Wales.

JOHN *(Astonished)*: He's always had a fancy for royalty, and now he's gone stark mad. But mad or not, Gammer Canty and I will cure the likes of you.

NARRATOR: John Canty drags the boy to his home, believing the Prince is his son Tom. The next day, at the palace, several lords come into the Prince's room, where a table is elaborately spread for dinner.

Listen as the men talk together.

ST. JOHN: What do you think, Lord Hertford?

HERTFORD: It worries me, Lord St. John. The King is near his end and my nephew is mad; mad he will mount the throne, and mad he will remain. God protect England. She will need it!

ST. JOHN: But—have you no doubts as to—as to—

HERTFORD: Speak on—doubts as to what?

ST. JOHN: I am loath to say what is on my mind, and you so closely related to him, my lord. Beg pardon if I offend you, then, but seems it not to you that his manner and speech differ in some trifles from what they were before? He did not recognize his own father and he insists that he is not the Prince!

HERTFORD: Peace, my lord, you utter treasonous words. Remember the King's command.

ST. JOHN (*Concerned*): True, true, I did forget myself. Yes, he must be the Prince. There could not be two in the land who look so much alike.

HERTFORD (*A little doubtfully*): An impostor would claim to be the Prince. Has there ever been an impostor who would deny this? No, this must be the Prince gone mad. We must help him all we can. Ah, it is the Lord Head Cook.

COOK: Everything is ready for the Prince's dinner.

ST. JOHN: Good. Call in the other attendants. Lord Hertford and I have a message from the King.

COOK: Yes, my lord.

HERTFORD: Lord St. John, I understand your questioning, but you must do all you can to hide your doubts. It is up to us to see him through this.

ST. JOHN: I'm sorry, my lord. I should not have even mentioned such thoughts.

HERTFORD: Lord Head Cook, are the others coming?

COOK: Yes, my lord.

NARRATOR: Three court attendants enter the room: the butler, the groom, and the page. They bow to Hertford and St. John.

HERTFORD: Good afternoon, gentlemen. We have called you here to relay a special message from His Majesty, the King. Word has reached him that there is talk in the palace that the Prince has gone mad. Lord St. John will read to you the declaration of the King. I shall fetch His Highness, the Prince.

ST. JOHN (*Reading*): "In the name of the King. Let none listen to this false and foolish matter, upon pain of death, nor discuss the same, nor carry it abroad. In the name of the King."

NARRATOR: Hertford and Tom enter. Tom sits at the table, awkward and ill at ease. He picks up the napkin and looks at it curiously, for he has never seen one before.

TOM: Please take this away. I am afraid it might get soiled.

HERTFORD: Your Highness had best retire early this evening, so you will not be tired for the city's banquet tomorrow.

TOM	*(Surprised)*: Banquet?
ST. JOHN:	Your memory plays tricks on you, Your Highness. The King did promise a banquet in the city in your honor. Do you not recall?
TOM	*(Still puzzled)*: Yes, yes. I recall it now.
GROOM:	What is the trouble, Your Highness?
TOM:	I crave your help. My nose itches terribly. Pray, tell me—what is the royal custom in such a matter? I cannot bear it much longer.
GROOM:	Lord Head Butler, what do you think? There has never been a case like this in all of England's history!
BUTLER:	Alas, there is no hereditary Nose Scratcher!
COOK:	What shall we do?
GROOM:	What's to be done?
TOM:	I hope I do not offend you, gentlemen, but I can wait no longer. I *must* scratch my nose.
HERTFORD:	Ah, here comes the page.
PAGE:	Your Highness.
HERTFORD:	Tell the page to rise, Your Highness.
TOM:	Yes, Page. Rise and come forward.
PAGE:	Your Highness, His Majesty the King requests the Great Seal.[4] He says that it is most urgent.
TOM	*(Bewildered)*: The Great Seal? Methinks I have forgotten about that, too!
HERTFORD:	The Great Seal which, during his illness, the King

---

4. Great Seal: the most important seal of a country or state, stamped on official documents as proof of their approval by the government.

gave to you as a symbol of your approaching responsibilities.

TOM: Oh, yes, the Seal. Tell my father I have forgotten where I put it, but shall think upon it most carefully.

PAGE *(Hesitantly)*: Yes, Your Majesty.

TOM: I am finished with my meal, my lord, and am in need of a rest.

HERTFORD: Lord Head Butler, pray clear away the table.

ST. JOHN: We shall leave you now, Your Highness, but shall return to remind you of your duties at the city's banquet.

TOM: Good, my lord. *(Pause)* I miss my mother, Nan, and Bet, though I cannot speak the same for my father and Gammer Canty. A city banquet in my honor! If I'm reminded of enough of the manners I've forgotten, I might begin to like it here. Ah! What book is this? "The E-ti-quette of the English Court." *(Happily)* This should be of great help!

NARRATOR: A few weeks pass. Now we go to the Cantys' room in Offal Court. John Canty enters dragging the Prince with him.

JOHN *(Angrily)*: Enough of your nonsense! This is your last chance to say who you really are or suffer the same beating as you had yesterday, and the day before, and the day before that one, too.

PRINCE: 'Tis ill breeding in such as you to command me to speak. I tell you now, as I told you before, I am Edward, Prince of Wales, and none other.

GAMMER (*Cackling*): So, 'tis still the Prince he is. Still too fancy for his own Gammer and his father, I warrant. 'Tis my turn to help him realize who he is. (*She laughs wickedly.*)

MOTHER: Oh, please do not hurt him today, husband. He is near ill with fatigue and hunger. My poor boy! Your foolish ideas have taken your wits away and are breaking my heart.

PRINCE: I tell you, your son is well and has not lost his wits, good dame. If you would let me go to the palace where he is, the King, my father, will return him to you.

MOTHER: The King your father! My child, do not say such things. They might mean death for you and the ruin of all of us. Call back your wandering memory and look upon me. Am I not your mother?

PRINCE (*Reluctantly*): I do not like to grieve you, kind madam, but you are not my mother.

GAMMER: 'Tis royalty he still is—too fine for his own family.

JOHN (*Sarcastically*): How dare you ladies stand in the Prince's presence? Upon your knees and do him reverence!

MOTHER: More rest and food will cure his madness. I'll fix him some soup with what scraps I can find. Come, Gammer, please help me.

GAMMER: I'll help you, but the soup will be for me and his father first.

JOHN: There'll be little rest for any of us unless you lower your royal self to begging soon. The rent is due tomorrow and you have not yet begged a single penny.

PRINCE: Offend me not with your sordid matters. I tell you again, I am the King's son. Oh—who are these men?

JOHN: Ah, Hugo and Ruffler. Where have you been these many months? It is long since I have seen you.

HUGO: We've been in prison, that's where we've been. We were suspected of stealing a deer from the King's park. They kept us in prison a few months, but could not prove us guilty. They gave us a good whipping for causing them so much trouble, then set us free.

PRINCE: But why would they whip you if you were innocent? That is not just!

RUFFLER *(Laughing)*: You young ones have such strange ideas. As if justice mattered in dear old England! We were lucky to escape with our lives; many innocents there be in prison, waiting to be hanged or burned as witches.

MOTHER: Here's some soup, Tom. 'Twill do you good to drink it.

PRINCE: Thank you, good madam. Your kindness will be remembered.

MOTHER: Oh, Tom, you talk as if your wits had left you. Please have the soup; perhaps it will restore your health and your memory.

JOHN: After you're finished bothering with "His Royal

Highness," what about some food for the rest of your family?

MOTHER: Forgive me. I'll fix some for you now.

JOHN: Well, "Your Majesty," I hope that soup pleases your royal tongue.

PRINCE: I do not mean to offend your kind wife, sir, but I cannot eat this without the proper service.

JOHN: Is that so? Then you'll be starving, you will, before you find any "service" around here.

HUGO: The boy is ill, John Canty. Here's how you do it, Tom.

NARRATOR: Hugo takes the bowl in his hands and drinks a large portion of the soup.

PRINCE: I command you to stop!

RUFFLER: Come, Hugo, leave "His Majesty" to his dinner.

HUGO: But there is big news, John Canty. Word has got about that the King is dead!

NARRATOR: The Prince looks up, startled, then buries his head in his arms. His shoulders are shaking with sobs. John Canty looks at the Prince, shakes his head and smiles.

JOHN: Little meaning that has for me. The new King is probably no better than his father.

RUFFLER: 'Tis heard that the young Prince will be crowned King before long. Then we shall see how much he cares for justice.

PRINCE *(Explosively)*: Enough of this treason! I shall see that justice be done to you and to all the others who were ill-treated.

HUGO: Why, Tom Canty, who be you to talk such?

PRINCE *(Solemnly)*: I am Edward the Sixth, King of England.

JOHN: Mates, my son is a dreamer, a fool, and stark mad. Mind him not. He thinks he is the King.

PRINCE *(Turning toward him)*: I am the King, and as justice will be done these two men for their suffering, so will you be punished for treating me as you have.

JOHN: So you threaten me now! I shall go out with my friends here for a while and when I return, you'd best have begged the pennies for the rent or we'll see who's punishing whom around here. Come, Hugo, come Ruffler, we'll tell the others you've returned. *(Mockingly)* Good day, Your Majesty.

HUGH and
RUFFLER: Good day, Your Majesty.

PRINCE: My father is dead and the pauper is an impostor. He must be more clever than I thought, or surely his rude manners would have betrayed him by now. I must get back to the palace, and I will.

NARRATOR: It is the day of the Coronation. At Westminster Abbey, Tom Canty is to be crowned King of England.

HERTFORD: A glorious day for all of England it is today, Lord St. John.

ST. JOHN: That it is, my lord—a day that will be long remembered.

HERTFORD: Did you mark how well the young King has been

feeling and behaving of late?

ST. JOHN: Yes, I did. Perhaps his madness has left him at last.

NARRATOR: The sound of trumpets and drums is heard. The King is announced. Tom Canty, looking downcast, slowly approaches the throne.

HERTFORD: My liege, people see your downcast head and take it for a bad omen. Lift up your head and smile upon your subjects.

TOM: I am sorry, my lord, but as I came here, I saw my poor mother in the crowd. She recognized me, but I did not speak to her. I betrayed my own mother.

ST. JOHN: He has gone mad again!

HERTFORD: Your Majesty, we must proceed with the Coronation. Where is your kingly bearing?

TOM: I do not feel very kingly now, but let the ceremony begin.

NARRATOR: At this moment, the real Prince forces his way into the room. He is dressed in Tom Canty's poor clothes but he holds up his hand and speaks with authority.

PRINCE: Stop the ceremony at once!

LORD: Look there!

LADY: How did that pauper get in here?

LORD: I think he looks like the Prince.

PRINCE: I forbid you to set the crown of England upon that head. I am the King!

NARRATOR: Guards rush forward and seize the real Prince for they do not recognize him. Tom steps down from the throne and speaks.

TOM *(Imperiously)*: Let him go! He is the King!

HERTFORD: Mind not His Majesty. His malady is touching him again. Seize the pauper.

TOM: On your peril! Touch him not. He is the King! Your Majesty, let poor Tom Canty be first to swear his loyalty to you.

ST. JOHN: My lord, do you mark the resemblance between them?

HERTFORD: 'Tis an astonishing likeness! By your favor, sir, I desire to ask certain questions.

PRINCE: I will answer them, my lord.

HERTFORD: If you are the true King, tell me how many servants were there at the palace when you left?

PRINCE *(Quickly)*: Four hundred and nineteen.

HERTFORD: What was the color of the curtains in the late King's bedchamber?

PRINCE *(Quickly)*: Royal blue, of course.

HERTFORD: The answers are correct, but they prove nothing.

ST. JOHN: Wait! I have a question on which hangs the throne. Where is the Great Seal? Only he who truly was the Prince of Wales can answer that.

PRINCE *(Confidently)*: There is nothing difficult about that. Lord St. John, go to my room in the palace. In the left-hand corner farthest from the door, you will find in the wall a brazen nailhead. Press on it and a little jewel chest will fly open. No one else in the

TOM: world knows about the chest. The first thing you will see will be the Great Seal. Bring it here.

TOM: Why do you hesitate? Haven't you heard the King's command? Go!

PRINCE: Tom, you are indeed loyal to help me in this way. I have suffered much these past weeks.

TOM: And I, though I like the comforts of royalty, dearly miss my mother and my friends at Offal Court. I have been most concerned about your welfare.

PRINCE: I have seen much unhappiness and injustice, but when I rule England, I hope what I've seen will help me. I shall give my people the justice they deserve.

TOM: I hope Your Majesty will not mind, but I have already released and pardoned many prisoners.

PRINCE: I do not mind at all, and you shall be rewarded for your generosity and loyalty to me.

NARRATOR: Lord St. John returns carrying the Great Seal.

ST. JOHN: The Great Seal of England!

TOM: Now, my King, take back these regal clothes and give poor Tom, thy servant, his rags again.

LADY: Arrest the impostor!

LORD: To the tower! Hang him.

PRINCE: I will not have this. Were it not for him, I would not have my crown again. Hear my first proclamation as Edward the Sixth: Whereas Tom Canty has been a king, he shall continue to wear royal clothes and all will pay him reverence. He will have the protection of the throne and the support of the crown. He shall be known by the honorable title of the King's Ward.

ALL: Long live the King! Long live the King's Ward! Hurrah!

The End

Meet the Author: **Mark Twain**

Mark Twain is one of America's greatest authors. His books *The Adventures of Tom Sawyer* and *The Adventures of Huckleberry Finn* have been read and loved by countless numbers of young people.

Twain moved with his family when he was four years old to Hannibal, Missouri, on the Mississippi River. Here, in this river town, Mark Twain grew up. Years later when he wrote *The Adventures of Tom Sawyer* and *The Adventures of Huckleberry Finn,* he drew his characters from people he knew in Hannibal. Aunt Polly is like his mother, while Tom Sawyer is a combination of himself and several other boys. Twain's family was poor. His father died when Twain was eleven, so Twain left school to become a printer.

In 1857, while living in Cincinnati, he decided to go to South America to seek his fortune. He boarded a riverboat for New Orleans and while steaming down the Mississippi, he changed his mind. He decided to be a river pilot instead. Later, he wrote a book about life on the Mississippi. He said that he learned a great deal about people while he was a pilot.

When Twain became a writer, he used the pen name Mark Twain. (His real name was Samuel Clemens.) *Mark Twain* is an old river term meaning "the water is two fathoms, or twelve feet, deep."

RESPONDING TO LITERATURE

1. If you were presenting this play, would you emphasize its humorous or its serious side? Explain your answer.

2. At the end of the play, the Prince is now King, and the Pauper is the King's Ward. Imagine that the two boys tell each other of their experiences. What important events do you think each boy would tell?

3. What changes did the Prince and the Pauper make in their lives and how do you think the changes affected each one?

4. The Prince and the Pauper come from very different backgrounds, yet they become friends. Why do you think they do?

5. If you could trade places with anyone for a week, who would that be? Explain.

A Seeing Poem

by Robert Froman

A SEEING POEM HAPPENS WHEN WORDS TAKE A SHAPE THAT HELPS THEM TO TURN ON A LIGHT IN SOMEONE'S MIND

APPRECIATING AUTHOR'S CRAFT

Thinking About Setting

In some stories, the exact setting is not important. Where the characters live or when the story takes place are not as important as what the characters do. In other stories, the setting is important.

Twain uses setting as an important element of his story. Think of how essential the time and place are in *The Prince and the Pauper.* Twain sets the story in a time when royalty had absolute power and the common person had few rights. The details about how servants scrambled to do what the Prince asked tell you how royalty lived. Tom, the Pauper, wasn't sure if the Prince could even scratch his own nose! The setting of the story in this period of history gives great importance to the role-switch.

Writing About Setting

Imagine that you are the Prince in a different time and place; it could be past, present, or future. Write a play scene about the Prince and someone he meets in a new setting. For example, the Prince could meet a famous baseball player, a rock singer, or a TV star. (For ideas about writing, look at The Writer's Handbook.)

Prewriting Copy the chart on the next page. Add two more examples that tell about the setting. Then fill in details about the time and setting for your play.

16th century
Prince's chamber

Writing Read the following scene:

Let's Change Places
Characters: **PRINCE, TOM**   Setting: Prince's chamber

TOM: We boys of Offal Court have sparring matches and races, and in the summer we wade and swim in the canals and the river.

PRINCE: It would be worth my father's kingdom to enjoy that just once!

TOM: We dance and sing around the Maypole, and roll in the mud sometimes too.

PRINCE: Oh, say no more! If only I could wear clothes like yours just once and run barefoot through the mud—I think I would give up my crown for that!

TOM: If I could wear such fine clothes as yours just once—

PRINCE *(Quickly)*: Would you really like that? Then it shall be.

Notice the play format: a title, list of characters, setting, small capital letters followed by a colon for a speaker's name, parentheses and italic type for stage directions.

Use the details from your setting to write a scene between the Prince and a new character. Have each character speak more than once.

Revising Read your draft to a partner and discuss how clear your setting is and now revise your draft, checking your play format. Now write your final copy.

Presenting Rehearse your play with a partner. Change your voice to fit the part of the character you are playing. For example, if you are playing the Prince speak in a haughty, refined manner.

EXTENDING YOUR READING

Expressing Yourself
Choose one or more of these activities:

Design a King Edward the Sixth Coin Use your imagination to design a coin showing the likeness of the new king. On the other side, draw what you think the Great Seal might look like. Look at a quarter or any other coin to give you ideas.

Prince and the Pauper Sequel Make up a scene for a sequel to the play and perform it for your class. Focus on what might happen to Tom's father and Gammer for their treatment of the Prince.

Tower of London When the Prince learns that Gammer mistreats Tom, the Prince wants Gammer sent to the Tower. Look up the Tower of London in an encyclopedia and make a brief report to your class about it.

Design a Playbill Design the cover for a playbill. On the inside, list the different parts in the play. You could also tell about the setting of the play, or give information about Mark Twain.

A Picturesque Poem Robert Froman uses words to show a lightbulb in his poem on page 501. Turn on a light in your mind and see what picturesque poem you can write. Perhaps you can write a seeing poem about a crown.

More Books About the Theater

Theater Magic: Behind the Scenes at a Children's Theater
by Cheryl Walsh Bellville, Carolrhoda Books, Inc. Have you
ever wondered how scenery and costumes are made, or how
stage make-up can totally change a face? These questions
and more are answered through many beautiful photographs
and a factual text.

Stage Fright by James Howe. Atheneum Publishers. When
he gets a part in a summer stock play, young Sebastian
Barth is excited, especially since he'll be acting alongside
the famous and beautiful Michaele Caraway. When oddly
frightening things begin happening around and to Michaele,
Sebastian's talents as a detective become more important
than his acting.

The Magic If: Stanislavsky for Children by Elizabeth Y.
Kelly. National Educational Press. How do professional actors
prepare themselves to play a dramatic role? How do they
make their characters come alive and be believable on
stage? You don't need to be an actor to learn how it's done
behind the scenes. This book will tell you all about it.

Supermouse by Jean Ure. William Morrow and Company.
Mrs. Bruce is upset when a well-known dancer offers her
older daughter Nicola a role with her mime troupe. Mrs.
Bruce has always favored her younger daughter Rose. The
sisters became rivals for the same role, and because of it
Nicola finds out about herself.

Student Handbook

Handbook of Literary Terms

Pages 507–517

Alliteration	Foreshadowing	Myth
Autobiography	Free verse	Narrative poem
Biography	Haiku	Nonfiction
Characterization	Historical fiction	Personification
Conflict	Humor	Plot
Drama	Imagery	Point of view
Fantasy	Lyric	Rhyme
Fiction	Metaphor	Setting
Flashback	Modern realistic fiction	Symbolism
Folk tale	Mood	Theme

Guide to Literature

Pages 518–523

Science Fiction	Realistic Animal Novels
Legends	Stories About Other Lands

Writer's Handbook

Pages 524–531

Glossary

Pages 532–541

Handbook of Literary Terms

Alliteration

repeated sounds, usually consonants, at the beginning of words or in accented syllables

(See "Jim" on page 43 for an example of alliteration.)

Autobiography

See Handbook entry for **Biography.**

Biography

any account of a person's life

In a **fictionalized biography,** a writer will use the facts of a person's life and create dialogue and dramatic incidents to make his/her subject come to life. (See Appreciating Author's Craft on page 142.) An **autobiography** is the account of a person's life, or part of a person's life, written by the person who lived it. (See *Homesick* on page 236.)

Harold Felton learned the facts about Elizabeth Freeman's life through the research he did. But he had no way of knowing the exact words spoken by Freeman or the precise feelings she experienced. As he wrote, he had to imagine what Bet may have said and how she probably felt. In this excerpt, notice how Felton brings Bet to life with a description of the thoughts and feelings that reveal her inner turmoil:

Bet was forlorn. She wanted to forgive Mistress Ashley and she did forgive the poor woman who had so little control of herself. Yet Bet wanted her freedom. She didn't know what she would do as a free person. She would find it difficult, maybe impossible, to find work for wages. She would be lucky to find a place to live as comfortable as the Ashley household.

The long days passed. She was closely watched and had no way of again talking with Mr. Sedgwick, or anyone else who might help her. She began to think it was foolish to believe that anyone would come to her aid. Who would help a slave with no money and no property? Her heart was filled with emptiness as she went about her daily chores.

What if Elizabeth Freeman were still alive today? What questions would you ask her about her life and her struggle for freedom if she were able to answer you herself?

Characterization

the method an author uses to help the reader become acquainted with a person, or character, in a story

The author develops character by describing physical characteristics, speech, and actions. The author also reveals character by the attitudes and actions of other characters. (See Appreciating Author's Craft on page 228.)

Conflict

the struggle or clash between two opposing forces in a story

(See Appreciating Author's Craft on page 328.)

Drama

a story to be acted on a stage or before motion picture, television, or video cameras in which dialogue and action are used to tell the story

(See *The Prince and the Pauper* on page 480.)

Fantasy

a story that is set in an unreal world and is often about incredible characters

(See Appreciating Author's Craft on page 228.)

Fantasies are about characters that could never exist and events that could never happen. Yet a skilled writer can capture readers' imaginations and make them believe, at least for a while, in the fanciful world that the writer invents.

In the following excerpt from the fantasy *Dragon of the Lost Sea,* Shimmer, the dragon princess, describes her encounter with the enchantress Civet. In spite of the incredible situation depicted in this passage, readers hold their breath awaiting its outcome.

Lithe as a cat, Civet strode to the very edge of the pool and leaped down. At her word of command, the roots of the nearby trees suddenly slipped out of the rocky floor and rose like gritty tentacles to wrap themselves around my legs and body. One even caught me across the mouth like a gag. I shut my eyes, straining every muscle as I pulled and wiggled, but even my immense strength could not break their stony grip. To my right I could hear Thorn grunting as if he, too, were trying to break free.

Then I thought of shrinking myself or changing into some more slippery shape, like that of a snake. Desperately I sketched a magical symbol in the air with my claw; but without a spoken spell to power the sign, my claws were simply scratching the air.

Dragon of the Lost Sea is filled with unexpected and magical events. In your opinion, what is the most amazing thing that happens in the story? Explain why you choose that event as the most amazing. What surprises you most about Shimmer? about Thorn? about Civet?

Fiction

literature that tells about imaginary people and happenings

Types of fiction include modern realistic fiction, historical fiction, science fiction, and fantasy.

Flashback

an interruption in the action of a story, play, or work of nonfiction to show an episode that happened at an earlier time

In *The Eyes of the Amaryllis,* on pages 366–467, the author interrupts the action of the story to tell about Jenny and her father's trip to Gran's. In the first chapter, Jenny and her father are already at Gran's house.

Folk tale

a tale, legend, or superstition originating and handed down among a people or nation

(See *The People Could Fly* on page 336.) Folk tales can be found in all parts of the world. They were passed down orally from one generation to the next.

In *The People Could Fly,* Virginia Hamilton wrote down the folk tales that had been told by American slaves. Hamilton wrote: "Remember that these folk tales were once a creative way for an oppressed people to express their fears and hopes to one another."

This passage tells what happens just as a slaveowner is about to kill an old slave named Toby:

> And he sighed the ancient words that were a dark promise. He said them all around to the others in the field under the whip, ". . . *buba yalie . . . buba tambe . . .*"
>
> There was a great outcryin. The bent backs straightened up. Old and young who were called slaves and could fly joined hands. Say like they would ring-sing. But they didn't shuffle in a circle. They didn't sing. They rose on the air. They flew in a flock that was black against the heavenly blue. Black crows or black shadows. It didn't matter, they went so high. Way down the plantation, way over the slavery land. Say they flew away to *Free-dom.*

What hopes and fears are expressed

509

in this passage? in "Carrying the Running-Aways"? in "The Talking Cooter"? If the children in your school were to tell a folk tale, what hopes and fears might be expressed?

Foreshadowing

an author's use of hints or clues to suggest events that will occur later in a narrative

In *Rebecca of Sunnybrook Farm,* the author hints at the troubles that await Rebecca in this sentence:

> There were thick gathering clouds in the sky, but she took no notice of them save to be glad that she could raise her sunshade.

Free verse

poetry that follows no set pattern or rhyme, meter, or line length

(See "Direction" on page 327 for an example of free verse.)

Haiku

a type of poetry popular in Japan usually consisting of three lines

Haiku usually refers to a wonder of nature and suggests a mood, thought, or attitude. Haiku is a word picture with few words. The reader uses his/her own imagination to fill in the details. (See "A Moment of Wonder" on page 287 for examples of haiku.)

Historical fiction

fiction that is set in the past

The setting of the story can tell the reader how people lived in that time. The themes of historical fiction often relate to the time period of the story and our own time as well.

The author of historical fiction must know as much as possible about the period in which the story takes place. Notice how Elizabeth George Speare weaves accurate historical details into this excerpt from her story *The Sign of the Beaver:*

> When the cabin door opened and the Indian entered, Matt hastily pulled himself up. Now, with clear eyes, he saw that there was nothing in the least strange about this man. He was dressed not so differently from Matt's own father, in a coat of some rough brown cloth and

leggings fringed down the side. His face was smooth-shaven, and so was his whole head, except for one long black topknot. When he saw that Matt was awake, his stern face was lighted by a wide smile.

Speare's story not only entertains the reader but also helps the reader understand what people's lives were like in the Maine wilderness in 1768. Now imagine that *you* were living in Maine in 1768. Pretend that Matt and Attean never met and you have to introduce them to one another. What would you tell each of them about the other to get them off to a better start?

Humor

a tone in a story resulting from the author's style, types of characters, unexpected situations, and how the characters react to those situations

(See Appreciating Author's Craft on page 180.)

Imagery

words that help the reader experience the way things described in a story or a poem look, sound, smell, taste, or feel

(See "This Land Is Your Land" on page 255 for an example of imagery and Appreciating Author's Craft on page 256.)

Lyric

a poem, usually short, expressing a basic, personal emotion such as grief, happiness, love, or melancholy

(See "Truly My Own" on page 75 for an example of a lyric poem.)

Metaphor

a comparison of two things that are somewhat alike

The comparison is not directly stated—that is, you have to figure out for yourself how the two things are alike.

> Once, when the sky was
>   very near the earth,
> a woman hoeing in her garden
>   took off her necklace
> and hung it in the sky.
> The stars are her silver necklace.
> —*from the Hawaiian Islands*

This poet uses a metaphor to compare the stars in the sky to a silver necklace. You know that the stars are not really a necklace, but in what way are they alike? Do you think the comparison is a good one? Why or why not?

Write a metaphor that describes one of the following things: the moon, rain, snowflakes, fog, autumn leaves. How are the things you compared alike? Explain why you think your comparison is a good one.

Modern realistic fiction

fiction that represents life as it seems to the average person.

Realistic fiction is set in a believable time and place, with characters who seem real and who are involved in action that holds the reader's interest. (See Introducing *Jake* on page 10.)

This example of realistic fiction is an excerpt from *Jake.* Notice that Jake's day begins just as any student's might—except that Jake has a special problem.

> I got up out of bed and pulled up the window shade. A cloudy gray day. It looked like it might rain. If only it would rain. We'd have an extra day in which to look for a coach.
>
> I made breakfast and that included milk and with Lenny's snores still ringing in my ears, I went off to school. It began to sprinkle. Rain harder, I prayed. Rain real hard and wash out our game.
>
> I'd never before prayed for a rained-out game.

The events in *Jake* take several unexpected turns before Jake's problem is resolved. Think back on the past few weeks. What unexpected complications have you had to face? Were you able to overcome them? How?

Mood

the atmosphere or feeling in a literary work

The setting, objects, details, and words all help create the mood. (See Appreciating Author's Craft on page 472.)

Myth

a tale by an unknown author about gods and goddesses or other supernatural beings

A myth was often used to explain something about the world that people didn't understand. (See Introducing Myths: Stories That Explain Why on page 82.) Myths were passed on by word of mouth from one generation to the next before they were finally written down.

Narcissus and Echo is a Greek myth that explains what causes an echo. This is what the goddess Hera says when she discovers that Echo has tricked her:

"Wretched creature!" she cried. "I know what you have done. I see the gift you have been given. And I would not have it said that my husband is more generous than I. So I too shall reward you for what you have done. Because you have used your voice for lying, you shall never be able to say anything to anyone again—except the last words that have been said to you. Now try lying."

"Try lying," said Echo.

Today we know the scientific explanation for the things in nature, such as echoes, that were once explained in myths. What if you lived many hundreds of years ago? You might have used a myth to explain snow to your children. Write a brief story in the style of a myth to explain one of the following qualities of snow: what snow is, why it snows, why each snowflake is different, why it snows in some places and not in others, or why snow melts in the spring. Don't forget to include a god or goddess in your myth.

Narrative poem

a poem which tells a story of an event or a series of events; it may be fictional or true

(See "Aunt Sue's Stories" on page 356 for an example of a narrative poem.)

Nonfiction

literature that deals with real people and events rather than imaginary ones

Types of nonfiction include histories, biographies, and other informational books. (See *Commodore Perry in the Land of the Shogun* on page 264 for an example of nonfiction.)

Writers of nonfiction must be meticulous regarding the accuracy of information they present. In *Commodore Perry in the Land of the Shogun,* Rhoda Blumberg combines accuracy with a fascinating look at an important historical event. In this excerpt, Blumberg describes Perry's landing on Japanese soil.

Perry proved to be a first-class showman, for he planned and staged a dramatic entrance. First, the marines formed two lines on the wharf. Then came sailors, marching to the lively music of two bands. Ships' cannons saluted when Commodore Perry disembarked. Bands played "Hail, Columbia" when he landed. Perry was flanked by two tall handsome black bodyguards, who proved to be sensational. The Japanese had never seen black men before.

In this selection you learned that Japan was shut off from the rest of the world for over two hundred years. Do you think this was a good thing or a bad thing for Japan? Use the information in the selection to help you decide. Then explain your opinion.

Personification

giving human qualities to animals or inanimate objects

These human qualities may include traits, such as pride or kindness, and abilities, such as speaking or dancing.

Reread the poem, "Hold Fast Your Dreams" on page 141. In this poem, dreams are personified. They require shelter and they grow, just as people do.

Think how you could personify the following animals and inanimate objects: a bee, a puppy, a clock, a road. Then write a sentence to personify each of them. Which was the easiest for you to personify? Why?

Plot

Point of view

a series of events selected by the author to present and bring about the solution of some conflict

In a carefully constructed plot, the events are arranged in a pattern so that each event follows from the one before it. The pattern of events leads to the climax, or turning point, of the story. The conflict is solved in the conclusion. (See Appreciating Author's Craft on page 44.)

the author's choice of a narrator, or speaker

This choice affects the amount and kind of information the reader will be given. The narrator may be an observer of the action. When a story is told from this point of view, the pronouns *he, she, it,* or *they* are often used. The narrator may also be a character in the story who can reveal only his or her own thoughts and feelings and what he or she is told by others. (See Appreciating Author's Craft on page 256.)

Rhyme

two or more words having the same last, or ending, sound

In poetry, the last words of lines often rhyme.

Look back at the poem "The Paint Box" on page 227. Identify the rhyming words in "The Paint Box." How many different rhyming sounds are there?

Now write two rhyming lines to describe a friend of yours.

Setting

the time and place of the events in a story

The setting may be directly stated, or it may only be suggested. Sometimes the setting is very important to the events of the plot. Other times it is not. The setting may help create a mood or feeling, or it may show how a character feels. (See Appreciating Author's Craft on page 228 and on page 502.)

Symbolism

the use of a person, place, event, or object that has a meaning in itself but suggests other meanings as well

(See *Rebecca of Sunnybrook Farm* on page 78.)

The use of symbols adds a richness in meaning to the selection. In this excerpt from *Rebecca of Sunnybrook Farm,* Rebecca sees the withered rose as a symbol.

. . . She smoothed it (her dress) out carefully, pinched up the white ruffle at the neck, and laid it away in a drawer with an extra little sob at the roughness of life. The withered pink rose fell on the floor. Rebecca looked at it and thought, *Just like my happy day!* Nothing could show more clearly the kind of child she was than the fact that she instantly perceived the symbolism of the rose and laid it in the drawer with the dress as if she were burying the whole episode with all its sad memories. It was a child's poetic instinct with a dawning hint of woman's sentiment in it.

What did the rose symbolize to Rebecca?

If you were an author, what might you use to symbolize each of the following: joy, sorrow, goodness, evil, poverty, wealth? Explain why you think the symbols you chose will convey your meaning to a reader.

Theme

the meaning behind the things that happen in a piece of literature

Sometimes the theme is stated directly, but most often it is not. (See Appreciating Author's Craft on page 76.)

How Can I Find a Book I'll Like?

- Look for more of what you know you will like such as other books in a popular series, more books by a favorite author, or books on your special interest. Use the subject, title, and author indexes of the card catalog to develop a personal file of books you'd like to read.

- Talk to friends, family, teachers, or librarians about books they like. Make a list of the books they suggest and take it with you to the library.

- Find out if there is a book about a movie or television show you enjoyed. After reading it, decide which is better, the book or the show.

- Look at books recommended by other young people called "Children's Choices." Ask your teacher or librarian for a copy of the list. Read what it says about the books for older readers and choose one that sounds good to you.

- Browse in the library and pick up a book whose cover appeals to you. Read the information on the book jacket, but don't stop there. Read the opening paragraphs of the first few chapters. Thumb through the remaining pages, noticing pictures, size of print, and overall length. Decide if the book is one you might enjoy.

What characteristics does good science fiction have?

- The realistic future world of a good science fiction novel is created through the use of known scientific facts.

- The main characters in a well-written science fiction story are credible beings whose fate becomes important to you as you read.

- Effective science fiction tells a suspenseful story that would be important in any setting.

- Good science fiction focuses on the effects of technology on human beings, not just on the technology itself.

What makes science fiction fascinating to read?

- You can shake up your thinking and imagine what changes may come in the future.

- You can escape to an imaginary world.

- You can enjoy adventures that seem real.

- You can participate in conflicts between human beings and creatures from other times or worlds.

What are some science fiction novels I might like?

The Forgotten Door. Alexander Key, The Westminster Press

Aliens in the Family. Margaret Mahy, Scholastic, Inc.

The Lotus Caves. John Christopher, Macmillan.

The Awakening Water. G. R. Kesteven, Hastings House, Publishers.

Norby: The Mixed-Up Robot. Janet and Isaac Asimov, Walker Publishing Company.

What characteristics do good legends have?

- Good legends tell stories about real, but unverified events of long ago.

- Effective legends focus on a strong central character and read like a story that could be told around a campfire.

- A first-rate legend maintains the dignity of the people and culture it describes.

- A kernel of truth about life can be discovered in legends, but well-written legends never "preach" to the reader.

Why is it fun to read a legend?

- You can enjoy a story that is so good it has lasted for many generations.

- You can relate to a hero or heroine who cleverly outwits enemies and overcomes obstacles.

- You can discover a nonhistorical explanation of how things happened in the past.

- You can learn a great deal about people from other times and other cultures.

What are some legends I might enjoy?

The Sword and the Grail. Constance Hieatt, Thomas Y. Crowell Company.

The Adventures of Odysseus and the Tale of Troy. Padraic Colum, Macmillan.

William Tell. Nina Bawden, Lothrop, Lee & Shepard.

Jackaroo. Cynthia Voigt, Atheneum.

The Stolen Fire; Legends of Heroes and Rebels from Around the World. Hans Baumann (translated by Stella Humphries), Pantheon Books, Random House.

What characteristics do good realistic animal stories have?

- The animal characters in well-written realistic animal stories are consistently animals, not animals with human thoughts and traits.

- The situations and adventures that make up the plot are appropriate for real animals.

- The actions of the animal characters in the story illustrate the way real animals would act and react.

- The setting of good realistic animal stories is authentic and scientifically correct.

What makes good animal stories attractive to readers?

- You can experience the love and loyalty between an animal and its owner as you read the book.

- You can learn about nature and the characteristics of animals that interest you.

- You can enjoy challenge and adventure that reflect important ideas about man's relationship with animals.

- You can make discoveries about yourself as you read about an animal's interactions with his world.

What are some realistic animal stories I might enjoy?

Justin Morgan Had a Horse. Marguerite Henry, Macmillan.

Old Yeller. Fred Gipson, Harper & Row.

The Cry of the Crow. Jean Craighead George, Harper & Row.

A Stranger at Green Knowe. Lucy M. Boston, Harcourt, Brace & World, Inc.

Along Came a Dog. Meindert De Jong, Harper & Row.

What characteristics do good stories about other lands have?

- By presenting strong visual images of the characters and the setting, good stories about other lands help the reader understand differences between countries.

- Well-written stories about foreign lands give information about the feelings and reactions of the people, rather than only facts about a country.

- Effective stories about other lands give a true representation of ethnic groups of a region and avoid stereotyping a race or nationality.

- Stories may be translated into English. The translator keeps the story the same, but adapts the language to make it fit meanings and expressions in our country.

What makes stories about other lands fun to read?

- You can learn about life in other cultures as you read a good story.

- You can discover that people in other countries have thoughts and feelings much like yours.

- You can meet people behind the facts you learn in social studies and geography lessons.

What are some stories about other lands I might like?

The Ark. Margot Benary-Isbert (translated by Clara and Richard Winston), Harcourt, Brace & World, Inc.

The House of Sixty Fathers. Meindert De Jong, Harper & Row Trophy Book.

When Hitler Stole Pink Rabbit. Judith Kerr, Coward, McCann.

The Winter Time Was Frozen. Els Pelgrom (translated from Dutch by Maryka and Rafael Rudnik), William Morrow and Company.

Born to Dance Samba. Miriam Cohen, Harper & Row.

How Can I Share a Book That I Enjoy?

- Write a headline and a short news story about a major event in your book. Remember that a good headline attracts the reader's attention and focuses on the main idea of the story.

- Compose a descriptive poem to highlight the differences between two main characters. Use the following pattern:

  Line 1 First character's name
  Line 2 Two adjectives describing the first character
  Line 3 Three "ing" verbs for both characters
  Line 4 Two adjectives describing the last character
  Line 5 Second character's name

- Create a pamphlet to "sell" your book. First, look at other advertising pamphlets for ideas. Next, fold a sheet of paper into thirds. Put the title and an illustration on the cover. Inside the pamphlet, put quotations, leading questions, riddles, or other lures to make classmates want to read your book.

- Plan a party for the characters in your book. Be sure the refreshments, decorations, music, and entertainment are suitable for the setting that the author created.

- Choose an interesting new vocabulary word from your book. Work with a partner to prepare a one-minute skit or demonstration that uses props to show classmates the meaning of the word.

- Devise a "Wanted Poster" for a villain or mean character in your book. Be sure to include all necessary information such as physical description, fingerprints (you can substitute your own), and location of last sighting.

- Develop a different solution to a major problem in your book. Write a letter to persuade the main character to accept your solution instead of the author's solution.

This handbook will help you write well in response to the literature you have been reading. It answers the kinds of questions that you might ask when you are doing your writing assignments for Appreciating Author's Craft in this book as well as when you are doing other writing assignments. It is divided into four parts, one part for each step of the writing process: prewriting, writing, revising, and presenting. The handbook also explains four types of writing: narrative, explanatory, descriptive, and persuasive/analytical.

Prewriting

1. I know the topic I'm going to write about, but how can I organize my ideas and narrow my topic?

There are many ways to organize ideas. One way is to use a chart, such as the one on page 44. Another way to narrow a topic is to use a web, or cluster diagram. This is a visual way to show how a main topic, subtopics, and details are related to one another.

To make a cluster diagram, first write the main topic and circle it. Then write a related subtopic below it and circle it. Draw a line to connect it to the main topic. Last, list details related to the main topic and to the subtopic and draw lines to connect them to the appropriate circles. Notice in the cluster diagram below that the four events under *What Happened* are narrower than the topic *What Happened*. Note also that *What the Print-Alls Planned* and *What Happened* are centered and that the details are clustered around them.

2. When I'm given a writing assignment, what is my first task?

When you are asked to write, your first task is to determine your purpose for writing and your audience. Your audience is the people who you want to read your work. It may be your teacher, your classmates, a friend, a writing partner, your family, or perhaps even someone you don't know. To determine your purpose, ask yourself, "What *type* of writing am I being asked to do?" Study the following chart to help you better understand your purpose for writing.

Type of Writing	Purpose	Examples
narrative	• to tell a story (real or imaginary) about something that happened to you, to someone you know, or to a character in a story you have read • to tell how you feel about something • to tell the events in the order in which they happened	• narrative paragraph • personal narrative • new incident in a story • play scene • imagination tale
explanatory	• to focus on a person and highlight the topic of interest • to request information or to inform someone about a problem	• news story • business letter
descriptive	• to paint a picture in words by using sensory details that help the reader see, hear, feel, taste, or smell what you describe, such as a conflict	• descriptive paragraph • journal entry
persuasive/ analytical	• to state an opinion and give supporting reasons in order to convince others to share the opinion • to collect facts, analyze them, and reach a conclusion • to summarize a story	• persuasive paragraph • summary paragraph • book review

Writing

1. Sometimes when I sit down, I just can't get started. What can I do then?

There are several ways to get started. Here are some suggestions.

Prepare Your Workplace Find a quiet, well-lighted place to work, either at home, at school, or at the community library. Be sure to have everything you need on hand. Include an extra pen or sharpened pencil and have plenty of paper. Avoid distractions; sit at a table by yourself and tune out noise and conversation.

Review the Task Take a minute to review your notes and remind yourself of the task you are about to do. Then make up your mind to do it.

Just Begin Don't stare at the blank page in front of you. Pick up your pen or pencil and write down something about your first idea. Sometimes just the physical act of writing will start your mind working. You can even imagine that your writing muscles are directly connected to your brain and are stimulating ideas and opinions. If the first few sentences don't work, keep trying until you have a good beginning. Remember to write on every other line so you'll have room to revise your work later.

2. What is a first draft?

A first draft is like a trial run or a rehearsal. The purpose of a first draft is to get your ideas down. Don't stop writing even if you feel you don't like everything you are saying. When you are writing a first draft, don't worry about perfect spelling, punctuation, or capitalization. If you stop to correct these types of errors, you may lose your train of thought.

1. I have just written my first draft. What do I do next?

It is helpful to pause, read over your first draft, and "listen" to yourself. Think about your big point. Is it clear? Will it make sense to your audience? Also think about the overall direction your writing is taking. Does your draft reflect the criteria for the specific type of writing you have been asked to do? The chart below offers some information on what makes a specific type of writing good.

Type of Writing	What Makes It Good
narrative	• keep to one main idea • tell the events in time order • use signal words such as *first, next, then,* and *last* to make the order clear
explanatory	• begin with a topic sentence that tells what you intend to explain • follow the topic sentence with details that support the main idea • tell the steps in order • use examples to clarify or illustrate the steps • use signal words such as *first, next, then,* or *for example* to connect your ideas
descriptive	• keep to one main idea • choose words that help your reader see, feel, hear, smell, and taste what you describe • be sure the details support the main idea • use spatial order—describe your topic from a particular position, such as left to right—to organize the paragraph
persuasive/analytical	• keep your audience in mind in order to choose ideas and language that will appeal to them • state your opinion in your topic sentence • use facts and reasons to support your opinion • use signal words such as *in addition* and *furthermore* to connect your reasons • draw conclusions based on facts • put the most persuasive reasons last

2. What should I do when I revise?

First, revise your content. Get together with a small group, a friend, or your teacher, and have them listen as you read your first draft. Ask for comments on what is good about your writing and how it could be made better. Take notes on what is said and use the notes to help you make changes.

3. How do I make changes?

There are four kinds of changes to make when you revise— adding, taking out, reordering, and proofreading. They are explained below. Remember that you can use the information you gathered in Prewriting, as well as your notes of others' comments, as you work through these changes.

Adding Information Reread your draft and check to see if you have left out any important information. Perhaps you forgot a major event in a narrative paragraph, or left out an important reason that supports your opinion in a persuasive paragraph. Add any missing or new information to your revision.

Taking Out Unnecessary Information Check to see that you have kept to your topic. Take out any sentences that don't keep to your topic. Also examine your paper for any unnecessary words. Can you say the same thing in fewer words?

Moving Words, Sentences, and Paragraphs The order of your words, sentences, and paragraphs determines how clear your writing is. Compare your draft with your notes. Have you told things in the right order? You may have to move a sentence or two, or even entire paragraphs. Use scissors and tape or paste to cut and arrange parts of pages.

Proofreading Your final task in revising is to check your paper for mistakes in spelling, punctuation, capitalization, and form. Use the proofreading marks at the top of the next page to help you make these changes.

4. How can I be sure I've done a thorough job of revising?

You can use the Revision Checklist on the next page to check yourself.

Proofreader's Marks

=	Make a capital.	ℯ	Take out something.
/	Make a small letter.	⌐→	Move something.
⊙	Add a period.	¶	New paragraph.
∧,	Add a comma.	ⓢₚ	Correct spelling.
∧	Add something.		

Revision Checklist

Content
- ✔ Does each paragraph have a clear main idea?
- ✔ Do all the sentences in each paragraph keep to the main idea?
- ✔ Are the events, steps, or reasons in the correct order? Should some information be moved around?
- ✔ Is each sentence clear and concise?
- ✔ Have I chosen words that say exactly what I mean?
- ✔ Have I removed information that doesn't keep to the topic?
- ✔ Is there any information missing that I should add?
- ✔ Have I used language appropriate for my purpose and audience?
- ✔ Are all my facts and figures accurate?

Mechanics
- ✔ Is each sentence capitalized and punctuated correctly?
- ✔ Are all the sentences complete?
- ✔ Is each word spelled correctly?
- ✔ Do the subjects and verbs agree?
- ✔ Have I kept the correct verb tense throughout?
- ✔ Is each paragraph indented?
- ✔ Is there a special form for this kind of writing? If so, have I followed that special form?
- ✔ Is my handwriting as clear as I can make it?

1. What are some ways I can present my writing to others?

There are many ways to share your writing. Here are some suggestions.

Read Aloud Read your paper aloud to your audience. Invite discussion by asking such questions as, "What did I describe?" "Were you able to predict that my story would end the way it did? Why or why not?"

Display Mount your paper on some colored construction paper or create illustrations for it. Then display your work on the bulletin board in your classroom.

Be a TV Producer You can put on a TV show to share your story with your classmates. Construct a TV from a box with a "screen" that has been cut out, two dowels, and a strip of brown wrapping paper.

Write the screen title and author (your name) on the left of the paper strip. Then draw pictures showing events from your story. Leave a little space between pictures. Then write a script, which you will read as you move your pictures across the screen.

When you have finished your drawings, tape the ends of the paper strip to the dowels inside the box. Turn the dowels until all of the strip is on the dowel at the right. To present your TV show, turn the dowel on the left.

To make your TV show more interesting, create some commercials that tie in with the subject of your story. For example, if your story is set in a snowstorm, you could write a commercial about boots.

2. How can our class work together to present our writing?
Here are some ways your class can work together.

Hold a Young Author's Conference Follow these steps:
a. Organize a special day for presenting and honoring the writing of students in your class.
b. Invite interested parents, students from other classes, and special guest speakers, such as a local author and your English teacher.
c. On the day of the conference, meet with classmates to share writing, talk about writing problems, listen to guest speakers, and read some of your writing aloud.
d. Collect pieces of writing from students at the conference and publish them in a class or school magazine.

Start a Class Newspaper Follow these steps:
a. Choose a small group to be in charge of the newspaper.
b. As a class, think of a name for your newspaper. Then discuss the types of news stories, features, cartoons, and other information you could include.
c. Decide when and how often you will publish.
d. Work in teams to revise and proofread all pieces.
e. Distribute your newspapers in and outside the school.

Present a Class Play Turn a story into a play. Work with a few of your classmates to assign parts and rehearse. Put on the play for your classmates or other classes.

Start a Class Library Would you like to make your writing available for everyone to read? Start a class library. Bind your class's personal narratives, research reports, and other works together and keep them in a special place in the classroom. You might also offer your class books to the school library.

Glossary

How to Use the Pronunciation Key

After each entry word in this glossary, there is a special spelling, called the **pronunciation.** It shows how to say the word. The word is broken into syllables and then spelled with letters and signs. You can look up these letters and signs in the **pronunciation key** to see what sounds they stand for.

This dark mark (′) is called the **primary accent.** It follows the syllable you say with the most force. This lighter mark (′) is the **secondary accent.** Say the syllable it follows with medium force. Syllables without marks are said with least force.

Full Pronunciation Key

a	hat, cap	**i**	it, pin	**p**	paper, cup	**ə**	stands for:
ā	age, face	**ī**	ice, five	**r**	run, try		a in about
ä	father, far			**s**	say, yes		e in taken
		j	jam, enjoy	**sh**	she, rush		i in pencil
b	bad, rob	**k**	kind, seek	**t**	tell, it		o in lemon
ch	child, much	**l**	land, coal	**th**	thin, both		u in circus
d	did, red	**m**	me, am	**ŦH**	then, smooth		
		n	no, in				
e	let, best	**ng**	long, bring	**u**	cup, butter		
ē	equal, be			**u̇**	full, put		
ėr	her, learn	**o**	hot, rock	**ü**	rule, move		
		ō	open, go				
f	fat, if	**ô**	order, all	**v**	very, save		
g	go, bag	**oi**	oil, toy	**w**	will, woman		
h	he, how	**ou**	house, out	**y**	young, yet		
				z	zoo, breeze		
				zh	measure, seizure		

A

adz or **adze** (adz), a cutting tool for shaping heavy timbers. It is somewhat like an ax but with a blade set across the end of the handle and curving inward. *n., pl.* **adz·es.**

adz

an·cient (ān'shənt), **1** of times long past: *In Egypt, we saw the ruins of an ancient temple built six thousand years ago.* **2** of great age; very old: *Rome is an ancient city.* **3** a very old person. 1,2 *adj.,* 3 *n.* —**an'cient·ness,** *n.*

au·di·ble (ô'də bəl), able to be heard; loud enough to be heard: *Without a microphone the speaker was barely audible. adj.*

a·venge (ə venj'), get revenge for: *avenge an insult. They fought to avenge the enemy's invasion of their country. v.,* **a·venged, a·veng·ing.**

B

bog·gy (bog'ē), soft, wet, and spongy; marshy; swampy: *boggy ground. adj.,* **bog·gi·er, bog·gi·est.**

brig (brig), ship with two masts and square sails set at right angles across the ship. *n.*

C

ca·pa·cious (kə pā'shəs), able to hold much; large and roomy; spacious: *a capacious closet. adj.*

ca·reen (kə rēn'), lean to one side or sway sharply; tilt; lurch; tip: *The speeding car careened around the corner. v.*

a hat	i it	oi oil	ch child	ə stands for:
ā age	ī ice	ou out	ng long	a in about
ä far	o hot	u cup	sh she	e in taken
e let	ō open	u̇ put	th thin	i in pencil
ē equal	ô order	ü rule	ᴛʜ then	o in lemon
ėr term			zh measure	u in circus

chat·tel (chat'l), piece of property that is not real estate; any movable possession. Furniture, automobiles, and animals are chattels. *n.*

clam·ber (klam'bər), climb, using both hands and feet; climb awkwardly or with difficulty; scramble: *The children clambered up the cliff. v.*

cli·ent (klī'ənt), person for whom a lawyer, accountant, or other professional person acts. *n.*

clum·si·ly (klum'zə lē), in a clumsy manner; awkwardly. *adv.*

coax (kōks), **1** persuade by soft words; influence by pleasant ways: *She coaxed me into letting her borrow my bicycle.* **2** get by coaxing: *The baby-sitter coaxed a smile from the baby. v.*

com·mence (kə mens'), begin; start: *The play commenced at eight o'clock. v.,* **com·menced, com·menc·ing.**

con·demn (kən dem'), **1** express strong disapproval of: *We condemn cruelty to animals.* **2** declare not sound or suitable for use: *The bridge was condemned as unsafe. v.*

con·temp·tu·ous (kən temp'chü əs), disrespectful; scornful: *a contemptuous look. adj.* —**con·temp'tu·ous·ly,** *adv.*

coot·er (küt'ər), any of several turtles of the southern and eastern U.S. *n.*

cut·lass (kut'ləs), a short, heavy, slightly curved sword, used in former times especially by sailors. *n., pl.* **cut·lass·es.**

D

dam·age (dam'ij), **1** harm or injury that lessens value or usefulness: *The accident did some damage to the car.*

2 damages, *pl.* money claimed or paid by law to make up for some harm done to a person or his property: *The person who was hit by the car asked for $25,000 in damages. n.*

daw·dle (dô′dl), waste time; idle; loiter: *Don't dawdle so long over your work. v., daw·dled, daw·dling.*

de·tour (dē′tur), **1** road that is used when the main or direct road cannot be traveled. **2** use a detour: *We detoured around the bridge that had been washed out.* 1 *n.,* 2 *v.*

di·a·logue or **di·a·log** (dī′ə lôg), **1** conversation: *Two actors had a dialogue in the middle of the stage.* **2** conversation written out: *That book has a good plot and much clever dialogue. n.* [*Dialogue* is from Greek *dialogos,* which comes from *dia-,* meaning "between" and *logos,* meaning "speech."]

dire (dīr), causing great fear or suffering; dreadful: *the dire results of an earthquake. adj.*

dis·dain·ful (dis dān′fəl), looking down on, or considering someone or something beneath oneself; proud and scornful. *adj.* —**dis·dain′ful·ly,** *adv.*

disdainful—She gave the children a disdainful look.

dumb·found (dum′found′), dumfound. *v.*

dum·found (dum′found′), amaze and make unable to speak; bewilder; confuse. *v.* Also, **dumbfound.**

E

e·man·ci·pa·tion (i man′səpā′shən), a setting free from slavery or restraint; release: *The emancipation of slaves in the United States was proclaimed in 1863. The discoveries of science have led to people's emancipation from many old superstitions. n.*

em·bla·zon (em blā′zn), **1** display conspicuously; picture in bright colors. **2** decorate; adorn: *The shield was emblazoned with a coat of arms. v.*

et·i·quette (et′ə ket), the customary rules for behavior in polite society: *Etiquette requires that we eat peas with a fork, not a knife. n.*

ex·as·pe·rate (eg zas′pə rāt′), irritate very much; annoy greatly; make angry: *Her continual lateness exasperated me. v.,* **ex·as·pe·rat·ed, ex·as·pe·rat·ing.**

F

far·thing (fär′ŦHing), a British coin equal to a fourth of a British penny. It is no longer used. *n.* [*Farthing* is from Old English *fēorthung,* which comes from *fēortha,* meaning "fourth."]

fig·ure·head (fig′yər hed′), **1** person who is the head of a business, government, etc., in name only, without real authority. **2** figure placed for ornament on the bow of a ship. *n.*

fin·ick·y (fin′ə kē), too dainty or particular; too precise; fussy. *adj.*

flab·ber·gast (flab′ər gast), INFORMAL. make speechless with surprise; astonish greatly; amaze. *v.*

for·feit (fôr′fit), **1** lose or have to give up by one's own act, neglect, or fault: *He forfeited his life by his careless driving.* **2** lost or given up as a penalty **1** *v.*, **2** *adj.*

a hat	i it	oi oil	ch child	ə stands for:
ā age	ī ice	ou out	ng long	a in about
ä far	o hot	u cup	sh she	e in taken
e let	ō open	u̇ put	th thin	i in pencil
ē equal	ô order	ü rule	ᴛʜ then	o in lemon
ėr term			zh measure	u in circus

G

ga·loot (gə lüt′), SLANG. an awkward or foolish person. *n.*

gawk (gôk), stare idly, rudely, or stupidly. *v.*

glade (glād), a little open space in a wood or forest. *n.*

glow·er (glou′ər), stare angrily; scowl fiercely. *v.*

glower—He **glowered** at me as I passed.

grist·mill (grist′mil′), mill for grinding grain. *n.*

ground·er (groun′dər), baseball hit so as to roll along the ground. *n.*

H

hoist (hoist), raise on high; lift up, often with ropes and pulleys: *hoist a flag, hoist sails. v.*

hov·er (huv′ər *or* hov′ər), **1** stay in or near one place in the air: *The two birds hovered over their nest.* **2** stay in or near one place; wait nearby: *The dogs hovered around the kitchen door at mealtime. v.*

hu·mil·i·a·ted (hyü mil′ē āt id), made to feel ashamed. *adj.*

hy·po·chon·dri·ac (hī′pə kon′drē-ak), person who imagines feeling ill, is often depressed, and worries unnecessarily about personal health. *n.*

I

im·mune (i myün′), **1** protected from disease, poison, etc.; having immunity: *Vaccination makes a person practically immune to polio.* **2** free; exempt: *Nobody is immune from criticism. adj.* [*Immune* comes from Latin *immunis,* meaning "free from duties or obligations."]

im·pos·tor (im pos′tər), person who pretends to be someone else in order to deceive or defraud others. *n.*

in·ces·sant (in ses′nt), never stopping; continual: *The incessant noise from the factory kept me awake all night. adj.* —**in·ces′sant·ly,** *adv.*

in·ci·den·tal·ly (in′sə den′tl ē), **1** aside from the main subject of discussion; as an incident along with something else: *She mentioned incidentally that she hadn't eaten.* **2** by the way: *Incidentally, are you coming to the meeting? adv.*

in·com·pre·hen·si·ble (in′kom pri-hen′sə bəl), impossible to understand. *adj.*

in·ept (in ept′), **1** without skill or aptitude. **2** awkward; clumsy: *an inept performance. adj.* —**in·ept′ly,** *adv.*

in·flec·tion (in flek′shən), a change in the tone or pitch of the voice: *We usually end questions with a rising inflection. n.*

in·iq·ui·ty (in ik′wə tē), **1** a very great injustice; wickedness. **2** a wicked or unjust act: *the many iniquities of slavery. n., pl.* **in·iq·ui·ties.**

in·sa·tia·ble (in sā′shə bəl), not able to be satisfied; extremely greedy: *The boy had an insatiable appetite for candy. adj.*

in·so·lent (in′sə lənt), boldly rude; intentionally disregarding the feelings of others; insulting: *You were insolent to turn your back on me while I was talking to you. adj.* —**in′so·lent·ly,** *adv.*

in·ter·me·di·ar·y (in′tər mē′dē-er′ē), person who acts between others to bring about an agreement; person who acts for another; go-between: *The teacher acted as intermediary for the students with the principal. n., pl.* **in·ter·me·di·ar·ies.**

in·vin·ci·ble (in vin′sə bəl), impossible to overcome; unconquerable: *Our basketball team seemed invincible. adj.*

ir·i·des·cence (ir′ə des′ns), display of changing colors; change of color when moved or turned: *the iridescence of mother-of-pearl. n.*

ir·re·press·i·ble (ir′i pres′ə bəl), not able to be restrained; uncontrollable: *irrepressible laughter. adj.*

ir·ri·ta·ble (ir′ə tə bəl), **1** easily made angry; impatient: *When the rain spoiled her plans, she was irritable for the rest of the day.* **2** more sensitive than is natural or normal. *adj.*

J

jin·rik·i·sha (jin rik′shə *or* jin-rik′shô), a small, two-wheeled carriage with a folding top, pulled by a runner, formerly used in the Orient. *n., pl.* **jin·rik·i·shas.** Also, **rickshaw** or **ricksha.** [*Jinrikisha* is from Japanese *jinrikisha,* which comes from *jin,* meaning "man," *riki,* meaning "strength," and *sha,* meaning "cart."]

jinrikisha

L

loath (lōth), unwilling or reluctant: *They were loath to admit that they were wrong. adj.*

M

may·hem (mā′hem), **1** crime of intentionally maiming or injuring a person. **2** needless or intentional damage: *The stampeding cattle caused great mayhem on the ranch. n.*

med·dle (med′l), busy oneself with or in other people's affairs without being asked or needed: *That busybody meddles in everyone's business. v.,* **med·dled, med·dling.**

N

ne·go·ti·ate (ni gō′shē āt), **1** talk over and arrange terms; confer; consult: *Both countries negotiated for peace.* **2** arrange for: *v.,* **ne·go·ti·at·ed, ne·go·ti·at·ing.**

ne·go·ti·a·tion (ni gō′shē ā′shən), a negotiating; arrangement: *Negotiations for the new school are finished. n.*

nim·bus (nim′bəs), **1** halo. **2** a bright cloud surrounding a god, person, or thing. **3** a low, dark-gray layer of rain or snow clouds. *n., pl.* **nim·bus·es, nim·bi** (nim′bī).

non·cha·lant (non'shə lənt *or* non'shə länt'), without enthusiasm; coolly unconcerned; indifferent. *adj.* —**non'cha·lant·ly,** *adv.*

a hat	**i** it	**oi** oil	**ch** child	**ə** stands for:
ā age	**ī** ice	**ou** out	**ng** long	a in about
ä far	**o** hot	**u** cup	**sh** she	e in taken
e let	**ō** open	**ù** put	**th** thin	i in pencil
ē equal	**ô** order	**ü** rule	**ᴛʜ** then	o in lemon
ėr term			**zh** measure	u in circus

O

om·i·nous (om'ə nəs), unfavorable; threatening: *Those black clouds look ominous. adj.* —**om'i·nous·ly,** *adv.*

o·ver·se·er (ō'vər sē'ər), person who oversees others or their work. *n.*

P

page[1] (pāj), one side of a leaf or sheet of paper: *a page in this book. n.*

page[2] (pāj), **1** a youth who attends a person of rank. **2** a youth who was preparing to be a knight. *n.* [*Page*[2] came into English about 700 years ago from French *page,* and perhaps can be traced back to Greek *paidos,* meaning "child, boy."]

pa·go·da (pə gō'də), temple having many stories, with a roof curving upward from each story. There are pagodas in India, China, and Japan. *n., pl.* **pa·go·das.** [*Pagoda* is from Portuguese *pagode,* which came from Sanskrit *bhagavatī,* meaning "goddess."]

pas·sion·ate (pash'ə nit), **1** having or showing strong feelings: *She has always been a passionate believer in human rights.* **2** easily moved to a fit or mood of some emotion. **3** resulting from strong feeling: *He made a passionate speech against death sentences. adj.* —**pas'sion·ate·ly,** *adv.*

pau·per (pô'pər), a very poor person; person supported by charity. *n.*

pe·di·a·tri·cian (pē'dē ə trish'ən), doctor who specializes in pediatrics. *n.*

pe·di·at·rics (pē'dē at'riks), branch of medicine dealing with children's diseases and the care of babies and children. *n.* [*Pediatrics* comes from Greek *paidos,* meaning "child," and *iasthai,* meaning "to heal, cure."]

pew·ter (pyü'tər), **1** alloy of tin with lead, copper, or other metals. **2** made of pewter: *a pewter mug.* **1** *n.,* **2** *adj.*

pin·cers (pin'sərz), **1** tool for gripping and holding tight, made like scissors but with jaws instead of blades. **2** the large claw or pair of claws of crabs, lobsters, etc. *n. pl., or sing.* Also, **pinchers.**

pagoda

pincers—of a crab

plan·ta·tion (plan tā′shən), a large farm or estate, especially in a tropical or semitropical region, on which cotton, tobacco, sugar cane, rubber trees, etc., are grown. The work on a plantation is done by laborers who live there. *n.*

pla·teau (pla tō′), **1** plain in the mountains or at a height considerably above sea level; large, high plain; tableland. **2** a level, especially the level at which something is stabilized for a period. *n., pl.* **pla·teaus, pla·teaux** (pla tōz′).

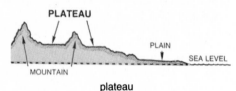

plateau

po·mar·ro·sa or **po·ma·ro·sa** (pō mə rō′sə), rose apple; a tropical tree bearing a large edible berry that has a strong roselike fragrance. *n.*

post·pone·ment (pōst pōn′mənt), a putting off till later; a putting off to a later time; delay: *The postponement of the picnic disappointed the children. n.*

pre·pos·ter·ous (pri pos′tər əs), contrary to nature, reason, or common sense; absurd; senseless; foolish: *That the moon is made of green cheese is a preposterous notion. adj.*

prow (prou), the front part of a ship or boat; bow. *n.*

Q

quag·mire (kwag′mīr′), soft, muddy ground; boggy or miry place. *n.*

quar·ry (kwôr′ē), place where stone is dug, cut, or blasted out for use in building. *n., pl.* **quar·ries.**

quiz·zi·cal (kwiz′ə kəl), **1** teasing; mocking: *a quizzical smile.* **2** questioning; baffled: *She had a quizzical expression on her face. adj.*
—quiz′zi·cal·ly, *adv.*

R

rec·i·ta·tion (res′ə tā′shən), **1** a saying over; a repeating; a telling of facts in detail. **2** a reciting of a prepared lesson by pupils before a teacher. **3** a repeating of something from memory. **4** a poem, story, etc., repeated from memory. *n.*

re·quite (ri kwīt′), pay back; make return for; make return to (a person): *requite kindness with love. v.,* **re·quit·ed, re·quit·ing.**

re·splend·ent (ri splen′dənt), very bright; shining; splendid: *a gown resplendent with jewels, a face resplendent with joy. adj.* **—resplend′ent·ly,** *adv.*

rick·shaw or **rick·sha** (rik′shô), jinrikisha. *n.*

ric·o·chet (rik′ə shā′), **1** the skipping or jumping motion of an object as it goes along a flat surface: *the ricochet of a stone thrown along the surface of water.* **2** move with a skipping or jumping motion: *The bullets struck the ground and ricocheted through the grass.* **1** *n.,* **2** *v.,* **ric·o·cheted** (rik′ə-shād′), **ric·o·chet·ing** (rik′ə-shā′ing).

S

sap·phire (saf′īr), a clear, hard, usually blue, precious stone. *n.*

sar·cas·tic (sär kas′tik), sneering; cutting: *"Don't hurry!" was my brother's sarcastic comment as I slowly dressed. adj.* **—sar·cas′ti·cal·ly,** *adv.*

seek (sēk), **1** try to find; look for; search: *seek for something lost.* **2** try to get: *Some people seek wealth. v.,* **sought, seek·ing.**

seer (sir), person who foresees or foretells future events; prophet. *n.*

se·ren·i·ty (sə ren′ə tē), **1** peace and quiet; calmness. **2** condition or state of being calm or unruffled. *n.*

snare (sner *or* snar), **1** noose for catching small animals and birds: *They made snares to catch rabbits.* **2** catch with a snare: *One day they snared a skunk.* 1 *n.*, 2 *v.*, **snared, snar·ing.**

snarl[1] (snärl), **1** growl sharply and show one's teeth: *The dog snarled at the stranger.* **2** a sharp, angry growl. 1 *v.*, 2*n.* —**snarl'er**, *n.* —**snarl'ing·ly**, *adv.*

snarl[2] (snärl) a tangled or knotted mass: *The yarn was all snarled and twisted.*

snip·er (snī'pər), person who shoots at someone from a hidden place; a hidden sharpshooter. *n.*

so·phis·ti·cat·ed (sə fis'tə kā'tid), **1** experienced in worldly ways; changed from natural simplicity. **2** very complex and advanced in design: *sophisticated laboratory equipment. adj.*

sor·did (sôr'did), **1** dirty; filthy: *a sordid back street, a sordid shack.* **2** mean; low; base: *sordid behavior. adj.* —**sor'did·ly**, *adv.* —**sor'did·ness**, *n.*

sought (sôt), past tense and past participle of **seek.** *For days she sought a job. They were sought and found. v.*

squad·ron (skwod'rən), **1** part of a naval fleet used for special service: *a destroyer squadron.* **2** formation of eight or more airplanes that fly or fight together. *n.*

sta·lac·tite (stə lak'tīt), a formation of lime, shaped like an icicle, hanging from the roof of a cave. It is formed by dripping water that contains lime. *n.*

sta·lag·mite (stə lag'mīt), a formation of lime, shaped like a cone, built up on the floor of a cave. It is formed by water dripping from a stalactite. *n.*

a hat	**i** it	**oi** oil	**ch** child	**ə** stands for:
ā age	**ī** ice	**ou** out	**ng** long	a in about
ä far	**o** hot	**u** cup	**sh** she	e in taken
e let	**ō** open	**ů** put	**th** thin	i in pencil
ē equal	**ô** order	**ü** rule	**ᴛʜ** then	o in lemon
ėr term			**zh** measure	u in circus

sta·tion (stā'shən), **1** place to stand in; assigned post: *The policeman took his station at the corner.* **2** building or place used for a definite purpose. **3** place or equipment for sending out or receiving programs by radio or television. **4** assign a station to; place: *She stationed herself just outside the main doorway.* **5** social position; rank: *A serf was a person of humble station in life.* 1-3,5 *n.*, 4 *v.*

stat·ure (stach'ər), height of a person: *a young woman of average stature. n.*

stew·ard (stü'ərd *or* styü'ərd), person employed on an airplane, a ship, etc., to look after passengers; flight attendant. *n.*

sub·mis·sive (səb mis'iv), yielding to power, control, or authority; obedient; humble. *adj.* —**sub·mis'sive·ly**, *adv.* —**sub·mis'sive·ness**, *n.*

suf·fo·cate (suf'ə kāt), **1** keep from breathing; hinder in breathing. **2** gasp for breath; choke. **3** die for lack of oxygen. *v.*, **suf·fo·cat·ed, suf·fo·cat·ing.**

T

ten·ant (ten'ənt), person paying rent for the temporary use of the land or buildings of another person. *A tenant farmer is a person who lives on and farms land belonging to another. n.*

tithe (tiᴛʜ), **1** one tenth. **2** one tenth of one's yearly income, paid for the support of the church. **3** make or pledge such a payment. 1,2 *n.*, 3 *v.*, **tithed, tith·ing.**

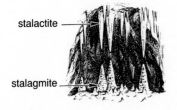

stalactite

stalagmite

trance (trans), **1** state of uncon-
sciousness somewhat like sleep. A
person may be in a trance from illness
or from hypnosis. Some people can
even put themselves into a trance. **2** a
dreamy, absorbed condition that is like
a trance: *She sat in a trance, thinking
of her past life. n.* [*Trance* came into
English about 600 years ago from
French *transe*, which comes from
transir, meaning "pass away," and can
be traced back to Latin *trans-*, meaning
"across," and *ire*, meaning "go."]
—**trance'like'**, *adj.*

trance—The hypnotist placed her in a
trance, so that she was able to lie
completely stiff between the chairs.

trans·for·ma·tion (tran'sfər-
mā'shən), a changing in form or ap-
pearance; a changing in condition,
nature, or character: *the transformation
of a caterpillar into a butterfly. n.*
trans·gress (trans gres'), **1** break a
law, command, etc.; sin. **2** go beyond
(a limit): *Their manners transgress the
bounds of good taste. v.*
trans·gres·sion (trans gresh'ən), a
transgressing or a being transgressed:
*the transgression of a law, to commit a
grave transgression. n.*
trans·lu·cent (tran slü'snt), letting
light through without being transparent:
Frosted glass is translucent. adj.
—**trans·lu'cent·ly**, *adv.*

trans·par·ent (tran sper'ənt *or* tran
spar'ənt), **1** letting light through so that
things on the other side can be dis-
tinctly seen: *Window glass is
transparent.* **2** easily seen through or
detected: *a transparent excuse.* **3** frank;
free from pretense or deceit: *a person
of transparent honesty. adj.* —**trans·
·par'ent·ly**, *adv.* —

transparent—A plant seen through
transparent glass.

translucent—The same plant seen
through translucent glass.

tran·spire (tran spīr'), take place; happen: *I heard later what transpired at
the meeting. v.,* **tran·spired,
tran·spir·ing.**
trea·son (trē'zn), betrayal of one's
country or ruler. Helping the enemies of
one's country is treason. *n.*

trea·son·ous (trē′zn əs), relating to or involving treason. *adj.*

tri·dent (trīd′nt), a three-pronged spear, especially the spear carried by Neptune, or Poseidon, god of the sea. *n.* [*Trident* is from Latin *tridentem,* which comes from *tri-,* meaning "three," and *dentem,* meaning "tooth."]

tur·moil (tèr′moil), state of agitation or commotion; disturbance; tumult: *Unexpected guests put us in a turmoil. n.*

a hat	**i** it	**oi** oil	**ch** child	**ə** stands for:
ā age	**ī** ice	**ou** out	**ng** long	a in about
ä far	**o** hot	**u** cup	**sh** she	e in taken
e let	**ō** open	**u̇** put	**th** thin	i in pencil
ē equal	**ô** order	**ü** rule	**ŦH** then	o in lemon
ėr term			**zh** measure	u in circus

U

un·dis·ci·plined (un dis′ə plind), without proper control; untrained. *adj.*

V

venge·ance (ven′jəns), punishment in return for a wrong; revenge: *She*

swore vengeance against her hateful enemies. n.

vin·dic·tive (vin dik′tiv), **1** bearing a grudge; wanting revenge: *A vindictive person is unforgiving.* **2** showing a strong tendency toward revenge: *a vindictive act. adj.* —**vin·dic′tive·ly,** *adv.* —**vin·dic′tive·ness,** *n.*

W

woe·be·gone (wō′bi gôn′), looking sad, sorrowful, or wretched. *adj.*

Word List

The following words all appear in the glossary. Those followed by an asterisk are introduced optionally in the Teacher's Edition.

Jake
clambering
exasperating
flabbergasted*
forfeit*
galoot
grounder*
hoisted
mayhem
quagmire*
postponement*

Rebecca of Sunnybrook Farm
dialogue
iniquity
irrepressible*
passionate*
recitation
resplendent*
transgression
transpired
undisciplined*
vindictiveness*

Myths: Stories That Explain Why
coax
glade*
hover*
meddle*
nimbus
pincers
pomarosa
sapphire
snare*
vengeance*

Mumbet: The Story of Elizabeth Freeman
chattel
client
damages*
grist mill
quarry
serenity*
sought*
suffocate*
tenant
turmoil*

Anastasia On Her Own
humiliated*
hypochondriac*
immune
incidentally
inflection
irritable*
pediatrician
quizzically
sarcastic*
sophisticated*

Dragon of the Lost Sea
avenging
cutlass
insolent
ominous
plateau*
ricochet*
sniper
stalagmite*
stalactite*
translucent*

Homesick, My Own Story
careening*
condemned*
dawdled
detour*
dire*
pagoda
requited
ricksha
steward
woebegone*

Commodore Perry in the Land of the Shogun
capacious
emblazon*
etiquette
incessant
inept*
insatiable
intermediary*
negotiation*
squadron*
tithe

The Sign of the Beaver
adz
boggy*
contemptuous*
disdainful
dumbfounded
finicky
glower*
incomprehensible*
nonchalant*
pewter

The People Could Fly
ancient
clumsily
commence
cooter
emancipation*
overseer*
plantation*
seer*
snarl*
trance

The Eyes of the Amaryllis
audible*
brig
figurehead
invincible*
iridescence
preposterous*
prow
submissive*
transformation*
trident

The Prince and the Pauper
farthing
gawk
impostor*
loath
page
pauper*
sordid*
station*
stature
treasonous*

Page 255: Excerpt from *This Land Is Your Land,* words and music by Woody Guthrie. TRO Copyright © 1956 (renewed 1984), 1958 and 1970 Ludlow Music, Inc., New York, NY. Reprinted by permission of TRO, The Richmond Organization, Essex Music Ltd., London and Essex Music of Australia Pty. Ltd. International Copyright Secured. All rights reserved.
Page 261: From *Commodore Perry in the Land of the Shogun* by Rhoda Blumberg. Copyright © 1985 by Rhoda Blumberg. Reprinted by permission of Lothrop, Lee & Shepard Books (A Division of William Morrow & Company, Inc.).
Page 287: "Two ducks swim to shore" by Hiroshige cited in *The Moment of Wonder: A Collection of Chinese and Japanese Poetry* edited by Richard Lewis. New York: The Dial Press, 1964.
Page 287: "The face of the dragonfly," and "What happiness" from *Haiku Vols. I–IV* edited and translated by R. H. Blyth. Reprinted by permission of the Hokuseido Press, Tokyo.
Page 293: From *The Sign of the Beaver* by Elizabeth George Speare. Copyright © 1983 by Elizabeth George Speare. Reprinted by permission of Houghton Mifflin Company and Victor Gollancz Ltd.
Page 327: "Direction" by Alonzo Lopez from *The Whispering Wind: Poetry by Young American Indians,* edited by Terry Allen. Copyright © 1972 by Terry Allen. Reprinted by permission of Doubleday & Company, Inc.
Page 333: From *The People Could Fly: American Folktales* by Virginia Hamilton, illustrated by Leo and Diane Dillon. Copyright © 1985 by Virginia Hamilton. Illustrations copyright © 1985 by Leo and Diane Dillon. Reprinted by permission of Alfred A. Knopf, Inc.
Page 353: "Virginia Hamilton" entry excerpted from *Something About the Author,* volume 4, edited by Anne Commire. Copyright © 1973 by Gale Research Company. All rights reserved. Reprinted by permission of Gale Research.
Page 355: "Cross Over the River" by Sam Cornish. Reprinted by permission of the author.
Page 356: "Aunt Sue's Stories" from *Don't You Turn Back* by Langston Hughes. Copyright 1942, 1947 © 1959 by Langston Hughes. Copyright 1932, 1948 by Alfred A. Knopf, Inc. Copyright renewed 1960 by Langston Hughes. Copyright © 1967, 1969 by Arna Bontemps and George Houston Bass, Executors of the Estate of Langston Hughes. Reprinted by permission of Random House, Inc.
Page 363: *The Eyes of the Amaryllis* by Natalie Babbitt. Copyright © 1977 by Natalie Babbitt. Reprinted by permission of Farrar, Straus and Giroux, Inc.
Page 468: Natalie Babbitt, "My Love Affair with the Alphabet," *Once Upon A Time,* p. 45. New York: G. P. Putnam's Sons, 1986.

Page 470: "The Noise of Waters" from *Collected Poems* by James Joyce. Copyright 1918 by B. W. Huebsch, Inc., 1946 by Nora Joyce. Reprinted by permission of Viking Penguin, Inc. and The Society of Authors, London, as literary representatives of the Estate of James Joyce.
Page 471: "The Sea" by James Reeves from *The Wandering Moon and Other Poems.* Copyright by James Reeves. Reprinted by permission of The James Reeves Estate.
Page 477: "The Prince and the Pauper" by Mark Twain, adapted by Elizabeth Brenner from *Favorite Plays for Classroom Reading* by Durrell and Crossley. Copyright © 1965, 1971 by Plays, Inc. Reprinted by permission.
Page 503: "A Seeing Poem" from *Seeing Things: A Book of Poems* by Robert Froman, lettering by Ray Barber. Copyright © 1974 by Robert Froman. Reprinted by permission of Harper & Row, Publishers, Inc. (Thomas Y. Crowell) and Robert Froman.

Artists
Section 1: Richard Sparks, 8–11, 20, 29, 34, 43, 45, 46
Section 2: Betty Maxey (John Walter and Associates), 48–50, 57, 64, 71, 77, 78; Charlotte Faubion, (border art) 50–56, 58–63, 65–70, 72–79
Section 3: Andrea Eberbach, 80–81, 84–92, 94–97, 99–104, 106–107
Section 4: David Cunningham, 112–116, 119, 121, 123, 126, 129, 133, 141, 144
Section 5: Diane deGroat, 146–147
Section 6: Chi Chung, 184–185, 188, 193, 197, 201, 205, 208, 212, 217, 222; Anthony Ma, 227
Section 7: Tom Herzberg, (map) 232–233, (border art) 234–235, 239, 246, 249, (border art) 254, 256
Section 8: George Suyeoka, 287
Section 9: Nathan Greene, 292–295, 303, 308, 314, 318, 323, 327–328, 330–331
Section 10: Leo and Diane Dillon, 332–333, 335, 338, 343, 347, 350, 355, 357
Section 11: Gino D'Achilli, 362–363, 367–368, 370–372, 374–378, 380–384, 386–393, 395–399, 401–408, 410–419, 421–425, 427–435, 437–441, 443–446, 448–454, 456–460, 462–467
Section 12: Handelan Pederson Inc., 476–479, 484, 489, 493, 500, 502, 504

Freelance Photography
Photographs not listed were shot by Scott, Foresman and Company.
Page 179: Bernard Arendt

Photographs
Page 41: Alfred Slote. Photo by Suzanne Coles-Ketcham. Courtesy Harper & Row.
Page 73: Kate Douglas Wiggin. Courtesy of Houghton Mifflin Co.

Acknowledgments continued on page 544